SANTA MONICA COLLEGE LIBRARY

3 5046 00146 5030

S0-AKF-632

OUTDATED MATERIAL

WITHDRAWN

WITHDRAWN

R119 .F548 1992
Fischer, Heinz Dietrich,
1937-
Medicine, media, and
morality : Pulitzer
Prize-winning writings on
health-related topics

**SANTA MONICA COLLEGE
LIBRARY**

**SANTA MONICA, CA 90405-1628**

DEMCO

# Medicine, Media and Morality

Pulitzer Prize-Winning Writings on Health-Related Topics

by Heinz-Dietrich Fischer

KRIEGER PUBLISHING COMPANY
MALABAR, FLORIDA
1992

SANTA MONICA COLLEGE LIBRARY
Santa Monica, California

Original Edition 1992


Printed and Published by
**KRIEGER PUBLISHING COMPANY**
**KRIEGER DRIVE**
**MALABAR, FLORIDA 32950**


Copyright © 1992 by Krieger Publishing Company

All rights  reserved. No part of this book may be reproduced in any form or by any means, electronic or mechanical, including information storage and retrieval systems without permission in writing from the publisher.
*No liability is assumed with respect to the use of the information contained herein.*
Printed in the United States of America.

FROM A DECLARATION OF PRINCIPLES JOINTLY ADOPTED BY A COMMITTEE OF THE AMERICAN BAR ASSOCIATION AND A COMMITTEE OF PUBLISHERS:

This publication is designed to provide accurate and authoritative information in regard to the subject matter covered. It is sold with the understanding that the publisher is not engaged in rendering legal, accounting, or other professional service. If legal advice or other expert assistance is required, the services of a competent professional person should be sought.

**Library of Congress Cataloging-In-Publication Data**
Fischer, Heinz Dietrich, 1937-
    Medicine, media, and morality : Pulitzer Prize-winning writings on
health-related topics / by Heinz-Dietrich Fischer.
        p.     cm.
    Includes bibliographical references and index.
    ISBN 0-89464-692-3 (alk. paper)
    1. Medical care. 2. Health. 3. Journalism, Medical. 4. Pulitzer
prizes.  I. Title.
    [DNLM: 1. Health--collected works. 2. Writing--collected works.
WZ 345 F529m]
R119.F548 1992
362.1--dc20
DNLM/DLC
for Library of Congress                                    92-11554
                                                              CIP

10    9    8    7    6    5    4    3    2

This book is dedicated to


*Professor Kenneth Koppel Goldstein*

- Graduate School of Journalism at
Columbia University in the City of New York -


the Pioneer in Medical Journalism Education

# PREFACE

Medical and health-related journalism has a long tradition in American mass media. To recognize the importance of medical reporting, quite a number of journalism awards were established over the past decades for this very specific field of writing. For example, the American Heart Association sponsors an award for heart and blood vessel diseases reporting; the Muscular Dystrophy Association offers a Prize for articles on muscular dystrophy and related disorders; the National Association for Mental Health recognizes journalism achievements on mental illness and treatment with a special award. In addition to these 'serious' honors there are quite a number of so-called medical awards which were mainly installed for PR purposes of the award donors rather than for excellence in medical resp. health-related writing.

In this context it may be astonishing that the most traditional and prestigious of all journalism awards in the world, the Pulitzer Prize system, never has established a special medical writing award category, although there exist fourteen annual Pulitzer Prizes for different fields of journalism. But over the decades, since its establishment in 1917, many medical or health-related articles have received Pulitzer Prizes in various Pulitzer award categories. Since these articles were entered under different reporting or editorial text categories, it was absolutely necessary to search through the complete bulk of Pulitzer Prize-winning stuff - totaling around one thousand exhibits, each of them containing quite a number of articles from award-winners.

So the present volume is not a representative sample but a nearly complete collection of - in a relatively broad sense - all medical or health-related articles ever awarded with a Pulitzer Prize up until the late 1980s. After the texts and their specific topics were at hand, it was a difficult task to categorize the articles. Finally, the author found a way to organize the heterogeneous material into six main chapters, each of them having three sub-chapters, and each subchapter containing two articles.

So this book presents altogether 36 Pulitzer Prize-winning texts on a variety of topics, ranging - in short - from ecological problems, health service and medical care questions to health conditions abroad. In this way, the book not only shows the broad spectrum of relevant topics but it also demonstrates different journalistic approaches, from on-the-spot news writing to investigative reporting to commentaries.

To realize the very time-consuming work of detecting relevant articles, the author considers it a great privilege that he received unlimited access to the Pulitzer Prize collection at Columbia University during the last couple of years. Mr. Robert C. Christopher, Administrator of the Pulitzer Prizes, and Mr. Edward M. Kliment, Assistant Administrator, kindly made available not only the award-winning exhibits from a time span of more than seventy years but also the jury reports and other background materials on the annual awarding procedures. Special thanks go to both of them as well as to a number of media representatives granting reprint permission for the Pulitzer Prize-winning texts presented in this volume.

Copyright clearances were especially done by William B. Brown (*The Advertiser*, Montgomery Al.), Ben Cason (*United Press International*), Robert J. Danzig (*Hearst Newspapers*), Mark F. Ethridge III (*The Charlotte Observer*), Howard R. Fibich (*The Milwaukee Journal*), Ashley B. Futrell Jr. (*Washington Daily News*, Washington, N.C.), James P. Gannon (*The Des Moines Register*), Leonard R. Harris (*The New York Times*), Joanne Heumann (*The Courier-Journal*, Louisville, Ky.), James Hoge (*Daily News*, New York), Don Kopriva (*Chicago Sun-Times*), Bill Kovach (*The Atlanta Constitution*), Christine P. Lemon (*International Herald-Tribune*), Lawrence A. Leser (*Scripps-Howard Newspapers*), Walter R. Mears (*The Associated Press*), Reg Murphy (*The Sun*, Baltimore, Md.), Cheryl Preston (*Los Angeles Times*), Joseph Pulitzer Jr. (*St. Louis Post-Dispatch*), Robert Richter (*The Sheboygan Press*, Sheboygan, Wi.), Madelyn A. Ross (*The Pittsburgh Press*), Irene Schwartz (*Newsday*, Long Island, N.Y.), Hal Seymour (*Minneapolis Star and Tribune*), James D. Squires (*Chicago Tribune*), Edward M. Storin (*The Miami Herald*) and Thomas E. Wark (*The Philadelphia Inquirer*).

The author also is indebted to Mr. Henry Bird (*The Sheboygan Press*), Mr. Frank J. Carroll (The Library of Congress, Washington, D.C.) and Mrs. Brigitte James (Library of the U.S. Embassy at Bonn/Germany) for special information. At the Ruhr University Bochum thanks go to Mrs. Ingrid Dickhut, Dr. Peter Gerlach and Mr. Jürgen Niemann (Department of Journalism and Communication) for valuable assistance during various phases of the preparation of the manuscript. A grant from the Ludwig Sievers Foundation (Cologne) provided the opportunity to research abroad; so special thanks go to Dr. Jürgen W. Bösche and Professor J. F. Volrad Deneke of that institution. Last but not least the editor wishes to say a merci to Professor Jon D. Franklin from the Department of Journalism at Oregon State University (Corvallis, Or.) who kindly permitted reproduction in this book of one of his two Pulitzer Prize Certificates, which he received for his outstanding contributions to medical journalism. Finally, the author is indebted to Miss Robin Harp who - as a native speaker - looked through the general as well as the special introductions to this volume.

January 1992                                                    H.-D. Fischer

# CONTENTS

# GENERAL INTRODUCTION:

## MEDICAL JOURNALISM AND THE PULITZER PRIZE SYSTEM

### - Several Aspects of Evolution, Ethics, and Education

by Heinz-Dietrich Fischer

"The emergence of philosophies of journalism education" in the United States started with the 'Pulitzer Principles', formulated in the early years of the twentieth century.[1] In one of his famous articles Pulitzer stated: "Before the century closes schools of journalism will be generally accepted as a feature of specialized higher education, like schools of law or of medicine."[2] Joseph Pulitzer, born 1847 in Hungary, "received a rudimentary education in a private school and at the hand of a special tutor."[3] At the age of seventeen he came to the United States, found his way to St. Louis, got a newspaper job, combined two local newspapers and made a fortune with the merger called *St. Louis Post-Dispatch*.[4] Later on he moved to New York City and bought the *World*.[5] He "multipled his fortune, gained an immense reputation and immense power", as Johnson states, "and gave two and a half millions to Columbia University to found a school of journalism. In his will... he left the school an additional endowment the income of which was to provide

---

[1] De Forest O'Dell, The History of Journalism Education in the United States, New York 1935, p. 55.

[2] Joseph Pulitzer, The College of Journalism, *The North American Review* (New York), Vol. 178/No. 5, May, 1904, p. 642.

[3] De Forest O'Dell, *op. cit.*, p. 55.

[4] Cf. Julian S. Rammelkamp, Pulitzer's *Post-Dispatch*, 1878-1883, Princeton, N.J., 1967.

[5] Cf. George Juergens, Joseph Pulitzer and the New York *World*, Princeton, N.J., 1966.

awards for distinguished achievement in journalism, literature and education. Such was the origin of the Pulitzer Prizes... ."[6]

The idea was born in the summer of 1902 when Joseph Pulitzer was 55 years old, intensely nervous and almost blind.[7] "During the previous year, as he was well aware," Hohenberg states, "the first prizes of world-wide significance had been bestowed on six distinguished Europeans through the munificence of the Swedish inventor of dynamite, Alfred B. Nobel, who had died in 1896. However, prizes were not then uppermost in Pulitzer's mind... ."[8] But within the next two years as the idea of establishing an award system became clearer, he included in his will a special agreement with Columbia University which says: "If the plan for awarding the prizes... shall not have been agreed upon by Columbia University and myself in my lifetime, then I direct that such prizes shall be awarded and paid in accordance with a plan to be agreed upon by my executors and the University... for... prizes and scholarships which shall be awarded or paid annually or otherwise as designated."[9] Richard T. Baker says that "from this small seed of an idea... came the prizes which... bear the donor's name and stand among the most coveted awards in American literature and journalism."[10]

The original plan of award contained the following ten Pulitzer Prizes: "1. For the best and most suggestive paper on the future development and improvement of the School of Journalism...; 2. For the most disinterested and meritorious public service rendered by any American newspaper...; 3. For the best history of the services rendered to the public by the American press...; 4. Five annual traveling scholarships...; 5. For the best editorial article written during the year, the test of excellence being clearness of style, moral purpose, sound reasoning, and power to influence public opinion...; 6. For the best example of a reporter's work during the year, the test being strict accuracy, terseness, the accomplishment of some public good commanding public attention and respect...; 7. For the American novel published during the year which shall best present the wholesome

---

[6] Gerald W. Johnson, The Lines are Drawn. American Life since the First World War as reflected in the Pulitzer Prize Cartoons, Philadelphia - New York 1958, p. 17.

[7] Cf. Don C. Seitz, Joseph Pulitzer. His Life and Letters, New York 1924, pp. 435 ff.

[8] John Hohenberg, The Pulitzer Prizes. A History of the Awards in Books, Drama, Music, and Journalism. Based on the Private Files over Six Decades, New York - London 1974, pp. 9 f.

[9] Quoted from De Forest O'Dell, op. cit., p. 108.

[10] Richard Terrill Baker, A History of the Graduate School of Journalism, Columbia University, New York 1954, p. 86.

## EXTRACTS FROM THE WILL OF JOSEPH PULITZER

### DATED APRIL 16, 1904

"·· III. If the plan for awarding the prizes contemplated by the agreements shall not have been agreed upon by Columbia University and myself in my lifetime, then I direct that such prizes shall be awarded and paid in accordance with a plan to be agreed upon by my Executors and the University. Such plan must, before its adoption, be approved by the Advisory Board, as then constituted and existing; and it must make provision for the following prizes and scholarships which shall be awarded or paid annually or otherwise as designated:

1st. Annually, for the best and most suggestive paper on the future development and improvement of the school of journalism, or for any one idea that will promise great improvement in the operation of the school, One thousand dollars ($1,000).

2d. Annually, for the most disinterested and meritorious public service rendered by any American newspaper during the year, a gold medal costing Five hundred dollars ($500).

3d. Annually, for the best history of the services rendered to the public by the American press during the preceding year, One thousand dollars ($1,000).

4th. Five annual traveling scholarships of Fifteen hundred dollars ($1,500) each, to be awarded as follows:

Three (3) to three different graduates respectively of the school of journalism who shall have passed their examinations with the highest honor and are otherwise most deserving, to enable each of them to spend a year in Europe, to study the social, political and moral conditions of the people, and the character and principles of the European press.

One (1) to the student of music in America whom the Advisory Board shall deem the most talented and deserving, in order that he

may continue his studies with the advantage of European instruction.

Another to an art student in America who shall be certified to the Advisory Board by the Society of American Artists as the most promising and deserving; or, if none be certified, then as the Advisory Board may select, in order that he may continue his studies in Europe.

5th. Annually, for the best editorial article written during the year, the test of excellence being clearness of style, moral purpose, sound reasoning and power to influence public opinion in the right direction, Five hundred dollars ($500).

6th. Annually, for the best example of a reporter's work during the year; the test being strict accuracy, terseness, the accomplishment of some public good commanding public attention and respect, One thousand dollars ($1,000).

7th. Annually, for the American novel published during the year which shall best present the whole atmosphere of American life, and the highest standard of American manners and manhood, One thousand dollars ($1,000).

8th. Annually, for the original American play, performed in New York, which shall best represent the educational value and power of the stage in raising the standard of good morals, good taste and good manners, One thousand dollars ($1,000).

9th. Annually, for the best book of the year upon the history of the United States, Two thousand dollars ($2,000).

10th. Annually, for the best American biography teaching patriotic and unselfish services to the people, illustrated by an eminent example, excluding, as too obvious, the names of George Washington and Abraham Lincoln, One thousand dollars ($1,000).

From: Columbia University (Ed.), Extracts from the Will of Joseph Pulitzer, undated, pp. 3, 5 f.

atmosphere of American life and the highest standard of American manners and manhood...; 8. For the original American play performed in New York which shall best represent the educational value and power of the stage in raising the standard of good morals, good taste, and good manners...; 9. For the best book of the year upon the history of the United States...; 10. For the best American biography teaching patriotic and unselfish service to the people... ."[11]

Because of numerous administrative hurdles the School of Journalism at Columbia University had not materialized before Joseph Pulitzer's death on October 29, 1911; the teaching started simultaneously with the commencement of the academic year of 1912.[12] Since Pulitzer had prescribed that the prizes - which were to be named after him - should be first awarded three years after the successful operation of the School of Journalism, at the earliest,[13] the official inauguration of the Pulitzer Prizes would not take place before 1915/16. According to Pulitzer's will, the awards were to be made in two steps. While he granted to the University's Trustees the right to bestow the awards, he rested in the Advisory Board of the Journalism School the principal authority for making recommendations to the Trustees.[14] The Board's first designated duty was to agree on a Plan of Award in 1915. However, no direct information about nominating juries in the awarding process was given. "This was the first signal," Hohenberg explains, "that the Board would regard all jury reports as advisory, that the Board would insist on its right to overrule juries and impose its own judgment on the contenders, and that the Board would, if necessary, select its own prize winners."[15] This precedent would influence from time to time the awarding of the Pulitzer Prizes.[16]

The new Plan of Award contained no surprises since it included all the prizes proposed in the Pulitzer will. "When the Board adjourned at 5:40 P.M. on May 24, 1915," John Hohenberg writes, "the course to be followed by the Pulitzer Prizes in its formative years was set for all practical purposes. Its members did not meet the following year, there being no business to warrant a formal session... In order to keep the

---

[11] Quoted from Heinz-Dietrich Fischer/Christopher G. Trump (Eds.), Education in Journalism. The 75th Anniversary of Joseph Pulitzer's Ideas at Columbia University (1904-1979), Bochum, FRG, 1980, pp. 15 f.

[12] Richard Terrill Baker, *op. cit.*, pp. 73 f.

[13] John Hohenberg, *op. cit.*, pp. 11 f.

[14] Cf. De Forest O'Dell, *op. cit.*, p. 109.

[15] John Hohenberg, *op. cit.*, pp. 23 f.

[16] Cf. Heinz-D. Fischer/Erika J. Fischer (Eds.), The Pulitzer Prize Archive. A History and Anthology of Award-winning materials in Journalism, Letters, and Arts, Munich - London - New York - Oxford - Paris 1987 ff.

Board fully posted," the president of Columbia University "circulated a letter to all members with notification that the first deadline for all nominations and exhibits would be February 1, 1917, and that the first Pulitzer Prizes would be announced at the Columbia Commencement in June, 1917. Thus, Pulitzer's dream materialized six years after his death and thus the Pulitzer Prizes, a frail craft of many masters, was launched directly into the tempest of World War I."[17] With the first announcement of the Pulitzer Prizes in 1917, a precedent was established which closely linked award-winning texts, especially in the journalism categories, with political events of the time:[18] In addition to the award for outstanding editorial writing,[19] the reporting award[20] also included a strong political component which became apparent, even before the first presentation of the prize. Thus, the award-winning editorial by Frank H. Simonds on the anniversary of the sinking of the Lusitania, and Herbert Bayard Swope's dispatches from Germany at war[21] served as foundations and models for the Pulitzer Prizes.

Since "Editorial Writing" and "Reporting" mainly focused on political aspects, to some extend the "Meritorious Public Service" category provided opportunity to honor other journalistic achievements.[22] But it lasted until 1938 when the Prize in this award category went to a newspaper which did not cover a political corruption story but a health-related one: The *Tribune* from Bismarck, North Dakota, earned the Pulitzer Meritorious Public Service Medal "for its news reports and editorials entitled, 'Self Help in the Dust Bowl.'"[23] And three years later it was the Pulitzer paper *St. Louis Post-Dispatch* which was honored in this award category "for its successful campaign against the city smoke nuisance."[24] The *Chicago Daily News* received an award in this category in 1963 "for calling public attention to the issue of providing birth control services in the public health programs in its

---

[17] John Hohenberg, *op. cit.*, p. 24.

[18] Cf. *ibid.*, pp. 28 ff.

[19] Cf. W. David Sloan, Pulitzer Prize Editorials. America's Best Editorial Writing, 1917-1979, Ames, Ia., 1980.

[20] Cf. W. David Sloan/Valerie McCrary/Johanna Cleary, The Best of Pulitzer Prize News Writing, Columbus, Oh., 1986.

[21] Cf. Erika J. Fischer/Heinz-D. Fischer, American Reporter at the International Political Stage. Herbert Bayard Swope and his Pulitzer Prize-winning Articles from Germany in 1916, Bochum, FRG, 1982.

[22] Cf. J. Russell Wiggins, Public Service Awards, *Columbia Library Columns* (New York), Vol. VI/No. 3, May, 1957, pp. 13 f.

[23] Columbia University (Ed.), The Pulitzer Prizes, 1917-1991, New York 1991, p. 4.

[24] *Ibid.*

area."[25] A decade later, *Newsday* from Garden City, N.Y., was awarded a Pulitzer Public Service Prize "for its definitive report on the illicit narcotic traffic in the United States and abroad, entitled, 'The Heroin Trail.'"[26] Another example is the *Charlotte Observer*. In 1981, this North Carolina paper earned a Pulitzer award "for its series on 'Brown Lung: A Case of Deadly Neglect.'"[27]

During its history the reporting category also experienced several changes: It originally embraced all fields - local, national and international reporting - thus ensuring a broader scope than only political news writing. So already in 1923 it covered for the first time science: A journalist from the *New York Times* won the award "for his reports of the proceedings of the convention of the American Association for the Advancement of Science held in Cambridge, Mass., in December, 1922."[28] In the following year the reporting award went to a reporter from the *San Diego Sun* "for his story of the eclipse of the sun."[29] A member of the *New York Times* won the 1930 award in this category "for his reports by radio from the Byrd Antarctic Expedition."[30] For their "coverage of science at the tercentenary of Harvard University" five journalists from different news media were the recipients of the Pulitzer general reporting prize in 1937.[31] And in 1946, a reporter from the *New York Times* won the award "for his eye-witness account of the atom-bombing of Nagasaki and his subsequent ten articles on the development, production, and significance of the atomic bomb."[32] In the following decades other Pulitzer reporting awards based on science journalism were given to several other newspapers.

Similar to the development in the Meritorious Public Service category, medical or health-related stories also appeared in the general reporting category since the early 1940's: In 1943 a reporter of the *Chicago Daily News* was so honored "for his graphic story of how a U.S. Navy Pharmacist's Mate under enemy waters in a submarine performed an operation for appendictis saving a sailor's life."[33] In the following year a group of journalists from the *New York Journal-American* received the prize for "the development and publication of a news story on August 12, 1943, which saved the life of a two-year old girl in the

---

[25] *Ibid.*, p. 7.
[26] *Ibid.*, p. 8.
[27] *Ibid.*
[28] *Ibid.*, p. 10.
[29] *Ibid.*
[30] *Ibid.*, p. 11.
[31] *Ibid.*
[32] *Ibid.*, p. 12.
[33] *Ibid.*

**Columbia University**
**in the City of New York**
GRADUATE SCHOOL OF JOURNALISM
OFFICE OF THE DEAN

May 1st, 1941.

Dr. Frank D. Fackenthal
Provost of the University

Dear Mr. Provost:

At the informal meeting of the Advisory Board today, the following recommendations were made for formal consideration tomorrow:

1. That the Pulitzer Public Service Prize be awarded to the St. Louis Post Dispatch for its successful campaign against the city smoke nuisance.

2. That a scroll be prepared containing the names of all foreign correspondents who have served daily newspapers and press associations since the beginning of the wars in Europe, the scroll to be signed by the members of the Advisory Board and presented to each man, or in case of death, to their families.

The Board voted also that a committee draft a special citation for The New York Times commending the public service value of its foreign news reports.

This is a Special Citation and not an honorable mention award.

3. For distinguished editorial writing, the Board recommends an award to Reuben Maury, editorial writer for the New York Daily News without naming any specific editorial.

4. That the reporter's prize be awarded to Westbrook Pegler for his reportorial work exposing scandals in the ranks of organized labor.

That the cartoon prize be awarded to Jacob Burck, The Chicago Times, for his cartoon "If I should die before I wake".

Faithfully yours,

Carl W. Ackerman
Dean.

Report of the 1941 Pulitzer Prize Jury in Journalism

Lutheran Hospital of New York City by obtaining penicillin."[34] In 1945 a reporter of the *San Francisco Call-Bulletin* earned the Pulitzer reporting award "for his campaign to encourage blood donations" in the previous year.[35] A dozen years later, a prominent member of the *New York Times* got a National Reporting award "for his five-part analysis of the effect of President Eisenhower's illness on the functioning of the Executive Branch of the Federal Government."[36] In the same category which was established in the late fourties, a member of *United Press International* was the 1964 award recipient "for his outstanding coverage of the assassination of President John F. Kennedy" in November of the preceding year.[37]

Also in the local reporting categories of the Pulitzer Prize system various awards were given for medical or health-oriented stories, several of them based on investigative reporting: In 1960 the award went to a journalist of the *Atlanta Constitution* "for the excellent reporting in his series of articles on mental institutions in Georgia."[38] Two years later a reporter of the *Chicago Tribune* earned the Pulitzer Prize "for his initiative in uncovering scandals in the Metropolitan Sanitary District of Greater Chicago, with resultant remedial action."[39] A reporter from the *Montgomery Advertiser* and *Alabama Journal* was the winner in 1970 "for his exposé of a commercial scheme for using Alabama prisoners for drug experimentation and obtaining blood plasma from them."[40] In the following year the award was given to a reporter of the *Chicago Tribune* "for exposing collusion between police and some of Chicago's largest private ambulance companies to restrict service in low income areas, leading to major reforms."[41] A journalist from the *New York Daily News* was the 1974 winner in the local investigative specialized reporting category "for his resourceful investigative reporting in the exposure of extreme abuse of the New York Medicaid program."[42]

In addition to scandal stories relating to aspects of health care costs,[43] Pulitzer Prizes were awarded for other types of medical articles as well. In 1976 staff members of the *Chicago Tribune* received the

---

[34] *Ibid.*
[35] *Ibid.*
[36] *Ibid.*, p. 24.
[37] *Ibid.*, p. 25.
[38] *Ibid.*, p. 13.
[39] *Ibid.*, p. 17.
[40] *Ibid.*, p. 18.
[41] *Ibid.*
[42] *Ibid.*
[43] Cf. Carl J. Schramm (Ed.), Health Care and Its Costs, New York - London 1987.

## Ambulance driver wins a Pulitzer

This ambulance driver is William Jones, Chicago Tribune reporter, named winner of the 1971 Pulitzer Prize for local investigative reporting. This is the fifth Pulitzer Prize awarded to members of the Tribune staff.

Posing as an ambulance attendant, Bill uncovered widespread abuses by some of Chicago's largest private ambulance companies. Sadistic treatment of the poor and ill. Phony fees. Police payoffs.

His six-part series resulted in 16 grand jury indictments, 10 of them against policemen. Two ambulance companies were barred from carrying welfare patients. Tough new laws were passed regulating private ambulance service. Civic leaders praised the articles for "performing a definite public service."

To this we add our own congratulations. We're proud of Bill Jones, and of all our staff. Because they believe a good newspaper should be a force for good in its community, they help make the Chicago Tribune the unchallenged leader throughout Chicagoland.

# Chicago Tribune

From: *Editor & Publisher* (New York), Vol. 104/No. 23, June 5, 1971, first cover p.

award because they had "uncovered widespread abuses in Federal housing programs in Chicago and exposed shocking conditions at two private Chicago hospitals."[44] The following year saw the prize awarded to two journalists from the *Philadelphia Inquirer* "for their reports on conditions in the Farview (Pa.) State Hospital for the mentally ill."[45] In the same year another Pulitzer award went to a member of the *Milwaukee Journal* "for her reports on the elderly and the process of aging."[46] In 1979 a science writer for the *Baltimore Evening Sun* was honored in a newly established feature writing category "for an account of brain surgery."[47] A staff member of the *New York Times* earned a Pulitzer Prize in the same award category in 1983 "for her memorable and medically detailed account of her struggle with toxic shock syndrome."[48] In the following year a team of reporters from *Newsday* won a general local reporting award "for their enterprising and comprehensive coverage of the Baby Jane Doe case and its far-reaching social and political implications" to other birth-defected children.[49]

From 1985 on, the Pulitzer Prize system was enriched by two new award categories entitled ""Explanatory Journalism" and "Specialized Reporting." In the first mentioned category - which is defined as "journalism that illuminates significant and complex issues" - the winner was a journalist from the *Baltimore Evening Sun* who received the award "for his seven-part series 'The Mind Fixers,' about the new science of molecular psychiatry."[50] The "Specialized Reporting" award was to be given to "a distinguished example of reporting on such specialized subjects as sports, business, science, education or religion."[51] In 1986 the award winners in this Pulitzer Prize section were two reporters of the *Pittsburgh Press* who earned the honor "for their investigation of violations and failures in the organ transplantation system in the United States."[52] From that time on, medical or health-related stories could be awarded in five different Pulitzer Prize reporting categories, therefore increasing the chances for such articles to win an award. From time to

---

[44] Columbia University (Ed.), *op. cit.*, p. 18.
[45] *Ibid.*
[46] *Ibid.*, p. 15.
[47] *Ibid.*, p. 31.
[48] *Ibid.*
[49] *Ibid.*, p. 15.
[50] *Ibid.*, p. 20.
[51] Columbia University (Ed.), The 69th annual Pulitzer Prizes..., New York, April 24, 1985, p. 2.
[52] Columbia University (Ed.), The 70th annual Pulitzer Prizes..., New York, April 17, 1986, p. 2.

# ENTRY FORM FOR A PULITZER PRIZE
## *In Journalism*

### (TO BE FILED BY FEBRUARY 1)
Postmark acceptable but not recommended

ENTRANT _____
(name in full; team entries are limited to 3 individual names)

HOME ADDRESS _____

PRESENT OCCUPATION AND ORGANIZATION _____

DATE AND PLACE OF BIRTH _____

PLEASE ENCLOSE ENTRANT'S Biography ☐ and Photograph ☐ $20 Handling Fee ☐ and check boxes accordingly.

The following Pulitzer Prizes in Journalism are awarded for material in a United States newspaper published daily, Sunday or at least once a week during the year. Check appropriate box. Please note that unless indicated otherwise, exhibits are limited to 10 articles.

| | Check Here |
|---|---|
| 1. For a distinguished example of meritorious public service by a newspaper through the use of its journalistic resources which may include editorials, cartoons, and photographs, as well as reporting, a gold medal. (No more than 20 articles may be submitted for each exhibit.) | 1 |
| 2. For a distinguished example of reporting within a newspaper's area of circulation that meets the daily challenges of journalism such as spot news reporting or consistent beat coverage, Three thousand dollars, $3,000. | 2 |
| 3. For a distinguished example of investigative reporting within a newspaper's area of circulation by an individual or team, presented as a single article or series, Three thousand dollars, $3,000. | 3 |
| 4. For a distinguished example of explanatory journalism that illuminates significant and complex issues, Three thousand dollars, $3,000. | 4 |
| 5. For a distinguished example of reporting on such specialized subjects as sports, business, science, education or religion, Three thousand dollars, $3,000. | 5 |
| 6. For a distinguished example of reporting on national affairs, Three thousand dollars, $3,000. | 6 |
| 7. For a distinguished example of reporting on international affairs, including United Nations correspondence, Three thousand dollars, $3,000. | 7 |
| 8. For a distinguished example of feature writing giving prime consideration to high literary quality and originality, Three thousand dollars, $3,000. (No more than 3 articles [1,500 words or more] or 5 articles [1,500 words or less] may be submitted for each exhibit.) | 8 |
| 9. For distinguished commentary, Three thousand dollars, $3,000. | 9 |
| 10. For distinguished criticism, Three thousand dollars, $3,000. | 10 |
| 11. For distinguished editorial writing, the test of excellence being clearness of style, moral purpose, sound reasoning, and power to influence public opinion in what the writer conceives to be the right direction, due account being taken of the whole volume of the editorial writer's work during the year, Three thousand dollars, $3,000. | 11 |
| 12. For a distinguished example of a cartoonist's work, the determining qualities being that the cartoon shall embody an idea made clearly apparent, shall show good drawing and striking pictorial effect, and shall be intended to be helpful to some commendable cause of public importance, due account being taken of the whole volume of the artist's work during the year, Three thousand dollars, $3,000. | 12 |
| 13. For a distinguished example of spot news photography in black and white or color, which may consist of a photograph or photographs, a sequence or an album, Three thousand dollars, $3,000. (No more than 20 photographs may be submitted with each exhibit.) | 13 |
| 14. For a distinguished example of feature photography in black and white or color, which may consist of a photograph or photographs, a sequence or an album, Three thousand dollars, $3,000. (No more than 20 photographs may be submitted with each exhibit.) | 14 |

Signature of person sponsoring this entrant _____
(may be self)

Please print your name, title, and organization _____

Address _____

*(Please send entry form and exhibit by February 1 to Mr. Robert C. Christopher, Secretary, The Pulitzer Prize Board, at 702 Journalism, Columbia University, New York, N.Y. 10027. Telephone; 212-854-3841 or 212-854-3841. See reverse side for Plan of Award. Please make checks payable to Columbia University/Pulitzer Prizes.)*

From: Columbia University (Ed.), The Pulitzer Prizes in Journalism, New York, October, 1989, p. 1.

time it is also possible for medical or health-related articles to win in non-reporting award categories.[53]

Although a separate Pulitzer Prize category for medical or science reporting was never established, medical or health-related aspects surfaced in many of the past and presently existing award categories. Although the award-winning stories vary in theme and style, only one author, so far, has undertaken the risky job to classify Pulitzer Prize-winning texts of reporters. He tried to distinguish "narrative writing," "investigative writing," "profile writing," "descriptive writing," and "analytical writing."[54] Principally, one has to bear in mind that the Pulitzer Prizes as such represent a continuum which does not necessarily hold true to the basic conditions under which the prize-winners were determined.[55] Interpreting the original ground rules for awarding the Pulitzer Prize can be a complicated task. The awarding procedures are often in flux because of changes in the jury or swings in the attitude of the Advisory Board.[56] As mentioned before, the Advisory Board has a strong influence on the final determination of the award-winners and is able to include certain priorities in the awarding criteria.[57]

The advantage of this policy is that - in certain cases and years - political, economical or cultural reporting is not recognized to the exclusion of medical or health-related text material. So in the last two decades the juries as well as the Advisory Board increasingly placed medical reporting - in a very general sense - on the priority list during the annual awarding process. Therefore, over many decades a relatively great number of Pulitzer Prizes went to medical-oriented articles so that the Pulitzer award system covers many more medical aspects than any of the past - or still-existing special medical journalism prizes in the U.S.A.[58]

---

[53] Cf. John Hohenberg (Ed.), The Pulitzer Prize Story. News, Stories, Editorials, Cartoons, and Pictures, New York - London 1959; John Hohenberg (Ed.), The Pulitzer Prize Story II. Award-winning News Stories, Columns, Editorials, Cartoons, and News Pictures, 1959-1980, New York 1980.

[54] Cf. W. David Sloan et al., The Best of Pulitzer Prize News Writing, op. cit., pp. V ff.

[55] Cf. John Hohenberg, The Pulitzer Prizes, op. cit., pp. 232 ff.

[56] Cf. Heinz-Dietrich Fischer (Ed.), Outstanding International Press Reporting. Pulitzer Prize Winning Articles in Foreign Correspondence, Vol. 1, Berlin - New York 1984, pp. XIX ff.

[57] Cf. John Hohenberg, The Pulitzer Prizes, op. cit., pp. 21 ff.

[58] Cf. Heinz-Dietrich Fischer, Medizinpublizistische Ehrenpreise in den Vereinigten Staaten - eine erste Bestandsaufnahme, in: J. F. Volrad Deneke/ Wilhelm Roessler/Paul Swertz (Eds.), Aktuelle Fragen der Sozialmedizin. Festschrift zum 65. Geburtstag von Herbert Viefhues, Bochum, FRG, 1985, pp. 94 ff.

and abroad.[59] "Because the fields of medical information, communication of scientific information, biosciences communications, health sciences information, have been growing with relative rapidity," as a competent author states,[60] this development is reflected in the Pulitzer Prize-winning texts on medical reporting as well. Like award-winning articles from other fields of journalism all the texts "have become a hallmark of excellence in American cultural life, of the working of a tradition of conscience in American journalism,"[61] as Hohenberg remarks and brings it at the point.

Although Pulitzer Prize-winning articles are generally considered as first-class journalism pieces, the Pulitzer Prize juries as well as the Advisory Board are not held responsible for any possible errors in the texts. There is no obligation of the Pulitzer Prize system to check any entry and article for aspects of truth and other ethical questions. So it happened, for example, that in 1973 two journalists of the *Knight Newspapers* won the Pulitzer national reporting award "for their disclosure of Senator Thomas Eagleton's history of psychiatric therapy, resulting in his withdrawal as the Democratic Vice Presidential nominee" in the preceding year.[62] "By concealing the machinations and politics behind a leak," Edward J. Epstein remarks, "journalists suppress part of the truth surrounding the story. Thus the means by which the medical records of Sen. Thomas Eagleton were acquired and passed on to the *Knight Newspapers* (which won the 1973 Pulitzer Prize for disclosing information contained in these records) seem no less important than the senator's medical history itself, especially since copies of the presumably illegally obtained records were later found in the White House safe..."[63] of a person involved in the Watergate case.

Despite that problem and similar occurrences from time to time "the Pulitzer Prizes... remain today the most prestigious journalistic awards."[64] But for this Prize system as well as for many others there are

---

[59] Cf.Heinz-Dietrich Fischer, Stimulans für medizinjournalistischen Nachwuchs durch fachpublizistische Ehrenpreise? Eine Skizze, in: Rolf Terheyden (Ed.), Beruf und Berufung. Zweite Festschrift für Johannes Binkowski, Mainz, FRG, 1989, pp. 96 ff.

[60] Stacey B. Day, Health Communications, New York 1979, p. 201.

[61] John Hohenberg, The Pulitzer Prizes, 1917-1957, *Columbia Library Columns* (New York), Vol. VI/No. 3, May, 1957, p. 13.

[62] Columbia University (Ed.), The Pulitzer Prizes 1917-1991, *op. cit.*, p. 25.

[63] Edward Jay Epstein, The American Press: Some Truths About Truths, in: John C. Merrill/Ralph D. Barney (Eds.), Ethics and the Press. Readings in Mass Media Morality, New York 1975, p. 68.

[64] William B. Blankenburg/Richard L. Allen, The Journalism Contest Thicket: Is it Time for Some Guidelines?, in: John C. Merrill/Ralph Barney (Eds.), *op. cit.*, p. 303.

still certain dangers which H. Eugene Goodwin describes as follows: "Today U.S. journalists have more than 400 contests they can enter, and leaders of the field are wondering aloud whether a good idea has not been carried too far. Three main problems result from the proliferation of journalistic awards: The first is that there are so many of them that all but a handful have lost significance as improvers of the breed. Second, the competition for the few prestigious journalism awards, such as the Pulitzer Prizes, is often so intense that journalists have been known to hype their articles in hopes of winning one of the big prizes. A third problem arises from a growing minority of the contests that are sponsored by vested interests who seem to be trying to get the news media to present material that might not otherwise get in print or on the air and to reflect a slant favored by the sponsor"[65] which also may be possible in the field of medical or pharmaceutical journalism awards.[66]

The biggest "flop" in the entire history of the Pulitzer Prizes happened in 1981 and was based on a medical-related story published in the *Washington Post* in the previous year. The paper which had received fame nearly a decade ago when it earned the Pulitzer meritorious public service award "for its investigation of the Watergate case,"[67] now had to confess that it was trapped by a journalistic hoax. The Columbia University's Office of Public Information announced in mid-April, 1981, the names of the annual Pulitzer Prize-winners which included a "feature writing" award for *Washington Post's* Janet Cooke "for her story of an eight-year-old heroin addict."[68] Only two days later another press announcement revised this decision by saying: "The Pulitzer Prize Board today awarded the 1981 Pulitzer Prize for feature writing to Teresa Carpenter of the *Village Voice*. The action by telephone poll of the Board's members followed the disclosure by the *Washington Post* that its reporter, Janet Cooke, had fabricated the story for which she had won the feature writing prize... The *Post's* executive editor... sent a telegram to members of the Board saying that Miss Cooke could not accept the award and had resigned from the newspaper. The board withdrew her prize. It was the first time in the 65-year history of the Pulitzer Prizes that an award was withdrawn because a story was false."[69]

---

[65] H. Eugene Goodwin, Groping for Ethics in Journalism, Ames, Ia., 1983, p. 79.
[66] Cf. Editor & Publisher (Ed.), Journalism Awards Directory. Prizes, Awards, Fellowships, 6th ed., New York 1978.
[67] Columbia University (Ed.), The Pulitzer Prizes 1917-1991, *op. cit.*, p. 8.
[68] Columbia University (Ed.),The 65th annual Pulitzer Prizes..., New York, April 13, 1981, p. 3.
[69] Columbia University (Ed.), Press Release, New York, April 15, 1981, p. 1.

# 6th Annual Directory of Journalism Awards

This Sixth Annual Directory of Journalism Awards continues a service instituted by EDITOR & PUBLISHER to provide an updated reference to the hundreds of opportunities for citations in the news media. The selections include prizes for people and publications in newspaper and magazine categories and in radio and television broadcasting—in both the United States and Canada.

Many of the listings are competitive; several are non-competitive awards that are generally regarded as being prestigious. Because the great majority of sponsors have imposed more specific and more demanding requirements for entries, the listings in this Directory give only basic information and direct the interested contestant to the organization or association which issues the entry forms. Unless otherwise noted the usual period of the competition is the calendar year. In most cases entry deadline dates are shown.

An annual edition of the Directory has become necessary because of the increasing number of prize competitions in the journalism fields and the dropout or revision of old ones. There are no fewer than 10 new prizes posted in this year's Directory.

A separate section contains information on special Fellowships and Scholarships for journalists. A complete register of scholarships for undergraduate journalism students may be obtained from The Newspaper Fund, P.O. Box 300, Princeton, N.J. 08540.

(Awards are listed by category. Name of award is listed in alphabetical order.)

## HIGHWAY SAFETY

AAA Highway Safety Awards. New Jersey radio stations and newspapers. $1,400 prizes. No editorials. Calendar year material. Entries before June 15 to: William J. Kohm Associates Inc., 312 Forest Avenue, Paramus, N.J. 07652. Sponsor: Public Affairs Council, AAA Automobile Clubs of New Jersey.

## SCIENCE

AAAS Science Writing Awards. U.S. Newspapers and magazines. $1,000 each in three categories from Westinghouse Educational Foundation. Expenses to annual meeting. Medical writing excluded. Entries before November 15 to: American Association for the Advancement of Science, 1776 Massachusetts Avenue, N.W., Washington, D.C. 20036.

1976 winners: Paul G. Hayes, *Milwaukee Journal;* Don Alan Hall, *Corval-*

*lis* (Ore.) *Gazette-Times;* Jonathan Eberhart, *Science News.*

## HEALTH CARE

AAFP Journalism Awards. The Family Doctor and health care. $2,000 prizes. Print media July through June. November deadline for entries on forms from: American Academy of Family Physicians, 1740 West 92nd Street, Kansas City, Mo. 64114.

1976 winners: Lewis Cope, *Minneapolis Tribune;* Dodi Schultz, *Today's Health;* Alton Blakeslee and Brian Sullivan, Associated Press.

## GEOLOGY

AAPG Journalism Award. Public understanding of geology. Conferred by: American Association of Petroleum Geologists, Box 979, Tulsa, Okla. 74101.

1977 winner: Dr. Philip H. Abelson, *Science.*

## HEALTH & HEALING

ACA Journalism Competition. Basic health habits and healing. All media. $200 prizes in five categories. Entries before March 15 on official forms from: American Chiropractic Association, 2200 Grand Avenue, Des Moines, Ia. 50312.

1976 winners: Kathy Craft, *Oregon* (U.) *Daily Emerald;* Jeff Holladay, *Oklahoma City Oklahoman* and *Times;* Alice Hornbaker, *Cincinnati Enquirer;* Joan Kilmer, *Buffalo Courier Express;* Matt Clark, *Newsweek;* Leonard Lear, *Bestways;* Gloria Hochman, *Philadelphia Inquirer;* Kenneth Lasson, *Washingtonian;* tv—Fred Greene, WINK, Fort Myers, Fla.; radio—KMOX Radio News; Carol Colman, WRFM New York; Michael D. Veley, Cornell U.

## NURSING

ACNHA Journalism Award. Long-term care and the professional administrator. Nominations to: American College of Nursing Home Administrators, 4650 East West Highway, Washington, D.C. 20014.

1977 winner: Grace Wilson, Minneapolis.

## CANCER

ACS Media Awards. Cancer treatment and research. Trophies to winners. September-to-August. Entries before September 15 on forms from: American Cancer Society, Suite 1900, 40 West 57th Street, New York, N.Y. 10019.

1977 winners: *New York Times* (Richard Severo), *Mason City* (Ia.)

**BARBARA REDDING, health reporter for the *Cincinnati Enquirer*, beams with her APHA plaque. Portable typewriter also went with her Ray Bruner Science Writing Fellowship.**

*Gazette* (Diane Cobb), *Minneapolis Tribune* (Lewis Cope), WIP-am Philadelphia (Patricia Shelton Miller), WOR-am New York (Penny Pinsker), WGAR-am Cleveland (Eric Braun), CBS tv (Good Times), 60 Minutes (Morley Safer), WGBH Boston, WBAL-tv Baltimore (Ron Smith and Amanda Arnold), WPIX-tv New York (Roger Field), WIIC-tv Pittsburgh (Beverly Byer).

## DENTISTRY

ADA Science Writers Award. Dental disease, treatment and research. Newspapers and magazines. $2,000 prizes from Lever Brothers Co. July-through-June. Entries before August 31 to: American Dental Association, 211 E. Chicago Avenue, Chicago, Ill. 60611.

1977 winners: Lucy Eckberg, *Winona* (Minn.) *Daily News;* Annette Stec, *Exploring* magazine. Honors to: Michael Unger, Long Island *Newsday;* Genell Subak-Sharpe, *Medical Opinion;* Lee Edson, *New York Times* Magazine; Dianne Hardisty, *Hanford* (Calif.) *Sentinel.*

## ARCHITECTURE

AIA Medal. Architecture. Photography, articles and criticism. Nominations to: American Institute of Architects, 1735 New York Avenue, N.W., Washington, D.C. 20006.

No medals awarded in 1977.

Elected to AIA College of Fellows: John Morris Dixon, *Progressive Architecture;* Mildred F. Schmertz, *Architectural Record.*

From: *Editor & Publisher*, 1978 Journalism Awards Directory. Prizes - Awards - Fellowships, New York 1978, p. 2.

The telegram of the executive editor of the *Washington Post* to the Advisory Board contained this passage: "It is with great sadness and regret that I inform you that Janet Cooke... has determined that she cannot accept the award. She told *Post* editors... that her story about an eight-year-old heroin addict was in fact a composite, that the quotes attributed to the child were in fact fabricated and that certain events described as eyewitnessed did not in fact happen. Janet Cooke was a particularly promising and talented young reporter. She regrets the events as much as the *Washington Post* regrets them. She offered her resignation, and the *Washington Post* has accepted it."[70] A couple of days later the newspaper apologized to its readers,[71] and there came up some fear of a general credibility crisis of American newspapers.[72] "When the falsity of Janet Cooke's story became known," Ed Lambeth describes the follow-up, "and when the injustice it had perpetrated on police and the black community became clear, the *Post* ran a special section explaining how its transgression occurred and highlighted on the front page the conclusions of its ombudsman's investigation. Among these conclusions were that the editors had ignored signs that the story of the boy heroin addict may have been untrue; that the emphasis on prizewinning at the *Post* 'clouded good judgment'... ."[73]

So vying for prestigious journalism awards like the Pulitzer Prize to some extent may become a problem for the integrity of journalistic achievement. "Although American journalists have a hard time on agreeing on many things," Goodwin remarks, "virtually all of them have come to accept accuracy and fairness as the most important of their professional standards. Both of these standards, of course, are ethical and professional or operational. Accuracy has been a more troublesome ideal for journalists than it might appear. For one thing, journalists have to do their work under deadlines, very demanding deadlines at times. The pressure to get the news out to the public while it is still fresh causes errors... A second difficulty in achieving accuracy has to do with expectations. Most people outside of journalism, and even many journalists, expect journalism to produce the 'truth,' forgetting... that news and truth are not the same thing. The facts that journalists *can*

---

[70] Quoted *ibid.*, pp. 1 f.
[71] Cf. Bill Green, Janet's World. The Story of a Child Who Never existed - How and Why It Came to Be Published, *The Washington Post* (Washington, D.C.), 104th Year/No. 135, April 19, 1981, p. 1, cols. 1 f.
[72] Cf. N.N., Von Watergate zu "Jimmygate". Ruhm, Reinfall und Schuldbekenntnis der 'Washington Post', *Der Spiegel* (Hamburg), Vol. 35/No. 19, May 4, 1981, pp. 168 ff.
[73] Edmund B. Lambeth, Committed Journalism. An Ethic for the Profession, Bloomington, Ind., 1986, p. 32.

produce sometimes add up to the truth, but journalists are seldom able to put sufficient facts together at a given time to be able to tell the truth about some news subject."[74] In cases of health or medical-related articles which use to be of special importance to the media recipients and potential patients this problem is significant.[75]

In this respect one may question how much medical ethics and journalistic ethics are congruent or very different from each other. This problem cannot be solved in short as special research is necessary to discuss this issue thoroughly. Therefore, it may be of interest to mention John Merrill's idea of an "Apollonysian" Journalist. He thinks that any journalist should "recognize the imperative of freedom, but that he should incorporate into his journalistic philosophy... two other emphases of tremendous importance: rationality and commitment. At the same time he must - and *will* with these philosophical dimensions - become a kind of journalistic scientist-artist, part Apollo and part Dionysus, a person who merges the perspectives of objective reason and existential subjectivity. Such a synthesis will produce a journalist who may well be called the 'Apollonysian': a person who thinks *and* feels, who is both rational *and* sensitive, who is both concerned with facts *and* with feelings, who is dedicated to the objective world 'out there' *and* to his subjective world 'in here.' He is, in essence, the rational synthesizer - the journalist who is able to *intentionally* develop a journalistic philosophy which merges the strains (or stances) of freedom, rationality and duty... The free journalist who tempers his journalism with reason, sensitivity and commitment *is a responsible journalist*".[76]

The journalists as well as the media "must assume obligation of social responsibility; and if they do not, someone must see that they do."[77] During the early days of journalism many journalists and publishers "were not likely to concern themselves with the ethical aspects" of the profession. But "by the middle of the nineteenth century, journalism had begun to attract men of education and principle who set high standards for their craft and tried to live up to them. Some such men formulated codes of ethics for their own staffs... As the twentieth century

---

[74] H. Eugene Goodwin, *op. cit.*, pp. 10 f.

[75] Cf. Heinz-Dietrich Fischer (Ed.), Handbuch der Medizinkommunikation. Informationstransfer und Publizistik im Gesundheitswesen, Cologne, FRG, 1988.

[76] John C. Merrill, The Imperative of Freedom. A Philosophy of Journalistic Autonomy, New York 1974, p. 183.

[77] Fred S. Siebert/Theodore Peterson/Wilbur Schramm, Four Theories of the Press. The Authoritarian, Libertarian, Social Responsibility and Soviet Communist Concepts of What the Press Should Be and Do, Urbana, Ill., 1963, p. 7.

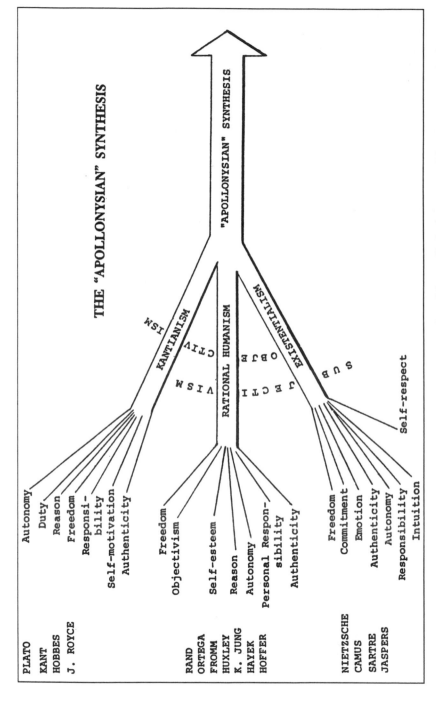

THE "APOLLONYSIAN" SYNTHESIS

"APOLLONYSIAN" SYNTHESIS

KANTIANISM

OBJECTIVISM

RATIONAL HUMANISM

EXISTENTIALISM

SUBJECTIVISM

PLATO — Autonomy
KANT — Duty
HOBBES — Reason
J. ROYCE — Freedom
— Responsi-bility
— Self-motivation
— Authenticity

RAND — Freedom
ORTEGA — Objectivism
FROMM — Self-esteem
HUXLEY — Reason
K. JUNG — Autonomy
HAYEK — Personal Respon-sibility
HOFFER — Authenticity

NIETZSCHE — Freedom
CAMUS — Commitment
SARTRE — Emotion
JASPERS — Authenticity
— Autonomy
— Responsibility
— Intuition
— Self-respect

From: John C. Merrill, The Imperative of Freedom. A Philosophy of Journalistic Autonomy, New York 1974, p. 187.

opened, publishers spoke more and more often of the duties which accompanied the privileged position of the press..."[78] In this group it was Joseph Pulitzer who wrote to defend his proposal for a school of journalism: "Nothing less than the highest ideals, the most scrupulous anxiety to do right, the most accurate knowledge of the problems it has to meet, and a sincere sense of its moral responsibility will save journalism from subversive business interests, seeking selfish ends, antagonistic to the public welfare... Commercialism has a legitimate place in a newspaper, namely, in the business office. The more successful a newspaper is commercially, the better for its moral side. The more prosperous it is, the more independent it can afford to be, the higher salaries it can pay to editors and reporters, the less subject it will be to temptation, the better it can stand losses for the sake of principle and conviction... ."[79]

Especially the medical journalist has to keep himself free from any influences or pressures from outside the media, i.e. pharmaceutical companies, PR agencies, etc., which sponsor certain products.[80] There are numerous other dangers, as well, as described by the American Medical Writers Association (AMWA): "The printed word can be very dangerous. False claims for medicines and false promises of cures for diseases still incurable, made in the mass media reaching the public, so-called 'health' books which become bestsellers, and many more such items of cultism and quackery cause great harm. They are used by charlatans to prey upon the faddists, the fearful, the ill, the dying. In professional practice, also, the printed word can be very dangerous. The quality of the medical information supplied to physicians is just as important as the quality of the product being described. Control of medical communication is just as important as control of potency, purity, and stability of drugs. Because medical communicators influence the health of the nation, they should have a code of ethics which emphasizes the following principles: 1. Competence..., 2. Accuracy..., 3. Completeness..., 4. Objectivity..., 5. Integrity..., 6. Documentation... This applies to every medical author, whether he is a physician in practice or research, a freelance writer, or an employee of a company or other organization... How well the art and science of medical communication continues to develop will depend on the degree of professionalism we instill into our calling."[81]

---

[78] *Ibid.*, p. 83.

[79] Joseph Pulitzer, *op. cit.*, p. 658 f.

[80] Cf. Heinz-Dietrich Fischer (Ed.), Medizinpublizistik. Prämissen - Praktiken - Probleme, Frankfurt a.M. - Bern - New York - Paris 1990.

[81] Harold Swanberg, History of the American Medical Writers' Association and its previous associated organizations, Vol. 1, Quincy, Ill., 1965, pp. 201 f.

To ensure the quality of its medical-related articles *Time* magazine has the policy that "stories about the law and medicine are reviewed by a lawyer and doctor before they are sent to the printers. The aim of this practice," Herbert Gans writes, "is to ensure accuracy, although the reviewers are free to question - but not to censor - criticism of their professions."[82] Besides these aspects there are several other potential barriers in medical journalism, too. "The bulk of medical writers," William B. Bean states, "float about in a linguistic fog and never forsake it for the world of clarity. Some care greatly, but by nature, by training, or by chance are so ill-attuned to the felicitous use of words that they recognize no stylistic lapses, their own or others. They do not even identify excellence when they see it... Despite billions of dollars in grants, institutes of one kind or another, project site visits, subsidies for research, committees assigning themselves to stamp out this and that, voluntary health organizations, we have never developed public health and preventive medicine to deal with grammar and excellence in speaking and writing. In short, we have no institutes for the care and feeding of spastic language, crippled sentences, chronically debilitated and injured grammar, and the malignant metastases of uncontrolled jargon..."[83]

There is also no guarantee that Pulitzer Prize-winning articles on medical or health-related topics are free from language or other deficiencies. This brings up the important question: how to educate writers and especially medical journalists? For example, the University of California at Santa Cruz Graduate Certificate Program in Science Communication believes "that it is not too late to make science and technology understandable to the average citizen" but the educational philosophy also states "that the job must be done by people trained both in science and in communication techniques, and no longer by generalists. Traditionally, developments in science and technology have been communicated to the public by reporters who are largely self-taught in science. Some of those science writers produce highly acclaimed reportage and editorial commentary despite their limited formal education in science. Others of them, however, are all but overwhelmed by the complexity of contemporary science and engineering, and their reporting often reflects their confusion... The UC Santa Cruz program responds to this new national

---

[82] Herbert J. Gans, Deciding What's News. A Study of CBS Evening News, NBC Nightly News, Newsweek, and Time, New York 1980, p. 270.

[83] William B. Bean, Medical Writing: Discrepancies between Theory and Practice, in: Stacey B. Day (Ed.), Communication of Scientific Information, Basel - Munich - Paris - London - New York - Sydney 1975, p. 6.

## AMERICAN MEDICAL WRITERS ASSOCIATION

### CODE OF ETHICS

**Preamble**

The American Medical Writers Association (AMWA) has compiled the following principles of conduct for all individuals involved in medical communication to guide them in their relationships with physicians, fellow writers, other health professionals, government agencies, and all others who may be affected by their communications. Writing is a powerful tool that influences the minds of readers in all walks of life. Therefore, medical writers should honor this code of ethics.

**Principle 1**

Medical writers have the duty to observe the laws and regulations pertaining to the documents they write, to uphold the dignity and honor of their profession and this Association, and to accept these ethical principles. They should not engage in any activity that may bring discredit to their profession or to the Association, such as writing papers or theses for individuals attempting to qualify themselves or preparing other fraudulent documents, and they should promptly expose any illegal or unethical conduct they detect in their profession.

**Principle 2**

Medical writers should hold accuracy and truth to be primary considerations and should provide well balanced, unbiased, undistorted information to the fullest extent of their capabilities. They should use authoritative (preferably original) sources as the basis for their writings and should give proper credit, including adequate documentation.

**Principle 3**

Medical writers should never knowingly write or condone the writing of medical information that does not meet high professional standards, whether or not such writings come under the purview of any regulatory agency. They should always try to prevent the perpetuation of incorrect information. They should write about a subject only when qualified to do so by training and experience or in collaboration with someone so qualified.

**Principle 4**

Medical writers should not function under conditions or terms which impair or impede proper application of their judgment and skills, which tend to lower the quality of their services, or which require unethical conduct.

**Principle 5**

Medical writers should constantly strive to enlarge and perfect their professional knowledge and skills. They should apply these fully and should actively participate in organizations that have as their objective the improvement of their profession.

**Principle 6**

Medical writers should respect the personal and confidential nature of professional records. They should not divulge, without proper authorization, any confidential patient, patent, or other private information to which they have access.

**Principle 7**

Medical writers may actively seek, through advertisements or other means, ethical professional assignments consistent with their talents and capacity to provide medical communication services. They should accept fair and reasonable remuneration for their services and should honor the terms of the contracts they sign.

**Principle 8**

Medical writers should not exploit their Association financially or otherwise, and should not use their Association or its publications or any activities of its members for their own personal gain.

Eric W. Martin, Ph.D., 1973
Revised June 1989

From: American Medical Writers Association (Ed.), Membership Directory 1990, Bethesda, Md., 1990, p. 80.

need by requiring that participants be not only proficient writers upon admission, but thoroughly grounded in science as well." This program includes such courses as "Reporting and Writing Science News," "Neurophysiology and Behavior," "Human Anatomy," etc.[84] Recently, the American Medical Writers Association created a special Educators Section "promoting and improving the teaching of medical communication and the training of medical communicators.[85]

Courses in science communication are also part of the educational program of the Graduate School of Journalism at New York's Columbia University, established by Joseph Pulitzer.[86] One of the basic courses in the curriculum, conducted by Professor Kenneth K. Goldstein, aimed "for a mixture of substance and technique in order to acquaint participants with the issues and people now important in the coverage of health/environment/science/technology areas." The course tried to "cover a variety of stories and develop a sound method for approaching each one, whether it is organ transplants or computer-assisted communications... During the course, a number of scientists and science writers will meet with the group... for close-up interviews..."[87] One part of the course dealt with "the new biology with specific stories on transplants, Recombinant DNA, genetic engineering, health care delivery, a sleep laboratory and other health/medical/biology topics."[88] Another course focused on "the most important ethical issues in contemporary science and medicine in order to give journalists a familiarity with the issues, with the resources that exist to analyze and document the ethical aspects of these issues, and with the ethical perspective on contemporary events in general."[89] The course concluded with a session on "Writing About Ethical Issues in Science and Medicine,"[90] also touching important questions of media morality by discussing health-related issues.

---

[84] John Wilkes, University of California, Santa Cruz: Graduate Certificate Program in Science Communication, in: Robert Bosch Stiftung (Ed.), Wissenschaftsjournalismus in den USA. Infrastrukturen, Ausbildungsangebote, Erfolgsgeheimnisse, Stuttgart, FRG, 1985, pp. 150 ff.

[85] Thomas A. Lang, Educators Plan First Plenary Session For Toronto Annual Conference, *AMWA Journal* (Bethesda, Md.), Vol. 6/No. 2, June, 1991, p. 33.

[86] Cf. Heinz-Dietrich Fischer, Trends zur Symbiose von Medizin und Kommunikationsmedien in den Vereinigten Staaten, *Deutsches Ärzteblatt* (Cologne), Vol. 79/No. 7, February 19, 1982, pp. 72 ff.

[87] Kenneth K. Goldstein, Health/Science/Evironment/Technology Reporting (at Columbia University), in: Robert Bosch Stiftung (Ed.), *op. cit.*, p. 160.

[88] *Ibid.*, p. 161.

[89] *Ibid.*, p. 168.

[90] *Ibid.*, p. 170.

The Columbia program also enables the students to write "a Master's Project on a science-related subject."[91] And from time to time alumni of Columbia's Graduate School of Journalism can be found among the annual Pulitzer Prize-winners in the field of medical or science reporting.[92] So the original Pulitzer intention to found a school of journalism and an award system for outstanding achievements in journalism and other fields over the decades resulted in an excellent record of educating and honoring journalists. The awarded texts from medical-related topics as well as from other areas of journalism offer proof of the success of that basic idea. As it was once stated by the president of Columbia University, Joseph Pulitzer "was first and foremost a journalist. But his horizons, like those of all good journalists, extended far beyond his own profession and when he decided to link a system of prizes to a university, he did so in the express hope that this would encourage 'public service, public morals, American literature and the advancement of education.'"[93] And John Hohenberg, a former administrator of the award system, concludes: "Whatever changes... have wrought in the Pulitzer Prizes, their appeal for journalists has remained constant and their fundamental purpose has not changed... For as long as these prizes stimulate the search for truth, they will be sought after in the United States and will do honor to the profession they represent,"[94] including the unique field of medical and health-related journalism.

This brings us back - to some extent - to ethical relationships between journalism and medicine. "The pharmacist and the physician," O. R. Strackbein states, "are the instrumentalities by which medication is prescribed and provided... Their licensing is attributable to this very fact. Also, they may be held liable in courts of law for any culpable injury they may inflict. The status of the press is radically and astoundingly different. If it commits what in other fields may be an actionable wrong it has the incredible power of punishing the complainant for his presumption to speak up; and the complainant cannot take his grievance to an impartial referee because none exists!... The press is also a purveyor of a commodity, namely, news and commentary... Distortion or suppression of the truth produces the effect of poisoning the public mind. In that respect the journalistic profession and that of the physician and pharmacist are analogous. Dispensing of drugs, to repeat, calls for a high degree

---

[91] Columbia University (Ed.), Graduate School of Journalism 1989-90 (program), New York 1989, p. 25.
[92] Cf. Columbia University (Ed.), The Alumni Directory, Graduate School of Journalism, New York 1975, pp. 1-98.
[93] Michael I. Sovern (Preface), in: Columbia University (Ed.), The Pulitzer Prizes 1917-1991, *op. cit.*, p. 1.
[94] John Hohenberg (Ed.), The Pulitzer Prize Story II, *op. cit.*, pp. 8 f.

# COLUMBIA UNIVERSITY

KNOW ALL PERSONS BY THESE PRESENTS THAT

## JON D. FRANKLIN

HAS BEEN AWARDED

### THE PULITZER PRIZE IN JOURNALISM

FOR

EXPLANATORY JOURNALISM

IN WITNESS WHEREOF IT HAS CAUSED THIS CERTIFICATE TO BE
SIGNED BY THE PRESIDENT OF THE UNIVERSITY
AND ITS CORPORATE SEAL TO BE HERETO AFFIXED
ON THE TWENTY-FOURTH DAY OF APRIL IN THE YEAR OF OUR LORD
ONE THOUSAND NINE HUNDRED AND EIGHTY-FIVE

PRESIDENT

PULITZER PRIZE CERTIFICATE OF A WINNER WITH MEDICAL ARTICLES

of competence. The same may be said of the gathering and dissemination of news and commentaries to the public. The analogy continues true. The disciplinary power that resides in the issuance and revocation of license is not applicable to journalism. Here the analogy breaks down."[95] So, as a consequence, journalism ethics and medical ethics may differ in cases when a decision has to be made whether 'hard' medical stories should be published in general news media or not. Probably several of the Pulitzer Prize-winning articles reprinted in this volume may bring up this question as well.

* * *

The following texts on medical and/or health-related subjects were taken from a number of Pulitzer Prize-winning entries in different journalism categories collected in the Pulitzer Prize archive room at the Graduate School of Journalism of Columbia University, New York. Although - in most cases - several award-winning texts by each prize-winner were available, it was possible to reprint only one complete text per author to limit the size of the book. The texts to be reprinted were selected to best illustrate the topics mentioned in the reasons for the award. Every reprinted article was checked in the original newspaper edition for accuracy because some of the texts from the entries showed gaps or other faults. The editor of this book added new headings to all of the reprinted journalistic texts in order to describe each topic as succinctly as possible because some of the articles were published several decades ago. At the same time the original headlines of each newspaper article remain as basic information, supplemented by detailed references to the original place of publication.

The references given to each article include precise specifications about the volume, number, page(s) and column(s) of the original newspaper edition to simplify the search for the journalistic texts for everybody. Subheadings and other typographical peculiarities in the original articles were left unchanged and un-edited. Corrections were made in the reprinted texts only in cases of obvious typographical errors or garbled lines in the original articles. The special introductory remarks to each chapter are based mainly on the following sources: (1) supplementary material from the Pulitzer Prize-winning exhibits; (2) unpublished jury reports from the Pulitzer Prize Office at Columbia University; (3) quotations from the official award-announcements by the Pulitzer Prize Board; (4) various publications by John Hohenberg on the Pulitzer Prize system; (5) a Pulitzer Prize Reporting book by William D. Sloan et al.[96]

---

[95] O. R. Strackbein, Tyranny of the Press, Washington, D.C. (1968), pp. 7 f.
[96] See chapter 7 of this book (First Orientation Bibliography).

# 1

# ECOLOGICAL DAMAGE TO THE LIVING CONDITIONS

## 1.1 POLLUTION AND ITS EFFECTS ON HEALTH

### 1.1.1 Special Introductory Remarks

For generations St. Louis was one of the dirtiest, smokiest big cities in the United States. The polluted atmosphere, especially in winter, retarded the city's growth, injured the health of its citizens and caused immense property damage. It was Joseph Pulitzer's own newspaper, the *St. Louis Post-Dispatch*, which in 1940 led an anti-smoke campaign using extensive and aggressive media coverage of this problem. Under the editorial leadership of Ralph Coghlan the campaign became an extraordinary success. So thought the Pulitzer Prize jury as well, which stated in its report: "This entry covers a high type of modern newspaper crusade. The evidence reveals that the campaign was carefully thought out and prepared. The *Post-Dispatch*... followed this through, until much to everyone's surprise St. Louis got rid of most of its smoke." So the Advisory Board in 1941 gave the Pulitzer Prize for Meritorious Public Service to the *St. Louis Post-Dispatch* "for its successful campaign against the city smoke nuisance" during the previous year.

In the summer of 1989, the editor of the North Carolina *Washington Daily News* was paying his home water bill in person at city hall. As he did, he noticed a new statement on the back of the bill: the town had been testing for chemicals in its water system. When he got back to the office, he called the notice to the attention of Betty Gray, one of four reporters on the small afternoon daily with a circulation of 10,500. Gray, digging intermittently as her other duties permitted, obtained a list of the 42 chemicals in the water and began checking it with private and state toxicologists. She was told that one of the chemicals was carcinogenic and that it was in the water of the town far above the level the U.S. Environmental Protection Agency considered safe. For a series of articles covering that story the *Washington Daily News* received a 1990 Pulitzer Public Service Prize "for revealing that the city's water supply was contaminated with carcinogens" in the year before.

## 1.1.2  Campaign against Air Pollution in St. Louis

[Source: Ralph Coghlan: We are on Our Way, in: *St. Louis Post-Dispatch* (St. Louis, Mo.), Vol. 92/No. 173, February 25, 1940, p. 2 F, cols. 2-3; reprinted by permission of the Pulitzer Publishing Company, St. Louis, Mo.]

St. Louis has been *talking* about smoke for 50 years. Now it has *done* something about it. The report of Mayor Dickmann's Smoke Elimination Committee, published today, shows how St. Louis can be made a smokeless city by the winter of 1942-43 - and how tremendous progress can be made toward that goal in the two intervening winters.

This is good news - excellent news. Just as a man who, after dreaming for years of building a home for his family, finally engages an architect to draw a set of blueprints, so St. Louis has at last reached the blueprint stage of smoke elimination. This blueprint is a remarkable document.

It is not merely the product of more than two months of grinding labor by the Mayor's committee; it represents the accumulated wisdom of many years as to how the city's major problem should be attacked; moreover, it arrives at a time when science has finally come to grips with the problem of making smokeless fuels out of cheap Illinois bituminous.

It is the last development particularly which distinguishes this smoke elimination report from all the reports that have gone before; it is the last development which should assure the people of this city that smoke, ruinous to health and property values, can be conquered.

\* \* \*

The committee's plan is based on two crystal-clear principles: 1. All who desire to burn high volatile (smoky) fuel must employ mechanical fuel-burning equipment to burn it smokelessly. 2. Those who are unwilling or financially unable to use mechanical equipment must use a smokeless fuel.

Under the first principle, citizens who prefer to heat their homes with cheap, raw bituminous must equip their furnaces with stokers. While stokers represent a capital investment, it is the committee's belief, founded upon careful study, that the use of stokers will result in "an economic saving in the fuel bill." Moreover, for citizens who take this course, the city should use its influence to see that stokers are made available at reasonable prices and on reasonable terms of payment.

Under the second principle, there is, for citizens of comfortable income, a wide range of choice. Numerous smokeless fuels, far more than sufficient for the city's needs, are already on the market. These include, of course, gas and oil, in addition to anthracite, by-product coke, petroleum coke, Pocahontas coal and Arkansas anthracite.

But since these fuels are beyond the purses of many of our citizens, the real heart of the problem lies in making available a smokeless fuel cheap enough for those in the lowest income brackets. It is here that the committee encountered its greatest difficulty and, as it may prove, achieved its greatest success.

* * *

To find a cheap smokeless fuel the committee made a wide survey of the field. It found that there are various processes for coking Illinois coal, either already in commercial operation or giving promise for such operation in the near future. It was able, in one instance, to institute negotiation "for a quadrupling of the output of one of those products and the making of it available at a very substantial reduction in price and at a cost which would be no burden to the consumer, heating quality considered."

It is expected that this product, along with others in the course of development - including the University of Illinois briquet - can be made available to consumers at a price of from $5 to $6 a ton. This price is higher than the prices now paid for the cheapest Illinois bituminous. However, the processed coal will be higher in heating value, and the total heating bill, other things being equal, will be no greater and possibly less than heretofore.

In this connection, the report cites the interesting fact, contained in a pamphlet issued by the United States Department of Labor, that St. Louis now enjoys the lowest coal prices of 19 large cities studied. A survey of the retail price of the same grade of coal in 19 large cities, including many in the Middle West, showed a range in price from $5.61 per ton to $17.51 per ton, and the average price of all to be $2.65 per ton higher than the St. Louis price. None was as low as the St. Louis price.

* * *

So even if it were not true that a clean processed fuel is of higher fuel content than raw coal, thus justifying a somewhat higher price, other considerations would no doubt cause the courts to approve an ordinance requiring the use of such fuel. Among these considerations, of course, would be the health of the community and the practical fact that smoke is costing the city millions of dollars annually in deterioration of property values, etc. A decade ago, the St. Louis Smoke Abatement League estimated this annual cost at more than $19,000,000. If that figure was accurate then, the cost is far greater today.

To give teeth and punch to its plan, the committee urges that the City of St. Louis should be authorized to engage in the purchase, sale and distribution of smokeless fuels under certain conditions. While the committee expresses the hope that "the less a municipality or governmental agency engages in business and interferes with the normal

FORWARD, ST. LOUIS!

channels of trade, the better, yet an emergency may exist which makes it most important that the credit and large buying powers of the city may be used in such an emergency."

To put it bluntly, this means that, while the committee hopes that the present system of private distribution will function efficiently and with due regard for the city's fuel needs, the city must be prepared for its failure to do so. In this case - and the Post-Dispatch, on behalf of coal dealers who have large investments here, joins the committee in hoping that the situation need not arise - the city would have certain obvious advantages in bargaining power and in exemption from certain governmental regulations that could be used with great effectiveness to lower the price of fuel to consumers.

If the coal dealers throw themselves wholeheartedly into the city's crusade to eliminate smoke, it may never be necessary to use the broad and sweeping powers suggested by the committee. But there is no question that they should be in the ordinance as a necessary protection. This is not a sham battle that is being fought. It is a real war.

* * *

As we have said, the report is a remarkable document. It is clear, thorough, realistic, beautifully and calmly reasoned, modestly yet powerfully stated. And among its other virtues is the fact that the committee, while unable to accept other suggested plans for smoke elimination, carefully analyzed them, one by one, giving cogent reasons for its rejection of each. Is education in the matter of burning cheap coal smokelessly a solution? The committee tells why it is not. Is natural gas the way out? The committee tells why it is not. Is district heating the answer? Again, the committee explains its negative answer. And, finally, on the question of whether or not the city should solve the smoke problem by building a municipal plant, the committee explains why it is unwilling, at this time, to favor such a plant.

So the blueprint is before us. It is, we believe, sound and workable in every major detail. And now comes the task of putting it into effect. It is up to the Mayor, the Board of Aldermen, the Division of Smoke Regulation - all supported by a sympathetic and co-operative citizenry - to clear the ground, set the stone, lay the bricks, fasten the joists, secure the timbers and make tight the roof. The slogan: A clean St. Louis by 1942.

### 1.1.3  Balance of Water Pollution in North Carolina

[Source: Betty Gray: Water dangers known in 1981, in: *Washington Daily News* (Washington, N.C.), Vol. -/No. 249, October 19, 1989, p. 1, cols. 1-2; p. 13, cols. 1-4; reprinted by permission of the Washington News Publishing Company, Washington, D.C.]

City officials knew about possible contamination of Washington's water supply by cancer-causing chemicals as early as 1981, newly-obtained documents reveal. Alerted by warnings in state and federal government publications, Jerry Cutler, Washington superintendent of water resources, sent samples of city tap water off for testing that year.

On Aug. 14, 1981, an Ashboro laboratory, Moore, Gardner & Associates, informed Cutler that the tests showed carcinogenic trihalomethanes at 908 parts per billion, more than nine times the maximum amount regarded as safe by the U.S. Environmental Protection Agency.

This was the first record of trihalomethanes in city water, five years earlier than officials have yet acknowledged. About two weeks later, Sept. 2, 1981, Cutler wrote a memorandum to Gilbert R. Alligood, then director of public works for the city, recommending the city pay for an engineering study of water treatment problems. Alligood is now an engineer with Rivers & Associates, consultant to the city on its proposed new water treatment plant.

One of the major problems identified by Cutler was trihalomethanes in the water. "At the present, they are nine times higher than the maximum contaminant level," his memo said. The alarming news was not made public. Since that information became available at least three city managers, three mayors, the state and the EPA have known of the problem, Cutler told the Daily News recently.

But there were no federal and state regulations forcing the city to act on the information, he said. What appeared to be more pressing problems and a scarcity of funds may also have played a role, he said. State and federal regulators have known for nearly a decade that trihalomethanes have been linked to cancer, Cutler pointed out. "They knew we had a problem by the potential of trihalomethanes," he said. "Knowing how our system operated, they knew we had a problem."

But towns between 3,300 and 10,000 population were only required to begin quarterly monitoring in January of this year. The U.S. Environmental Protection Agency first issued regulations for trihalomethanes in 1979 as part of the Safe Drinking Water Act. The law required phased-in monitoring and reporting for municipalities based on population size. In passing the federal Water Pollution Control Act and the Clean Water Act, both meant to protect the American public from hazards in surface water, Congress made provision for financial aid to communities to upgrade their sewage treatment facilities.

Not so with the Safe Drinking Water Act. The cost of improving drinking water is borne mainly by the utility and, eventually, the consuming public. Cutler's 1981 memo to Alligood put forward suggestions for upgrading and replacing equipment at the surface water plant or for replacing the surface water treatment plant with four wells and a groundwater treatment plant.

During this time, the city was beleaguered by a wastewater treatment plant that did not meet federal requirements and budget overruns in construction of a new electrical substation. A lack of money combined with the lack of federal and state requirements governing drinking water apparently combined to give top priority to the other problems. "The city's drinking water plant was operating within the law," Cutler said. "But our wastewater treatment plant was out of compliance so we had to take action on it."

An engineering study, completed Aug. 12, 1983 by Moore, Gardner & Associates and presented to Alligood, gave the city five alternatives in upgrading its surface water supply. Among them: drilling a well system north of Washington, moving the plant from Tranters Creek to the Tar River or blending water from the city groundwater well with water from Tranters Creek before the treatment process to lower the amount of organics in the water. Subsequent efforts to blend the water failed, Cutler said. On May 23, 1986, Cutler sent a memorandum to Russell Waters, city director of public works, which identified three contaminants in the city drinking water at or above concentrations allowed under the amended Safe Drinking Water Act.

Turbidity and aluminum were two of the contaminants. Trihalomethanes were the third. During a long-range planning meeting in February 1987, the Public Works Department requested $2,500,000 for water projects. The planning report said the projects were needed "to reduce the high levels of trihalomethanes in the finished water."

It said EPA and the state government required this in systems which served more than 10,000 people. "The City of Washington is near this population level," it said, noting that EPA was in the process of lowering the limit and had recently proposed new regulations for 83 specific chemical contaminants in drinking water which might have to be met over the next five years. Chloroform, one of the trihalomethanes in the water, was a known carcinogen, the report said.

Quarterly tests by Oxford Laboratories of Wilmington began this past January as required by the Environmental Protection Agency. The tests showed concentrations of about 338 parts per billion in tap water on

Jan. 6, 1989 and 934 parts per billion in tap water on April 3, 1989, far above the EPA limit. Oxford Labs sent written copies of the results to the state public water supply section and to the city.

As required under the Safe Drinking Water Act amended in 1986, the city sent written notices of the testing, but not the results, to its water customers. About 20 people asked for copies of the test results, Cutler said. Contamination of the city water supply became public knowledge after the Daily News obtained a copy of the report, and on Sept. 22 the state health director, Dr. Ronald Levine, told city residents they should

Mr. Gilbert R. Alligood
Page 2
September 2, 1981

8) Most plumbing and valves have deteriorated and need replacing.

9) Bulk lime feeding system

10) Control of Trihalomethanes in finished water. At the present, they are 9 times higher than the maximum contaminant level.

A complete rebuild, upgrade and control of Trihalomethanes, turbidity, coliform, etc. should be in the first proposal.

Ground water looks good when looking at cost to treat only.

The ground water supply is coming from the Castle Hayne Aquifer which Texasgulf is pulling 60 Mgd from it now, and N.C. Phosphate has a permit to pull another 60 Mgd from the Castle Hayne Aquifer.

The City of Washington is pulling 500 gpm from the Castle Hayne Aquifer, and we have seen a 15 foot drop in the drawdown at our well in the last four years. This drawdown could very well increase when N.C. Phosphate begins to pull another 60 Mgd from the Aquifer.

The second proposal should be to possible delete the Surface Water Treatment Plant and add four more wells and Ground Water Treatment Plants.

Without looking at the lower cost of treatment of the ground water and the possible drawdown level which N. C. Phosphate may have on our well water, we have the dry years to consider and the luxury of two sources of water.

The second proposal should show cost to build and operate four new Well Treatment Plants and meet the Primary Drinking Water Standards.

The third water proposal should show the upgrade and repair of the Surface Water Plant and keep the well water source as a second source of water.

The Safe Drinking Water Act Standards would have to meet the maximum contaminant levels for all parameters.

I feel Wm. F. Freeman Associates should do this water study because of their knowledge of our water sources and water systems.

Documents showing the early awareness of the water problem.

MOORE, GARDNER & ASSOCIATES, INC.
ENVIRONMENTAL LABORATORY
ASHEBORO, NORTH CAROLINA
EPA CERTIFICATION NO. NC002
ANALYTICAL REPORT

SAFE DRINKING WATER ACT     MGA CLIENT     SAMPLE
REPORT OF ANALYSES     NUMBER 280000(84)     NUMBER 16899

System: City of Washington (Surface Supply - Community Source)

Address: P.O. Box 1988, Washington, NC 27889

Date Collected: 7/22/81     Collected By: T. W. Woolard     Time Collected: 0915

Date Analyzed 7/23/81     Sample Point: Consumers Faucet

Type of Sample:     Chemists: . Johnson, Hayworth

| Parameter | Maximum Contaminant Levels (MCLs) | Contaminant Level Detected |
|---|---|---|
| Arsenic (mg/l) | 0.05 | |
| Barium (mg/l) | 1.0 | |
| Cadmium (mg/l) | 0.010 | |
| Chromium (mg/l) | 0.05 | |
| Iron (mg/l) | 0.3 | |
| Lead (mg/l) | 0.05 | |
| Manganese (mg/l) | 0.05 | |
| Mercury (mg/l) | 0.002 | |
| Selenium (mg/l) | 0.01 | |
| Silver (mg/l) | 0.05 | |
| Fluoride (mg/l) | * | |
| Nitrate (as N) (mg/l) | 10.0 | |
| Turbidity (NTU) (monthly average) | 1 | |
| (average of 2 consecutive days) | 5 | |
| pH (units) | $\geq 6.5$ | |
| Coliform Bacteria (# MPN/100mls) | * | |
| Endrin (mg/l) | 0.0002 | |
| Lindane (mg/l) | 0.004 | |
| Methoxychlor (mg/l) | 0.1 | |
| Toxaphene (mg/l) | 0.005 | |
| 2,4-D (mg/l) | 0.1 | |
| 2,4,5-TP (Silvex) (mg/l) | 0.01 | |
| Total Trihalomethanes (mg/l) | 0.1 | 908 ug/l |

WE HEREBY CERTIFY THAT ALL ANALYSES REPORTED WERE PERFORMED IN STRICT ACCORDANCE WITH
THE ANALYTICAL METHODS REQUIRED UNDER THE SAFE DRINKING WATER ACT (PUBLIC LAW 93-523,
DECEMBER 16, 1974) AS SET FORTH IN THE FEDERAL REGISTER, VOLUME 40, NO. 248- WEDNESDAY,
DECEMBER 24, 1975.
DATE August 14, 1981     CERTIFIED BY William H. Cobb III
Director of Laboratory Services

not drink the water, wash or cook fruits and vegetables in it, or take showers in it because they might inhale the steam.

The following day, a U.S. Marine Corps convoy set up water wagons around the city to provide its residents with clean water. In the past three weeks, city officials have taken emergency measures which reduced trihalomethane levels to a point where the advisory has been lifted except for the warning against drinking the water, using it in vaporizers or in preparing hot and cold drinks such as coffee or tea and juice from concentrates.

## 1.2    ENVIRONMENTAL INFLUENCE AND SYNDROMES

### 1.2.1   Special Introductory Remarks

Brown lung, or byssinosis, for a long time had been accepted as commonplace in the textile industry and existing regulations were largely ignored. The *Charlotte Observer* in 22 articles and eight editorials drew the anger and resistance of industry and government officials. Soon it became clear that the series lead to stricter enforcement and reform of protective law and regulation, and improvement in the health and working conditions of textile workers throughout the country. Because of its successful campaign the North Carolina newspaper, in the opinion of a Pulitzer Prize jury, was the "unanimous first choice for the 1981 Pulitzer Prize for Meritorious Public Service for its series on brown lung disease. It is a classic example," the report continues, "of how a newspaper can effectively and dramatically use its editorial resources to expose and draw public attention to an important and previously ignored problem - in this case a disease that disables and kills thousands of workers."

Two years before, another newspaper uncovered a story which was approaching a national tragedy: the nuclear accident on Three Mile Island. It was the *Philadelphia Inquirer* which observed, commented and analyzed many aspects of the disaster and so enabled its readers to learn about the existing dangers. The newspaper's entry to a Pulitzer Prize jury got high praise: "The coverage of the accident at the Three Mile Island nuclear power plant was distinguished both on a day to day basis as this story unfolded as well as for the remarkably detailed reconstruction of the nuclear accident by a team of reporters twelve days after the event. Newspapers had never before been called upon to cover a story precisely such as this one." The Advisory Board agreed to this proposal and awarded the Pulitzer Prize for Local General Spot News Reporting to the staff of the *Inquirer* "for coverage of the nuclear accident on Three Miles Island" in 1979.

## 1.2.2  Pulmonary Diseases in the Cotton Industry

[Source: Robert Conn: BROWN LUNG: A Case of Deadly Neglect - A Time Bomb Ticks Away in Millworkers' Lungs, in: *The Charlotte Observer* (Charlotte, N.C.), 95th Year/No. 24, February 3, 1980, p. 18 A, cols. 1-5; reprinted by permission of the Knight Publishing Company, Charlotte, N.C.]

Howard Kanupp, 64, hasn't been able to sleep through a night for years. "I jump up trying to get my breath," says Kanupp. "I sleep on two pillows. When I get up, I spit up all the time. I got me a spit can I carry around." You might think Kanupp - who breathes only 39 percent as well as a healthy man his age and height - has chronic bronchitis. He may. But because Kanupp, a Hickory millworker for 40 years, has been exposed to cotton dust, doctors also call his disease byssinosis. The symptoms are the same as chronic bronchitis.

Byssinosis, or brown lung, acquired during work with hemp, flax or cotton dust, begins with mild breathing disturbances such as shortness of breath. A worker can show initial symptoms the first day on the job. Over several decades, according to American doctors, byssinosis can progress to a chronic stage where it is irreversible and often fatal. British doctors say it can become chronic after as few as five years. Lung specialists have trouble diagnosing the disease because symptoms so closely resemble other chronic lung diseases.

There isn't an accepted diagnostic procedure for brown lung - the way a biopsy determines cancer. And a sick lung isn't distinctively brown, as the Ralph Nader-created word would imply. In an X ray, it may look just like the diseased lung of a chronic smoker, full of holes because the tiny air sacs, called alveoli, have been destroyed. Doctors diagnose brown lung by first taking a work history. Then they measure a worker's breathing capacity. When possible, they test this when he first returns to work from a weekend or vacation, then after he's been there about six hours. A sick worker's breathing usually will show some signs of impairment.

There are two distinct forms of the disease, according to most pulmonary (lung) doctors:

● Acute byssinosis, characterized by coughing, chest tightness and shortness of breath the first workday after a weekend (or vacation) away from the mill. Some doctors believe this occurs because the person's respiratory system has bounced back to near normal during time away from the mill. Then, when the susceptible individual comes in contact with cotton dust again, the reaction occurs that severely restricts breathing. This stage is considered reversible and symptoms disappear when the worker isn't exposed to cotton dust. During a worker's early years in the mill, there may be no discomfort beyond this point.

● Chronic byssinosis, or irreversible loss of lung function. People with chronic byssinosis may find walking a few yards or climbing stairs tires them.

Dr. Richard Schilling of Great Britain, a leading researcher on byssinosis, has said workers go through four stages before they become chronic. However, many Carolinas pulmonary doctors say they see patients who have never gone through the first stages, but are permanently disabled. They diagnose these patients as having chronic obstructive lung disease caused by cotton dust. In layman's words, they say the patients have bronchitis or emphysema, depending on the symptoms. A patient with chronic bronchitis coughs up mucus at least three months a year for two successive years; the mucus clogs his airways. In emphysema, the lungs lose elasticity and the victim develops a barrel chest from trying to breathe.

Perhaps 25 to 30 percent of millworkers are susceptible to brown lung, according to many medical experts, and if they work in an area with a high level of dust they will get the disease. These doctors don't know how long it takes - some people exhibit symptoms the first day on the job. Doctors see byssinosis primarily among people who work in the early production steps of the mill, opening and combing bales of cotton. Dust levels are highest there, and the dust contains more of the tiny pieces of cotton plant bract, the leaves around the white cotton boll, which researchers now think is a primary cause of brown lung. Byssinosis occurs less frequently among spinners and weavers, except in those mills where the entire process is in one or two large rooms, or where the ventilation system spreads dust throughout the building.

Smoking complicates the picture. The industry has long provided smoke breaks and smoking areas, but smoking seems to multiply the effects of cotton dust on the lungs. Many who get byssinosis also smoke, leading some doctors to say a disabled worker's damaged lungs are due only to smoking. Most Carolinas lung specialists, however, say they see the disease frequently in nonsmokers as well. Doctors treat acute byssinosis by providing face masks or recommending the worker move to a low-dust area or another job. For the chronically ill, doctors generally follow standard steps for chronic obstructive lung disease. Dr. Douglas Kelling of Concord says these steps include:

● Teaching the patient how he can help his condition. Particularly important are special exercises to help drain mucus from clogged lungs.

● Drugs. These include relaxers for muscles along the airways, spray inhalants and medicine to reduce inflammation.

"I KNOW IT HURTS DADDY'S LUNGS, BUT WHY DOES IT HARDEN THE HEARTS OF EVERYBODY ELSE?"

● Antibiotics at the first sign of any infection, pneumonia shots and annual influenza shots. Brown lung victims are more susceptible to lung infections and because of their weakened condition, are more likely to die.

Doctors also insist their patients stop smoking. Says Dr. Barbara Winn, a Laurinburg lung specialist: "They've got to quit smoking cold turkey or I won't care for them."


## 1.2.3  Fear of Diseases after a Nuclear Accident

[Source: Richard L. Papiernik/Fred Cusick/Mary Bishop: Under the nuclear gun - Three Mile Island has people worrying themselves sick, in: *The Philadelphia Inquirer* (Philadelphia, Pa.), Vol. 300/No. 94, April 4, 1979, p. 8 A, cols. 1-6; reprinted by permission of the Philadelphia Inquirer, Philadelphia, Pa.]

Since Friday, patients have been streaming into the Hamilton Health Center here, complaining of chest pains, stomach pains, back pains, hives and shortness of breath. They are not suffering from radiation sickness or any other physical malady, Dr. Samuel T. Clayton, a staff physician, said yesterday. They are suffering from tension and fear, the emotional fallout of the accident at the Three Mile Island nuclear-power plant southeast of here. "It's anxiety," Dr. Clayton said.

Elsewhere here, a psychologist told of a patient suffering recurring nightmares in which his home was invaded by evil forces. Another psychiatrist said hysterical patients were calling him constantly. And an obstetrician, besieged with calls from frantic pregnant women, said he "would have no problem recommending an abortion if there is fear that the fetus was exposed to radiation." Health officials confirmed that many people in the area of the nuclear-power plant had sought help for stress and anxiety-related maladies in the aftermath of the accident Wednesday that spread radiation outside the plant and, for a while, posed the threat of a melt-down.

And, said Dr. James L. Knestrick, a clinical psychologist, "the real problem just may not surface for weeks. It will really show up in excessive stress on people who already are having problems handling stress. I don't think a direct casual relationship will result, but there could be some people ending up being phobic about this. ... It is like war, when there is shelling and you know there is going to be a bombardment at a certain time so you can prepare for it and maybe you can handle it better. But if you know there is going to be a bombardment and you can never tell just when, then the anxiety increases. And what we are talking about here is an unseen threat. People may react later by being afraid to go outside, to breathe fresh air or to drink water. They may be so phobic about these things that they can't go on with their normal life-style."

Some people, Dr. Knestrick said, might react to the Three Mile Island incident by developing a healthy sensibility to their environment and the pollutants in it, but, he continued, others might react by curling up in a ball in a corner of the house or by thinking they should go and blow up the plant." Said a Harrisburg psychiatrist, Dr. Robert A. Fisher, "Starting last Wednesday, and last Friday and yesterday, my phone was ringing constantly. People were very frightened. "A typical reaction from a patient is, 'My God, what's going to happen? The thing's going to blow up. Should I go? Shouldn't I go?'" He said stress had been especially telling on people already suffering from psychological problems. "I have patients who evacuated on Wednesday, came back on Thursday, left on Friday and came back again yesterday (Monday)," he said. "People who have anxiety have a tendency to get upset about anything disturbing that happens."

Dr. Lawrence B. Silver's patients have another reason to be anxious. They are pregnant. "I've been getting call after call, and they are all the same. They ask, 'What should I do.' If they still have four to six weeks or more to go, I tell them to go visit relatives but don't go out to the middle of nowhere. I tell them to make sure they are in or near a city where there are hospitals available, just in case." Dr. Silver, who maintains an office in Middletown, which is three miles north of Three Mile Island, would not discuss whether anyone had come to him for an abortion as a result of the radiation fear. However, he said, he would have no problem recommending an abortion, particularly in the first three months of pregnancy, if radiation exposure was feared.

"The most critical time is the first trimester," he said. "It is when the fetus is most vulnerable. I have had calls from women who say they are five months or so pregnant and think they have been exposed to radiation. They ask if they should have an abortion. I tell them that they should just stay out of the area, that the baby is well formed at that point but they just couldn't take chances on staying around and that there should be no problems. But if they are, six or eight weeks pregnant, it is up to them to make the decision. All I know is that a baby is for a lifetime, and if the fetus is exposed to radiation that early, there could be real problems."

At the Hamilton Health Center, Dr. Clayton said that a major problem was that most of the patients with stress-related complaints are poor. "A good deal of our patients are relief patients," he said, "and a lot of them can't run away if they wanted to. They just don't have enough money to get out of Harrisburg." A typical patient, Dr. Clayton said, was an elderly woman. "She would come in and say that for the last four days she had back pain, flank pain, stomach pain, initially nausea but no vomiting." Most of the time, he said, reassuring words from the staff has helped, but sometimes the doctors find it best to treat the symptoms. "If you give them something for the stomach pain and the pain goes away," Dr. Clayton said, "they feel less anxiety."

Dr. Fisher noted that for those affected, proximity to the nuclear plant did not seem to heighten anxiety. In many cases, he said, it has been just the opposite. "Both Friday and yesterday (Monday), I spoke with a number of patients who live within the five-mile radius of Three Miles Island's" he said. "They were calmer than many of my patients who live farther away. I can't explain that. I think it's probably because they're living in the shadow of the towers. I think you can have an assurance if you can see what's going on. In other words, if you're going to blow up, you'd like to see the explosion."

Some experts linked the anxiety to general mistrust of official information about the power-plant crisis. "I think the worry of most people around here, staff and patients alike, is, 'Are we getting all the information and ... how much of that is factual and how much of it is theoretical?" said Ted Yanich, director of the outpatient department of Harrisburg Hospital's mental-health center. Dr. Leonard Cohen, a Harrisburg psychologist, said, "Typical of what's going on now is the general mistrust of government officials after the whole Watergate fiasco. And, unfortunately, there was that big mix-up in communications, which made matters worse."

Dr. Cohen cited the reaction of his daughter, who called him from West Virginia. "She ... begged us to leave. She said, 'They aren't telling you the truth about this. Get out now, while you can.' We did got to Chambersburg for a few days," Dr. Cohen said. Dr. Knestrick, describing the recurring dream of a patient, said it was about an evil force that just pervaded the house. No one could tell just what it was, but it was there, and it came into the house at night. "It's the kind of thing you see when a person feels surrounded by imminent danger. They feel they are vulnerable, but it's something in the air that they can't see or touch, like radiation."

## 1.3 FOOD SCANDALS AND OCCUPATIONAL DISEASES

### 1.3.1 Special Introductory Remarks

One young newspaper reporter, by vigorous, persistent, investigative reporting, was given credit by many knowledgeable observers for prompting the first federal reform in packing plant inspection since the 1906 Meat Inspection Law enacted during the administration of Theodore Roosevelt. It was Nathan K. (Nick) Kotz of the *Des Moines Register* and the *Minneapolis Tribune* who had done five-months research on the unsavory conditions prevailing in a large segment of America's meat industry. "The Kotz stories," the Pulitzer Prize jury report states, "exemplified the best in the traditional role of newspaper responsibility. Kotz developed his articles around a little known and largely ignored five-year old federal report on imperfections in the national meat inspection process. He followed through with excellent stories on the problem" which finally resulted in a new law. So in 1968, Nick Kotz earned the Pulitzer National Reporting award "for his reporting of unsanitary conditions in many meat packing plants, which helped insure the passage of the Federal Wholesome Meat Act of 1967."

More dangerous than coal mining, construction, or factory work, farming in 1983 rose to the top of the nation's list of hazardous jobs. Its on-the-job death rate was five times the national average for all industries: 1,900 American farmers died in work-related accidents that year, and 200,000 more were disabled. Equally distressing was the growing incidence of crippling diseases such as "farmers' lung" and "corn-growers' cancers" that appear to be linked to modern farming methods of raising livestock indoors and heavy use of chemicals to boost crop yields. Tom Knudson of the *Des Moines Register* wrote a six-part series on this problem, and his articles impressed the Pulitzer Prize jury which called it "a well-written, thoroughly-reported... account of a problem that has received virtually no public attention" before. Tom

Knudson received the 1985 National Reporting Pulitzer award "for his series of articles that examined the danger of farming as an occupation," published in the preceding year.


## 1.3.2  Hygienic Deficiencies in Slaughter-Houses

[Source: Nick Kotz: Some Intrastate Meat Plants of Big Firms Found Unsanitary, in: *Minneapolis Tribune* (Minneapolis, Mn.), Vol. CI/No. 60, July 23, 1967, p. 13 A, cols. 1-4; reprinted by permission of the Minneapolis Star and Tribune, Minneapolis, Mn.]

Federal investigators have discovered unsanitary conditions not only in small meat packing plants, but also in several plants operated by prominent national meat firms. The Minneapolis Tribune obtained last week investigation reports from all 50 states made by Agriculture Department (USDA) meat inspectors who looked into conditions in slaughtering and processing plants not under federal inspection.

Fifteen per cent of meat slaughtering and 25 per cent of processing, enough meat to feed 30 million persons, does not come under federal inspection because the meat does not cross state lines. The only USDA survey of nonfederally inspected plants was made five years ago. The investigation reports became public only last week, during a congressional committee debate over bills designed to strengthen federal and state meat inspection.

Rep. Neal Smith, D-Iowa, believes that few persons realize that some of the large national firms operate plants on an intrastate basis to meet slate and local competition and that these plants are not federally inspected. The federal investigators looked at relatively few instrastate plants operated by the large national firms,but the following were some of their findings:

At a Louisiana plant operated by one of the largest firms: "Meat barrels were rusty. Boning boards were old and caked with fats and meat juices." At a Florida plant operated by the same firm: "We could only open the door and look in the holding cooler, since the room was filled to capactiy. Since the cooler was so congested, footprints were present on the bellies."

At a Florida plant operated by another national firm: "This branch house is old and rundown. The sanitation is poor. Evidence of rats and mice were present on the second floor in the dry-storage area." At a Virginia plant operated by a national firm: "Some cockroaches were observed in the curing cellar where exposed meat is handled and stored. Meat-grinder bearings had much encrusted putrid material. Sausage was hung on unclean aluminum smoke sticks, and no attempt had been made to clean the sausage mixer. Some beef cuts hanging in the cooler showed evidence of soilage and had not been reconditioned by removing the soiled portions."

At a Texas plant operated by the same national firm: "Numerous carcasses and tubs of meat were observed to be contaminated with drippings from the ceiling. Paint, scale, rust, and plaster were scaling down from the walls and ceiling on the products through the plant. A majority of the hogs contained a great number of beater wounds on them which were grossly contaminated with tub water and hair. Other carcasses were found to have large chronic wounds on them."

The investigators, however, reported good conditions in some of the non-federally inspected branch plants operated by national firms. Smith, author of two bills designed to broaden federal inspection and strengthen inadequate state inspection, commented: "Some of the big companies have set up these intrastate branch plants strictly for the purposes of meeting local competition. They have been forced to resort to inferior practices. They can't compete without operating as the local plants do."

Dorothy Wheeler, an official of a large consumer cooperative, also expressed concern about the national firms as she testified in support of the wholesome meat act before the House Agriculture Livestock sub-committee. She said: "We are quite concerned over the fact that many large packing plants carefully retain their status as intrastate businesses so as to avoid federal inspection. This is even true of individual plants operated by some of the largest packing corporations in the country in states that have no inspection laws. We question the intent of such a practice."

Only 25 states have laws requiring mandatory inspection of slaughtering and processing. The USDA investigation showed abuses and inadequate inspections in many of these 25 states. The administration bill would tighten procedures to insure that unwholesome meat doesn't get into channels of human consumption. It would provide matching funds and technical help to states willing to come up to federal standards in their own inspection systems. Smith is sponsoring another bill that would bring far more large packers under federal inspection. This bill would require federal inspection of all firms considered in interstate commerce under provisions of the Taft-Hartley Act.

The American Meat Institute, representing the large packers, has indicated its displeasure at both bills. It has offered amendments that

Smith says would destroy the effectiveness of the proposed legislation. There are indications, however, that some of the largest national firms might urge passage of bill, before publicity from the USDA investigation leads to a general scandal.

### 1.3.3  Health Risks of American Farmers

[Source: Tom Knudson: Farm health woes grow, but little is being done, in: *Des Moines Sunday Register* (Des Moines, Ia.), Vol. 136/No. 91, September 23, 1984, p. 1 A, cols. 2-3; p. 3 A, cols. 1-6; reprinted by permission of the Des Moines Register and Tribune Company, Des Moines, Ia.]

America's largest and most productive business - agriculture - is slowly getting sick, and government is doing little to make farmers well. "Unless something is done soon, a very valuable resource - the American farmer - is going to be in trouble," said David Baker, a farm safety specialist at the University of Missouri.

Trouble already is at the door. Just last year, farming surpassed mining as the nation's most dangerous job, according to the National Safety Council. Fifty-five of every 100,000 farmers died in on-the-job accidents in 1983, five times the national average. The cost of farm accidents to the economy was more than $5 billion. That's just the beginning. The council's figures do not measure the more insidious health threats now afflicting agriculture. Those hazards, which scientists are just beginning to document, include leukemia and other cancers, hearing loss, stress, farmer's lung, hog lung and other maladies.

The farmer's mounting health woes - an offshoot of the industrial revolution on the farm - have received only scant attention from state and federal agencies, health officials and the public. The few programs that do exist to help farmers are uncoordinated, underfinanced and generally have accomplished little to deal with the growing toll of sickness and accidents on the farm. "There are no preventive programs to deal with these occupational problems," said University of Iowa associate professor Kelley Donham before the Joint Economic Committee of Congress last year. "Therefore, they may be expected to continue and their economic significance is likely to increase."

Donham told the lawmakers, "An effective program to protect the farmer has fallen between the cracks of various federal and state agencies." Here are some examples:

● The Occupational Safety and Health Administration, which is charged with protecting the health of America's workers, never sets foot on most farms.

● The U.S. Department of Agriculture (USDA), the farmer's traditional ally, largely has ignored farm health problems. Its safety program is short on money, manpower and training.

● Large federal research agencies, such as the National Institute for Occupational Safety and Health, often overlook farmers because they have less political clout than other worker groups.

● So little information is gathered about farm health and safety by government agencies that scientists still don't know the scope of many problems.

The deteriorating health on the farm has prompted a call for stronger medicine. The therapy would include a heavy dose of research, better training for rural physicians and safety specialists, the creation of a farmhealth lobbying group and the development of a national health and safety policy for agriculture. One of the loudest cries is for more research. "Agriculture is really the last frontier for occupational safety and health research," said James Merchant, director of the University of Iowa's Institute of Agricultural Medicine. "There's been a real lack of information about the problem."

But for now, the important questions remain unanswered. Does breathing hog dust and manure gas lead to permanent lung damage? What are the most common causes of farm accidents? How widespread is farmer's lung disease? Do pesticides trigger such cancers as leukemia and lymphoma in farmers? "These chemicals kill birds and everything else. Why wouldn't they be hard on humans, too?" asked Kathryn Dawes of Adel. Last year, her husband, Harold, a farmer, died of lymphoma. He was 63. "He always felt his sickness came from the chemicals," she said. "And I thought it was connected, too."

Scientists haven't had much luck squeezing money from federal agencies for farm health research. They say farmers, with less than 5 percent of the population, will never rivet the attention of Congress. As one scientist put it: "The wheel that squeaks the loudest gets the grease." "Farmers aren't very well known to the scientific community and the funding agencies," said Keith Long, former director of the U of I's Institute of Agricultural Medicine. "And their population isn't large. So it's much more difficult to get funds to study their problems." Farm health research, said Donham, "hasn't been a likely funded item because there is no consolidated group in agriculture to draw attention to these issues. Most research is awarded to occupational groups that have political clout."

There's another problem. Until scientists can document a health threat, the government isn't likely to spend money on it, and farm health researchers don't have the money to document the problems. "It's like the old story of the kid who gets out of school and can't get a job because he doesn't have experience," said Long, "and he can't get the experience because he doesn't have a job." Some work is being done. For example, Merchant received a $45,000 grant in 1983 to study the use of respirators among farmers. Donham is working on a $21,753 project with the American Lung Association on farm respiratory problems.

But many important areas are not being studied much. For example, there's hog lung, an ailment that strikes many swine confinement workers. In 1983, University of Iowa researchers submitted a grant proposal to the USDA to study air quality inside confinement units. The grant was turned down. "I don't think we've ever had any funding from the USDA," Donham said. "The agency is 90 percent production-oriented. That's is orientation. Health is not." "We would hack and wheeze and cough a lot of stuff up," said Robert Cook, 31, of Stuart, who worked in the dust of a hog confinement building. "I don't know if I ever got rid of it all."

Cook's problem turned critical in 1980 when he was exposed to deadly hydrogen sulfide gas while working in a manure pit at a hog confinement unit. "I had edema of the lungs," he said. "And shortly after that, my capillaries broke down and fluid was leaking into the tissues of my body. At the hospital the doctors told my folks that they didn't expect me to make it. I'm lucky, because a lot of people die from it." Cook's ordeal shadows him today. It has ravaged his eyesight and hearing and damaged his hip. The gas was only partly to blame. An infection he picked up at the hospital also did serious harm. For his misery, Cook received a worker's compensation payment of $128,000.

Then he sued the companies that supplied equipment and building materials for the confinement unit for $1.5 million. That was in 1982. The case was settled out of court just three weeks ago. "We can't disclose the exact settlement," said his lawyer, Randy Hefner. "But he'll be receiving monthly benefits for the rest of his life, plus periodic lump-sum payments." Cook, now a salesman for a Des Moines medical supply firm, is concerned about other confinement workers. "There needs to be more research, especially on the long-term respiratory problems," he said. "The hydrogen sulfide - that's scary, but it's more isolated. The dust is something that everybody who works in those units is going to encounter."

The USDA is just beginning to address farmers' health problems, but money still is short. "This is an area that we're going to be moving

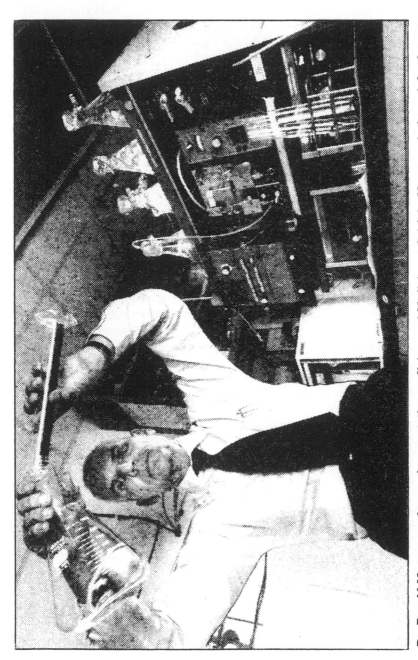

Dr. Donald Morgan, professor of preventative medicine and environmental Health at the University of Iowa Medical School, is shown working at the Institute of Agricultural Medicine at Oakdale. Morgan, who has a federal grant to assess the health hazards of pesticides, is using a chromatograph to do chemical analysis.

into. We're going to be hitting it a lot heavier," said Rollin Schnieder, who directs the agency's national farm safety program from an office in Lincoln, Neb. "Our research arm - the agricultural research service - has really been hit on funding the last five or six years," he said. "And the trend has been more toward funding soil conservation work. We know that work needs to be done in the farm health area. But the grants just have not been there." Traditionally, Schnieder's program has focused on safety - how to make tractors less dangerous, how to keep ladders from slipping and the like. Each state has been awarded $20,000 yearly to help support a farm safety specialist in its extension service. Iowa's extension safety specialist is David Williams at Iowa State University in Ames. Since the program expanded to all 50 states in 1975, the $20,000 grants have not increased and its overall budget has remained at $1,020,000. "We need to at least double, and maybe triple, the commitments we're making to the extension programs in the states," said Baker. Schnieder agreed: "Three million would be a lot more realistic. It would give us a much better program."

Extension's efforts today "are very meager in comparison to other industries," said Dennis Murphy, a farm safety specialist at Pennsylvania State University. "You have basically one person trying to deal with an entire state." Many are not trained for the job. "If someone wished to evaluate the field thoroughly, he would find that only a handful of the 50 extension specialists are trained as certified safety professionals," said Gary Erisman, a former extension safety specialist in Florida who now farms in Illinois. "Somewhere along the line, someone has gotten agricultural engineering and safety confused," he said. "They think that if one is an ag engineer, you're automatically a safety specialist. And that is not true." Farming's safety and health problems have caused some to question whether the extension's program is getting the job done. The safety program "is a voluntary educational service that farm people may choose to ignore," Murphy wrote in an article. And for a variety of reasons, too many do choose to ignore it." Said Baker: "Voluntarism is an important concept but I'm not sure it's the ultimate answer. It's hard to keep people motivated." Schnieder thinks otherwise. "We could go the route of West Germany," he said. "They have 160 inspectors for an area the size of Nebraska. And we have only one person here, that being me. Yet when you look at Germany's accident statistics, we're doing as good on a voluntary basis as they are with their inspectors. Extension runs on voluntarism. This is the route we have to follow."

Kendell Dickman of Coon Rapids was nearly killed last year in a farm accident. His coat got wrapped up in a spinning power take-off shaft on a tractor. The shaft had no protective shield. "I was trying everything I could to rip my coat off but the shaft had a hold of me," said Dickman, then a hired hand on a large farm. "It pulled me down and flipped me over so hard that my jaw split in half. My head hit so hard that I was just stunned. I didn't know what was going to happen next." Fortunately for Dickman, a co-worker arrived and shut the machine off. "Even two seconds more and I could have been killed," he said.

The accident happened on March 29, 1983, but Dickman still is recovering. "I'm just now getting the feeling back in my lip and bottom teeth," he said. "My arm was messed up, too. It's still kind of deformed. It has a dip in it." Most power take-off shafts are shielded, but this one wasn't "It was probably 15 years old, and I don't think it had ever had a shield on it," said Dickman, 24. "But you know, right after it happened they came out and put one on it... . They had one on there within half an hour after the accident."

The safety and health standards of the Occupational Safety and Health Act (OSHA) have almost no role in agriculture, and that's just the way most farmers want it. Consider the position of the American Farm Bureau Federation: "We continue to favor repeal of the Occupational Safety and Health Act." Some wonder if that attitude is too costly. "We continue to have accidents in agriculture and perhaps OSHA is just another piece in the puzzle that could be used to apply the brakes to our accident rate," said Gary Downey, president of the Iowa Farm Safety Council. "I think that if OSHA standards were applied from a practical standpoint and drafted by people familiar with agriculture, the agency could have a role in farming," said Downey, engineering director at the Grinnell Mutual Reinsurance Co.

Farming's opposition to OSHA helped shackle the agency in 1977 when lawmakers prohibited it from regulating farms with 10 or fewer employees. Ironically, such farms are the most dangerous. "OSHA's limited efforts in agricultural safety are not aimed where they are needed most; namely the smaller farm operations where the majority of fatal farm work accidents occur," wrote Murphy in "Professional Safety" magazine. The Center for Rural Affairs, a Nebraska-based farm group, said the OSHA rule, "which concentrates on the number of employees rather than the health risks of farm technology, misses the mark." Nationally, about 95 percent of all farms are exempt from OSHA coverage, Murphy reported. In Iowa, only 7,500 of the state's 153,700, farmers and farm hands are covered, according to the Iowa Bureau of Labor. Any attempt to reintroduce OSHA to agriculture would draw howls of protest. As Murphy wrote: "Old time feelings of independence and resilience are alive and well in rural America. ... There is something very un-American about the government coming on [a farmer's] property to tell him how to go about his business." OSHA itself hasn't helped the situation. After it was created in 1970, the agency drafted a bushel of farm-related rules and regulations, many of which were viewed as trivial. Farmers were warned about everything from rickety ladders to slippery cow manure. And OSHA was nearly laughed out of the Corn Belt. That attitude still exists today, but some say it's time for a change. "There is a need to move to a new level where cooperation, rather than conflict, will be the predominant mood," wrote Donald Pedersen in the Agricultural Law Journal.

"No doubt the kind of regulation that is being attempted can serve to advance the cause of safety and health if taken seriously by farm operators and their employees," said Pedersen, a professor at Capital University Law School in Ohio. Donham suggested something similar at a Farm Bureau meeting earlier this year. "Through leadership from the industry, stressing the uniqueness of agriculture, [OSHA's] regulative format can possibly be modified to emphasize education, research and consultation," he said. OSHA could help with one other thing: information. The agency collects health and safety statistics from industry, but none from the 95 percent of farms with 10 or fewer employees. That "leaves [scientists] with insufficient information to analyze emerging health problems of new technology," reported the Center for Rural Affairs. "This is unfortunate for farmers and workers alike." What little information exists in Iowa indicates that the farmer's health and safety are worsening. On the 1,400 larger farms where statistics are gathered (those with more than 10 employees), the number of fatal and non-fatal accidents and work-related illnesses jumped from 293 in 1979 to 840 in 1982. The overall picture is almost certainly much worse. Those 1,400 farms are only 1.2 percent of the 117,000 farms in Iowa. The most extensive dangers - which still are officially unrecorded - occur on the family farms. "The ones who are being wiped out are the family farmers," said John Patrimanas of the Iowa Bureau of Labor, which gathers information for OSHA. "But OSHA doesn't take them into consideration because the law doesn't cover them."

"The end result of inadequate data, poor public information and fragmented regulatory authority is injury, disability and possibly death for farmers and farmworkers," reported the Center for Rural Affairs. Safety and health specialists believe a solution is remote and the outlook gloomy. "I'd love to work myself out of a job," said Baker in Missouri. "But I don't think I'm going to. Not in my lifetime." "We know that progress is not being made," said Williams at ISU. "But we don't know why." "I'm afraid I don't have any solutions at all," said Downey at Grinnell Mutual. "I wish I did. I wish someone did."

# 2

# COMMERCIAL ASPECTS OF THE HEALTH SERVICE

## 2.1 DEFRAUDATION AND THE ORGAN DEAL

### 2.1.1 Special Introductory Remarks

William Sherman, an investigative reporter for the New York *Daily News*, concentrated for some time on such problems of the metropolitan area as health care and questionable alliances between politicians, judges and businessmen. In 1973, he was given a Medicaid card and assigned to find out what was wrong with New York's Medicaid program. Posing as a Medicaid recipient in physicians' offices, he found major abuses such as: a doctor who said he treated 300 patients in one day; unneeded tests, the use of drugs that were not approved, short quantities and weights on prescriptions; some psychiatrists who submitted bills to the city for more hours than there are in a day. Sherman worked closely with two city agencies, the Health Department and the Human Resources Administration. His series of 14 articles about the scandal was acclaimed by a Pulitzer Prize jury as good writing and painstaking investigation. Sherman earned the 1974 Pulitzer Prize for Local Investigative Specialized Reporting "for his resourceful investigative reporting in the exposure of extreme abuse of the New York Medicaid program."

Hints of violations in human kidney dealings led Andrew Schneider, public health writer for the *Pittsburgh Press*, and staff writer Mary Pat Flaherty on a ten-month trek that took them virtually around the world in 1985. They found that money, rather than medical need, often rules; that organs sales is a burgeoning industry; that covenants between donor and recipient were broken. And, above all, they found surgeons around the world coming face-to-face with the prospect of trade in human organs - another crisis in medical ethics. The two journalists heard stories of kidneys being taken from donors for one purpose then shipped off for another, etc. A Pulitzer Prize jury found the series of articles outstanding, and the Advisory Board awarded the 1986 Pulitzer Specialized Reporting Prize to Schneider and Flaherty "for their investigation of violations and failures in the organ transplantation system in the United States."

## 2.1.2 Abuse of the Medicaid Program

[Source: William Sherman: How Medicaid Paid $457,000 for Sesame Oil, in: *Daily News* (New York, N.Y.), Vol. 54/No. 184, January 25, 1973, p. 2, cols. 1-4; p. 30, cols. 1-5; reprinted by permission of the New York News, Inc., New York, N.Y.]

A 76-year-old Romanian-born physician, Emanuel Revici, announced to the world more than 20 years ago that he had developed a cancer drug. Since then, the doctor has claimed to have invented other drug remedies for alcoholism and narcotics addiction. His remedies have never received approval from the federal Food and Drug Administration.

So, city officials were dismayed last fall to discover they had paid out $457,000 in medicaid funds for his panacea for drug addiction - injections of sesame oil, sulphur crystals, and other still unidentified compounds at a voluntary hospital here. The funds went to Trafalgar Hospital, 161 E. 90th St., where Dr. Revici, a short, stout balding man, is a trustee and the director of internal medicine. There, on the third floor, between 1970 and 1972, according to the records of the Health Department, about 900 medicaid patients were injected with substances bottled variously under the names "Bionar," "Perse," and "425-Rex." The drugs were touted by Revici as a cure for heroin addiction.

Joseph A. Cimino, commissioner of the City's Health Department, said yesterday that the city had been unaware of Revici's activities at the hospital for two years. Dr. Cimino called the experiments "unlawful, potentially dangerous, and inadequately controlled." He added that use of a new drug without FDA approval is a violation of the city's Health Code. The city had no way of knowing what was going on, Cimino said, because the hospital made no mention of the use of the drugs on addicts. The Health Department, in its audit last November, was also surprised to find that the city had paid for experiments on 260 addicts who were hospitalized several days each with common colds.

These disclosures came as part of THE NEWS continuing Medicaid Probe series, an in-depth investigation into abuses in the city's $1.3 billion medical assistance program. Last Oct. 11, Jerome E. Driesen, the Health Department's director of psychiatry, visited Trafalgar Hospital, and, in a report, said the addicts were admitted for diagnosed diseases they did not have, and that even when a disease was appropriately diagnosed, it was not properly treated in many cases.

"In effect," Dr. Driesen wrote in his official report, "they were all brought in for withdrawal from physiological dependency on narcotics, barbiturates, or even alcohol. Then they were returned to the community without after-care." Recently, a reporter visited Dr. Revici at his office at the Institute of Applied Biology, 144 E 90th St. He is the scientific director there in addition to his position at the hospital, and it was there that he developed the drugs.

## TYPE A BORSCHT?

When asked under what sanction he conducted his experiments, since he did not have FDA approval, the doctor replied. "A state health official told me I could inject borscht into my patients if I wanted to. That was between me and my patients." He declined to identify the official. Referring to the development of his latest drug, "Bionar," used in experiments on addicts at the hospital, Revici said, "This produces the most amazing results of anything I have developed so far." Caressing a bottle of one of his drugs in his left hand while he spoke, Revici said, "After several injections, the addicts sat up and said 'My God, I feel normal again.'"

## WORKS 18 HOURS A DAY

He would not disclose the contents of Bionar except to describe it as "butyl-oxy-phenol... a combination of ether and other things in an oily substance." The doctor, who lives at 1111 Park Ave., insisted, "I'm not in it for the money. I work 18 hours a day to help people." Revici, a naturalized American citizen who was licensed to practice medicine in New York in 1947, was born in Romania in 1896. His father was also a physician. From 1921 until 1941, he said, he participated in research experiments in Bucharest and later in hospitals in France. In 1941, he fled from the Germans to Mexico, where he organized the Institute de Biologica Aplicado in Mexico City, the forerunner of his institute on E. 90th St.

In addition to those offices, the institute also occupies a laboratory at 161 E. 91st. St., where experiments in cancer research and other diseases are carried out on white rats and mice. "My theory of addiction treatment is that withdrawal pains are caused by an imbalance of fatty acids in the body," Revici said. "Too much fatty acid with no heroin to balance it off during withdrawal, and the addict feels pain and the need for the narcotic. Once we inject something that will neutralize the fatty acids," he said with a gleam in his eye, the addict feels no pain and loses his need for heroin."

## WORKS ON 2 ADDITIONS

His theory of acid and alkaline imbalance as causing disease and pain has also been applied in his drugs for cancer and alcoholism. In fact, he said, his drug called "Perse" was used to cure both drug addiction and alcoholism. Several years ago, he injected several thousand addicts with Perse, he said, "and we achieved remarkable results." The FDA denied him "investigational drug approval," because Perse contained selenium, a metal which is harmful when taken internally. Still, Perse was used in experiments on addicts at Trafalgar Hospital. "Once we took the selenium out of Perse, we had a drug similar to Bionar, but I didn't perfect it until about a year and a half ago," Revici said. "After three days of treatment with Bionar, the addict is completely free of any pain and any need for heroin." Again the doctor emphasized that he would realize "no financial gain" from the drug's sale, and said that he did not even have the patent rights to the drug.

An investigation of Health Department records and the interview with Revici revealed the existence of the Bionar Corp., with an address at 505 Park Ave. The Bionar Corp., it turns out, is connected with Compudat Scientific Systems and another company called Camin Industries. All three are presided over by Benjamin Payn, a 58-year-old businessman. A NEWS reporter and a photographer found Payn in his offices at the Park Avenue address. A smooth-talking, well-dressed man, Payn said that Camin Industries "is a firm in electrocoating and mechanical forming of metals." The company earned $2,449,396 last year, according to its financial statement.

"I met Dr. Revici two years ago and was impressed with his experiments," Payn said. "He needed money, and we gave him about $100,000 for his research. In return, he assigned us the patent rights for Bionar. We took over the financial and commercial interests in the drug, and quite frankly, we did see a large profit potential in it. It is much cheaper than methadone to produce and does not have methadone's addictive qualities. I don't expect to make any money out of the drug for a while," Payn concluded, "and maybe it will never earn any money."

## SULPHUR TREATMENT

The treatment of addicts with Dr. Revici's experimental drugs has been stopped at Trafalgar Hospital, according to the Health Department. But not before an exhaustive investigation by that agency showed that $457,000 in medical funds was paid out. Investigators for the Health Department found that most of the addicts were "walk-ins off street," and that others were referred to Trafalgar by doctors at Beth Israel Hospital. Dr. Revici told THE NEWS that in addition to patients treated with Bionar, and a similar drug he called "425" or "425-Rex", 3,000 other patients were injected with sulphur crystals. "We achieved marvelous results with the sulphur, but then the patients started getting stomach aches, so we had to discontinue it," Revici said.

Among the other drugs found in the third-floor medicine cabinets of Trafalgar by Health Department investigators was a drug labelled "Sleep in Water." Nurses who administered the substance intramuscularly said it was "used for sleep." Another drug found was "F C - 12." Mrs. Alice Scott, a registered nurse who works at the third-floor station, said it was "put on bread and then given to a patient to eat to stop abdominal pain." The nurses said that the drugs, including the Bionar and "425 - Rex" solutions, were ordered by Dr. Revici.

Nine nurses on three shifts injected the drugs into the patients last September, two years after the hospital started billing medicaid for the experiments. An analysis of patients' records by the Health Department last October revealed that several addicts treated with 425 Rex, a drug the Health Department found to be identical to Bionar in composition, exhibited nervousness, insomnia, and vomiting, right up until the time of their release.

## FUNDS TRANSMITTED

On Oct. 30, Revici, Payn, and the hospital administrator, Leo Lazarus, were called to the Health Department office at 330 W. 34th St. for an informal hearing. At the meeting, Steven Rosenberg of the Health Department charged that the patients were treated with experimental drugs, and that under city medicaid regulations, the hospital could not be paid for such a program. By then, however, the $457,000 had already been paid to the hospital. Dr. Rosenberg also charged that the patients were given Bionar before they received treatment for the ailments cited on the bills submitted to the hospital.

On Dec. 12, a second hearing was held, and this time a representative of the city Corporation Counsel's office concluded that the $457,000 should be returned to the city. Now, the city begins the long and ardous task of trying to recover the medicaid money. Last Week, Trafalgar Hospital was quietly suspended from the Medicaid Program, and Health Department officials are still unable to determine the effect of the drugs on the addicts. "We haven't been able to track down the addicts to find out what happened," said Dr. Cimino, the Health Commissioner.

## 2.1.3 Dealers and Deals in Human Kidneys

[Source: Andrew Schneider/Mary Pat Flaherty: Exploiting trust. Neglect and greed infect transplant system, in: *The Pittsburgh Press* (Pittsburgh, Pa.), Vol. 102/No. 132, November 3, 1985, p. 1, cols. 1-5; p. 18, cols. 1-6; reprinted by permission of the Pittsburgh Press Company, Pittsburgh, Pa.]

Born in wonder and nurtured by selfless acts, kidney transplantation is coming of age amid a climate of greed, manipulation and neglect. In Bombay, a slum dweller sells her kidney to a Saudi who needs a transplant. With some of the proceeds, she buys a television. In Tokyo, a loan shark allows some of his debtors to pay off with their kidneys. In Manila, Filipino prison inmates donate their kidneys for a chance at early parole. In Mexico City, a part-time organ broker says he's sent several paid donors to American hospitals for operations banned under the U.S. law against selling organs.

Thirty-one years after the first kidney transplant, the operation has become commonplace and highly successful, making kidneys one of the most sought-after commodities on the world market. The demand for kidneys generates price tags of more than $13,000 on the 5-ounce organs, almost seven times higher than the same amount of gold. A limited natural resource, kidneys are precious. Yet, internationally, they get less protection than whales or computer chips. As the first major human organ transplant to become routine, kidney transplants are pioneering a host of troubling questions about human exploitation and medical ethics, raising the specter of a harsh future divided between poor donors and powerful organ users.

Most of the dedicated professionals working with kidney transplants see that organs are found quickly for patients suffering slow deaths. But a less-reputable element is muscling into the kidney trade, building profits and reputations on the misfortune of others. A 10-month investigation by The Pittsburgh Press of kidney transplantation around the world found that money, rather than medicine, often sets the path of kidneys from donors to recipients. Last year, for example, while almost 10,000 Americans sat shackled to dialysis machines waiting for transplants, at least 300 of the kidneys gathered in the U.S. were deemed useless and sent abroad. Most of these castoffs went to Great Britain, Kuwait, Turkey and Japan, where surgeons report transplant success rates that rival those at the best U.S. centers.

In the exchanges, kidneys donated by trusting American families to help the sickest patients routinely passed into unregulated systems where the richest, not the sickest, got them. "It's always the rich who get them because it's only they who can afford to reimburse the costs of getting them over here," says Yoskiki Konoeda, transplant coordinator at Hachioji Medical Center of Tokyo Medical College. "We keep a special list of those who can pay." Exporting U.S. kidneys is just one of the dilemmas facing transplant experts. The buying and selling of human organs is another. While the United States, Britain and other Western countries largely use brain-dead cadavers as donors, cultural taboos restrict such donations in other countries. They depend on kidneys obtained from "paid, unrelated living donors" - the delicate phrase that coddles the indelicate business of black-market organs.

Most people can live normal lives with only one of their two kidneys, a reality that prompts poor people in several countries to sell a piece of themselves to wealthy patients. The most active live human organ network is centered in Bombay, where organ sales are legal and where vast slums have become human supermarkets where the world's privileged shop for kidney donors. The ethical, moral and legal problems besetting kidney transplantation aren't only on foreign soil, however. The Pittsburgh Press review found they also touch the very heart of the American transplant system through:

● Doctors who offer and deliver transplants to higher-paying foreign patients in a fraction of the time that it usually takes Americans to get a kidney.

● A noted surgeon who sidestepped an "Americans-first" policy among Chicago hospitals by taking his transplant service for foreign national patients on the road. The surgeon has a contract with a foreign government to coordinate transplants for its citizens, primarily using kidneys from brain-dead American donors.

● Organ brokers on at least three continents who skirt the U.S. ban on trafficking in organs by referring paid donors to America. Those black-market brokers - both covertly and openly - send paid donors to hospitals where the purchased kidneys are transplanted for premium prices into wealthy patients.

● A Houston psychotherapist who is suing the state of Texas to allow the sale of human organs because he believes people have a constitutional right to do so.

● A Washington, D.C., rock promoter who bills himself as a fund-raising consultant for anguished families needing money for expensive transplants. One 19-year-old mother says she gave him $10,000 collected by her neighbors for her infant's transplant. He operates in Maryland without a state license. Such activities lead some doctors to question whether the American transplant community is the moral fortress it holds itself out to be.

## AMERICAN CONNECTIONS

The distance between the world's muddy slums and its stainless steel and tiled surgical suites is not all that long, insists Dr. Terry Strom, director of immunology at Boston's Beth Israel Hospital and a member of the congressionally appointed National Task Force on Organ Transplants. "We talk of the buying and selling of organs in remote corners of the Third World but all too often it appears these activities lead directly to the operating rooms of hospitals in the United Kingdom and our country. How can we make believe we aren't involved?" How also can surgeons contend they're honoring the covenant they made with donor families, Strom asks. "This commercialization is horrendous," he says. "In addition to not doing what our benefactors - the donors of the kidneys - would have us do with their gifts, we then do something worse by passing them on to special people who get special privileges. That is outrageous."

The commercialization of kidneys sprouting at a rudimentary level between brokers and paid donors also has corporate blossoms. From its private hospitals in Great Britain, American Medical International Inc. - the world's fourth-largest hospital management firm - mounts an aggressive marketing campaign that solicits transplant patients throughout India and five other countries. The California-based corporation promises quick transplants using discarded American kidneys - a supply that American surgeons insist is small and irregular but which was dependable enough to allow AMI to do one transplant a week with American organs for the past six months, according to its British marketing director. Evolution of kidney transplants from experiment to enterprise leaves some of the field's leaders happy to be retiring.

"Without getting sensational at all, I think all these troubles are going to get much worse as transplantation gets better. In a way, I'm glad that I will not be doing transplants for many more years," says Dr. Roy Calne, a founding father of kidney transplantation who works at Cambridge University in England. Steps should be taken to regulate the industry now, "before there is a major, deeply entrenched criminal side to it," Calne says. "Common sense shows there are a lot of people, criminals presumably, who would be willing for money to go out and get the organs. They haven't got to get the organs literally. All they've got to do is shoot the person carefully through the head, then get him admitted to a small sanitarium on the outside of town. Suddenly, there is a donor of a specific blood group available. I could see that happening." Says Calne, "When you have commodities that could be life-saving or prevent you from being crippled or blinded and they are scarce, you immediately face the law of the marketplace degenerating into the law of the jungle."

## HOW KIDNEY FUNCTIONS

As human organs go, the kidney seems an unlikely candidate for so much attention. It is not nearly as imposing as a pulsating heart or the breath-giving lungs, but without it life can be unbearable. Only 4 inches long and 2 inches wide, a person's two kidneys serve as the body's waste disposal filters, clearing out noxious byproducts before they have a chance to build up to lethal levels. They also help regulate blood pressure and produce hormones that prevent anemia and brittle bones, but those are lesser functions. "It may sound funny to some but the bottom line is that without a kidney you can't pee and that makes life very difficult," says Mick Bewick, a London transplant surgeon. When it comes to kidneys, the body is blessed with an abundance of riches. Even with one kidney, a person still has about 25 percent more kidney function than he needs to lead a healthy life.

For reasons that are a mystery to scientists, once one kidney is removed from a person, his remaining kidney expands to compensate for the loss. It is that trait that, in part, encourage some surgeons to take a kidney from a living donor and transplant it into someone whose kidneys have failed. For living donors in developed countries, the surgical risk in kidney donation is minimal. However, they are left with only one kidney and have no back-up should they ever develop kidney disease themselves. For living donors in less-developed countries, the risks of donation come in follow-up care should they develop medical problems after surgery. For surgeons who prefer to use kidneys removed from brain-dead donors, the kidney has another endearing property. It is hardy, very hardy. Packed in the proper preservatives, a kidney from a cadaver donor remains usable in transplants for at least two days and, according to some surgeons, as many as three or four. Livers, by comparison, have a shelf life of eight to 10 hours; hearts, four hours.

## FINDING THE MATCH

Before transplanting a donor organ, most hospitals run matching tests that compare the chemistry of the donor's body with the recipient's. The matching is done by looking at specific markers - called antigens - on each cell. The antigens are hereditary and unique to each individual. "For years it was felt that in order to ensure a good outcome in a transplant each one of these antigens had to be matched perfectly with the donor organ or the body would produce antibodies or killer cells that would cause rejection of the transplanted organ. But (the anti-rejection drug) cyclosporine has changed a lot of that," says Mary Ann Palumbi, senior transplant nurse coordinator with the Pittsburgh Transplant

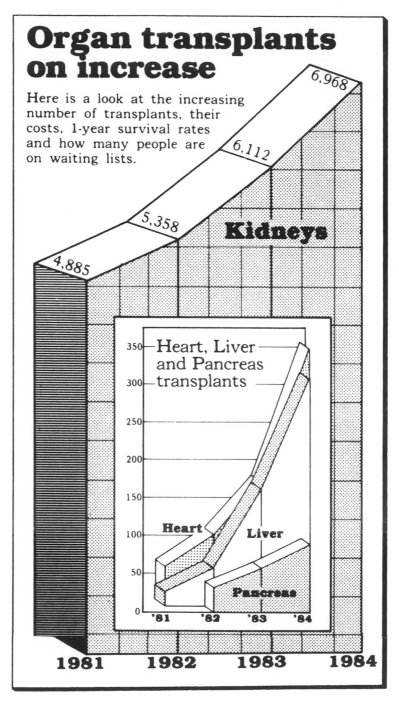

# Organ transplants on increase

Here is a look at the increasing number of transplants, their costs, 1-year survival rates and how many people are on waiting lists.

6,968

6,112

5,358

4,885

**Kidneys**

Heart, Liver and Pancreas transplants

350

300

250

200

150

100

50

0

Heart

Liver

Pancreas

'81   '82   '83   '84

1981     1982     1983     1984

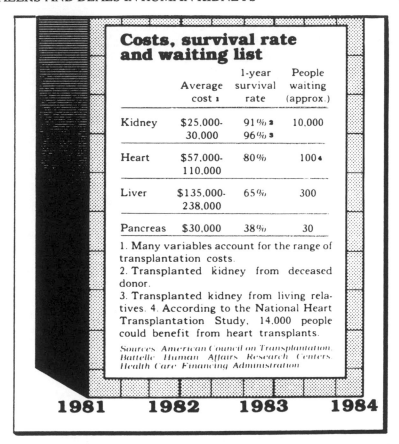

## Costs, survival rate and waiting list

|  | Average cost [1] | 1-year survival rate | People waiting (approx.) |
|---|---|---|---|
| Kidney | $25,000- 30,000 | 91% [2] 96% [3] | 10,000 |
| Heart | $57,000- 110,000 | 80% | 100 [4] |
| Liver | $135,000- 238,000 | 65% | 300 |
| Pancreas | $30,000 | 38% | 30 |

1. Many variables account for the range of transplantation costs.
2. Transplanted kidney from deceased donor.
3. Transplanted kidney from living relatives. 4. According to the National Heart Transplantation Study, 14,000 people could benefit from heart transplants.

*Sources: American Council on Transplantation, Battelle Human Affairs Research Centers, Health Care Financing Administration*

**1981        1982        1983        1984**

Foundation. Cyclosporine suppresses the body's natural rejection process of organs that aren't part of its original equipment. Honing their transplant techniques over the past three decades, surgeons have made kidneys a global medical commodity and taken transplantation from cottage industry to vast, commercial venture.

In the U.S. alone, 6,968 people had kidney transplants last year while another 10,000 were on waiting lists. In 1981, 4,885 people had kidney transplants, according to the federal Office of Organ Transplantation. The rapid expansion of their field leaves surgeons fretting about the potential for abuse. In July, the 20-member executive board of the International Transplantation Society met near Montreal to talk about just such fears. In a hunting lodge built by the captains of Canada's railroad industry, the captains of world transplantation took turns appalling each other with stories, rumors and bits of fact about organs sold in the hungry villages and stinking slums of the Third World; of money often deciding who gets the kidney. After 14 hours of exhausting deliberation, they adopted, 19-1, new ethical guidelines to halt such abuses. But even these advocates weren't certain their action was enough.

## MIDNIGHT MISGIVINGS

Over a midnight dinner, presidents of the ITS, the American Society of Transplant Surgeons and the British Transplant Society wondered what atrocities might be next - and what might already be eluding them. "We're looking over our shoulders, over our colleagues' shoulders. The storm clouds are gathering and you don't know when or where they'll hit. What else is out there?" asks Dr. Anthony Monaco, president of the American Society of Transplant Surgeons and a Boston surgeon. "We assume that everything is being done properly so we don't look hard for trouble. We've usually found out by accident or chance that we have a problem," says Dr. Robert Sells, president of the British Transplant Society.

Just such a chance alerted British surgeons to the export of human organs from the U.S. to England. The British didn't find out that U.S. kidneys were being routinely shipped into England until a British customs agent called one surgeon and asked about organs he found passing through London's Heathrow Airport in coolers. The agent was upset because dogs trained to sniff out drugs kept turning up human kidneys. "For the obvious, indelicate reasons, he was worried there was going to be an accident," says Sells. "That's how we  started talking about exports from the States. But we still don't have a good handle on it. And it's been more than a year."

## EXPORT MYSTERIES

Laxity and lack of basic information also plague the United States kidney transplant system - a $2 billion, tax-payer-supported industry funded through Medicare. No one, including officials within the U.S. Health Care Financing Administration who oversee it, has a good handle on the industry. Although thousands of Americans are waiting for kidneys, HCFA does not know how many are exported or why those kidneys leave. HCFA officials estimated that 100 kidneys were exported from the U.S. during the fiscal year ending June 30. But that figure likely is nearer to 300, according to a survey by The Pittsburgh Press of 185 transplant centers nationwide, as well as interviews with procurement directors, surgeons abroad who received the kidneys and internal HCFA reports obtained under the Freedom of Information Act. The 300 organs account for about five percent of the cadaver kidneys donated in the U.S. last year.

And while surgeons and procurement specialists contend the exported kidneys were surplus or compromised organs for which no recipient was available in the United States, the federal government can't be certain because of the lack of reliable data. The U.S. program was loose enough to allow Vinod Patel to get government permission to run an organ procurement agency out of his home in Kennedy, just outside Pittsburgh. Patel, an engineer who has no medical training, said he planned to get kidneys from traditional U.S. sources and "generous donors" in India and Brazil, two countries where cadaveric donation is minimal and organs almost always are bought. Before procurement coordinators prodded the White House to halt Patel in June, HCFA had issued him a Medicare provider number, which is the government promise of payment for any organs gathered by an organ-procurement agency.

## DELICATE SUBJECTS

Even organ groups that keep detailed records on kidneys are reluctant to release them for fear of how they'll be interpreted. The largest exporter of U.S. kidneys is the United Network for Organ Sharing, a Virginia-based organization that matches donated organs with waiting patients. Its executive director, Gene Pierce, at first declined a request by The Pittsburgh Press for destination and billing information to help track the exported kidneys. Pierce refused for four months, saying it was up to the executive board of UNOS' parent organization, the Southeastern Organ Procurement Foundation, to release the information. "Gene just doesn't think that information should be made public and I agree," said Dr. William Eagles, SEOPF's medical director. "We just don't want a lot of noise made about the kidneys we export. Nobody does. The public might not understand it and that could hurt our entire program." Pierce released some of the information in early October, after much of the information already had been supplied by the overseas surgeons who get American kidneys.

## BEHIND CLOSED DOORS

The secrecy shrouding kidney exports is typical of the closed dialogue surrounding much of the American transplantation program. In Park City, Utah, at an April meeting of 50 of the world's leading authorities on the artificial heart, Dr. Robert Jarvik barred the media from the gathering, claiming it would hinder "open, frank and candid discussion of the medical and ethical issues." While some say they understand Jarvik's desire for privacy, others contend it's unacceptable in the transplantation of human organs. "None of the decisions on human transplantation should be made behind closed doors," says Strom. "Donated organs are a public resource and secrecy in the deliberations of the ethical and procedural issues of transplantation will only compound the problems we have and further endanger the trust we have been given," he said.

The fear of violating a trust is most strongly expressed by professionals who deal with the donor's family; those at the very center of the American transplant program. Talking with grieving families about donating their loved one's organs is a draining ordeal. Most kidney donations are from donors who are brain-dead. Never easy to accept, death is even harder to accept when it comes as brain death. In that state, patients lie in the bed of an intensive-care or trauma unit looking as if they merely are asleep. They're warm to the touch. They breathe. Their chests rise and fall. But their brains are dead, and so are all chances of survival.

It often takes nurses and doctors hours, sometimes days, of tearful conversations, not only with the family, but occasionally with friends and neighbors, until all the questions are answered, and a covenant is established between the family and procurement professionals. "Talking about organ donation with the young mother and father of a 4-year-old struck by a car isn't much easier than talking to the wife of a 30-year-old shot in a hunting accident or the sister of a 52-year-old man with a brain tumor. It's all painful," says Diane Cantella, a supervising nurse at Allegheny General Hospital's trauma unit. "All of them have lost someone they loved. We offer them the chance to find something positive out of their tragic loss, to help someone else live. We trust the system and families trust us. If that trust is being violated anywhere down the line, then the entire system will fail. It just can't be allowed to happen."

## UNCERTAIN TRUST

Growing reports of abuse in the transplant system trouble the professionals who promise grieving families in good faith that organs will go to the medically appropriate patient based on urgency or the best match between organ and ailing recipient. "For years, people involved in procurement worked night and day to surround organ donation in an aura of trust. It was the only way we could get people to accept the highly unique premise of sharing parts of their deceased family members with strangers, so people they've never met, and probably never will meet, will live or have their lives improved," says Donald Denny, chairman of the National Task Force's committee on procurement and director of the Pittsburgh Transplant Foundation. Should the American public's support of organ donation ever falter, transplantation in this country will come to a halt. "We fear that, unless the abuses of the system are halted immediately, the damage to the trust that we've worked so hard to build will be irreparable," Denny says.

Where once the transplant community was tightly knit, it now has grown beyond chumminess and beyond the easy trust and monitoring that chumminess allow. In response, surgical groups are adopting tighter controls over their field. Following disclosures in May by The Pittsburgh Press that surgeons at Presbyterian University Hospital in Pittsburgh pushed 61 influential or wealthy foreign patients to the top of the kidney transplant list for non-medical reasons, several U.S. transplant societies adopted "Americans-first" policies for the distribution of cadaver donor organs. And there are indications that professional groups are readying for even greater battles as some of the issues raised in Pittsburgh - favoritism, line jumping, inflated billing - emerge on a world scale.

The International Transplantation Society, the American Society of Transplant Surgeons and the United Network for Organ Sharing - all groups with professional guidelines - are shopping for insurance protection in case of legal reprisals by people or institutions they may have to criticize. Within one week last month, the U.S. Justice Department received 14 phone calls seeking interpretations of the federal law banning trafficking in human organs. The glut of calls after a year of virtual silence prompted one harried Justice Department lawyer to ask "What the hell's going on out there?" What appears to be going on is that professional groups are struggling to get their own houses in order to stave off regulation by outsiders. Guidelines to expel doctors who sell organs, use

# Kidney charges in Chicago

Kidney charges to U.S. government can vary in the same city:

| | |
|---|---|
| Rush — Presby | **$7,100** |
| University of Illinois | **$7,279** |
| Loyola | **$8,320** |
| Northwestern University | **$8,500** |
| Children's Memorial | **$8,500** |
| University of Chicago | **$9,000** |
| Chicago Reg. Organ & Tissue Bank | **$13,500** |

*Source: Pittsburgh Press interviews*

paid organ donors, solicit patients or ignore patient waiting lists already have been adopted by the International Transplantation Society.

And - with a consensus among surgeons around the world - that may be the only step needed, says Dr. Peter Morris, ITS president: "I can see the time arising when, if you're not a member of one of these societies, it will be a little tough for you to stand up and proclaim yourself a transplant surgeon," says Morris, of Oxford University in England. Others in the field, however, foresee more stern legislative measures to control the rapidly developing field of human organ transplants. "There must be more control than the medical societies can provide," says Calne, who in addition to his post at Cambridge is president of the European Transplant Society. "We've really got no power to do anything but expel them from the society, but so what? We worked hard to expel someone from the British Transplant Society - there was great agonizing about it and they finally agreed to expel him - and then we found out he wasn't even a member."

Rules to stop abuses, says Calne, must be given the power of law - domestic and international law. Strom, the Boston immunologist, says the righteous disbelief of surgeons who dismiss reports of abuse must give way to a sense of personal responsibility and professional accountability "even if it takes legislation." Relying on peer pressure, says Strom, amounts to regulation by the regulated. And that is inadequate for so precious a commodity as kidneys. "Face it. Getting thrown out of one of these professional societies is like getting thrown out of the Book-of-the-Month Club."

Self-serving opportunists and entrepreneurs can't be allowed to erode the bedrock of trust on which transplantation is built, says Dr. Nicholas Tilney, chairman of the International Transplantation Society's ethics committee and a Boston transplant surgeon. "In all too many cases trust is being violated at both ends of transplantation: To the donor's family who often with great personal pain freely gives the gift of a loved one's organs, and to the American patient waiting on the list, assured that the donated kidneys are always fairly distributed on the basis of medical need and not financial status. A program where trust is so important cannot survive if there is deceit anywhere."

## 2.2 HOSPITALS AND THE RECRUITMENT OF NEW PATIENTS

### 2.2.1 Special Introductory Remarks

The probe of ambulance service in Chicago began after William Jones from the *Chicago Tribune* got a tip that policemen were taking bribes in return for referrals to certain ambulance companies. Jones knew at the outset that he could best see ambulance service from the inside. After taking a month-long advanced first aid course so that he would not be helpless in an emergency, he applied for his first job as an ambulance driver. On that job, he observed terrible conditions and listened to other drivers telling of unbelievable practices. Jones' six-part series in his paper received wide public attention. "Showing a high degree of initiative and resourcefulness," a Pulitzer Prize jury stated, Jones "uncovered for his readers corrupt companies handling ambulance cases often on a pay or no go basis. He used specific incidents tellingly, gave details he could have obtained no other way." For his work, Jones received the 1971 Local Investigative Specialized Reporting award "for exposing collusion between police and some of Chicago's largest private ambulance companies to restrict service in low income areas, leading to major reforms."

A team of task force reporters from the same newspaper in 1975 conducted investigations in two Chicago hospitals. At von Solbrig Memorial, they found filth, dangerous understaffing, unsound medical practices and violation of state and local regulations including a staff list of 50 doctors, of which only 18 practiced there, while others were dead or had never been there at all. At Northeast Community Hospital, which had a regular patrol to recruit derelicts with promises of free food and rest, the reporters uncovered: a haven of welfare loafers who could float for days on powerful tranquilizers; revolving-door-treatment of 300 alcoholics a month, for which the state was billed more than $2 million a year in public aid money. A Pulitzer Prize jury found the reporters' work "a hard-hitting and exclusive series, dramatically presented by first person reports based on infiltration of the hospital staffs. There is impressive additional detail of the situation that quickly resulted in closing the hospitals." *The Chicago Tribune* team received the 1976 Local Investigative Specialized Reporting award for "exposing shocking conditions at two private Chicago hospitals."

## 2.2.2 The Degenerating Transportation of Sick People

[Source: William Jones: Men of Mercy? Profit in Pain, in: *Chicago Tribune* (Chicago, Il.), 123rd Year/No. 158, June 7, 1970, p. 1, cols. 1-2; p.2, cols. 2-5; reprinted by permission of the Chicago Tribune Company, Chicago, Il.]

They are the misery merchants and they prowl the streets of our city 24 hours a day as profiteers of human suffering. Waiting in filthy garages scattered thruout the city, they prey on families faced with an urgent need for transportation and medical care for a loved one. They are the hustlers among the city's private ambulance operators and they are waiting for your call for help. Their business is big business in Chicago. The multimillion-dollar industry accounts for nearly 1 million dollars of Cook County's welfare fees each year. At the same time, the misery merchants are exacting a toll in needless suffering and sadistic treatment of the ill that may never be inventoried.

PLAY RUSSIAN ROULETTE

You may have to call the misery merchants this afternoon or tomorrow or next week. When you do, a member of your family may be gasping after a heart attack or screaming in agony after fracturing a hip or leg. As you frantically leaf thru the telephone directory to find an ambulance company, you unwittingly will be playing a game of Russian roulette with the person you are trying to help. The stakes are high. If you are poor or black or on welfare, they are even higher. I know because I worked as a misery merchant and this is how they operate:

1. A middle-age man lies gasping from an apparent heart attack in his north side apartment. His throat makes a rasping sound as he desperately tries to continue breathing. A two-man ambulance crew stands over his body, arguing with a friend of the victim that the $40 fee must be paid before the man is placed on the stretcher. They are told the victim has only two dollars in cash. The crew shrugs, then lifts the still gasping man onto a kitchen chair where he slumps across the table. As

they walk out of the apartment one of the attendants reaches across the table and pockets the two dollars.

### A PLEA IGNORED

2. An elderly black man, his body wracked with cancer, pleads with a private ambulance crew to handle him gently because even the slightest pressure causes extreme pain. The attendant in charge ignores his plea and grabs the man under the arms, drags him across the floor to the stretcher, and drops the patient. As the old man's face contorts in agony and breaks into a sweat, the attendant mutters to his fellow worker: "Next time the guy will walk to the stretcher."

3. An epileptic with a fractured hip lies in the rear of a police squadrol for nearly two hours until a private ambulance firm that makes pay-offs to policemen is able to respond to the call. Instead of taking the victim to a hospital in the squadrol, the police spend a dime to call a misery merchant. Then they wait until the ambulance - and the $10 pay-off - arrives. When the ambulance finally responds, the victim is ordered to crawl from the squadrol onto the stretcher. Hospital records later will be falsified to show that the victim was picked up at a neighbor's home.

### "SHE LOOKS ALL RIGHT"

4. An ambulance crew demands that a northwest side housewife with a broken back write out a $49 check as she lies in a hospital. When she complains that the pain is making it difficult for her to perform the task, they fill out the check and hand it back to her to sign.

5. An ambulance driver hurls insults at a black woman while her daughter waits for emergency transportation after suffering a miscarriage. The daughter is screaming. "She looks all right," the ambulance driver decides. "She can walk down the stairs." The apartment is on the third floor. It is raining and once outside the victim is ordered to crawl into the ambulance thru a side door.

These are a few of the incidents observed during a two-month investigation of the misery merchants by THE TRIBUNE and the Better Government association. The probe was prompted by complaints from other ambulance operators who told of pay-offs to police and firemen, welfare fraud, and sadistic treatment of the ill and injured.

### FEARED A SCANDAL

They feared a scandal that would damage the entire industry and volunteered their cooperation to end the activities. Working with George Bliss, B. G. A. chief investigator, I obtained a city ambulance attendant's license. My partner in the undercover probe was William Recktenwald, one of Bliss' top investigators. Despite warnings of what we would find as ambulance attendants, neither of us was ready for what we found in the world of the misery merchants. "It was the most sickening display of mistreatment of human beings I have ever encountered," Recktenwald reported. "I would go home completely outraged at what I had seen and heard." At one point, Recktenwald walked off the job after 31 hours on duty with only 40 minutes sleep. "I just couldn't take any more," he said.

### THREATENED WITH BEATING

At the same firm, several days earlier, an owner became suspicious of my credentials and threatened me with a beating if the company learned I was a private investigator. I managed to talk my way thru an interrogation by several employees and finished my 24-hour shift with the company. The owner will not know until he reads this story how correct his instincts were. The world of the misery merchant is a life filled with 24-hour shifts stacked on top of 24-hour shifts at pay rates as low as 87 cents an hour. Much of the time is spent in filthy, rat-infested store fronts, waiting for calls from the company dispatcher.

Your companions, for the most part, are people who entertain each other with bizarre stories about their treatment of the sick and suffering. One ambulance driver recalled how he became angered at a fireman who called his firm with a heart attack case. The fireman called the company even tho the ambulance had to travel across the city to answer the call, because the company deals in $10 pay-offs for welfare referrals.

### A CHEWING OUT

"I ran it [arrived at the victim's home] in 35 minutes," the driver said. "When I arrive the fireman was screaming at me so I told the fireman I'll keep the $10 and you keep the patient. I got about five blocks away when they [his company] call me on the radio and told me to return. I get back and got the patient. As I was taking him down the stairs he had a cardiac arrest. I shot him into St. Bernard's hospital but he was D. O. A. [dead on arrival] and [the company] chews me out for not taking him to County [Cook County hospital] because we'd get more mileage."

Ambulance companies charge one dollar a mile as part of their fee. Another driver, who described himself as the south side manager of a large ambulance company, told Recktenwald that it was company policy "never to use sheets on welfare recipients. I don't lift them right either, unless I have to," the driver said. "I just swing them." The licensing of these attendants and ambulance drivers as well as others, is controlled by the City Vehicle commission and the department of health. According to the city code, a prospective ambulance attendant must complete a standard and advanced first aid course before he is licensed.

### EASY TO QUALIFY

The city permit is similar to those carried by cab drivers and is known in the industry as a "hard card." In practice, a "hard card" is issued after a person enrolls in the advanced course. The only other requirements are a $5 license fee, police clearance, and a tuberculosis test. Both Recktenwald and I were working as attendants within minutes after we reported for work at several different companies. We received no instructions in the use of oxygen or the proper handling of a stretcher case before we were sent out on emergency calls. One operator hired me over the phone and I worked for the company two days without ever showing my "hard card."

If there is one statement that speaks for all the misery merchants, perhaps it came one night after we answered a possible child food poisoning call in a south side housing project. We had taken the 12-year-old girl and her mother to County hospital about midnight and were returning to the south side. The driver, who also is a vice president and general manager of the ambulance company, was ridiculing the child's mother for calling an ambulance because "the kid burped." "Some of the guys working for me get too close to these cases," the general manager observed. "Now take me. I can watch a nigger die right next to me and never take my eyes off the road."

## 2.2.3  How Hospitals Attract Alcoholics

[Source: Pamela Zekman/William B. Crawford/Jay Branegan: Gets welfare cash - Hospital hunts patients, in: *Chicago Tribune* (Chicago, Il.), 129th Year/No. 252, September 9, 1975, p. 1, cols. 1-4; p. 6, cols. 1-4; reprinted by permission of the Chicago Tribune Company, Chicago, Il.]

An employee of Northeast Community Hospital regularly patrols Near North Side streets in a red truck or hospital van recruiting patients among the derelicts possessing public welfare cards, with promises of food and rest. Desk clerks at seedy flophouses in the Near North and Uptown areas daily send residents to the hospital at 6970 N. Clark St., the largest private alcoholic treatment center in the city. A Northeast Community physician holds regular office hours once a week in a flophouse that supplies the hospital with more patients than any other single source.

From all over the city, private ambulance companies take public aid recipients, easily able to use other transportation on expensive rides to Northeast, a violation of public aid regulations. In some cases, ambulances carrying "emergency" cases bypass other hospitals to go to Northeast, another public aid violation. A Tribune task force investigation found that this is the way Northeast Community gets most of the 300 patients that its alcoholic treatment unit serves every month in a revolving-door process. The hospital, for these and other patients, last year received more than $2 million in welfare funds. It is guaranteed $78 a day for each public aid patient.

The passport into Northeast's patient-supply network is the Medicaid green card, which pays for hospitalization, drugs, and the costly ambulance rides to and from the hospital. The green card, issued by the state Department of Public Aid, identifies a person as eligible for state-paid medical care. Reporter William Crawford temporarily obtained a green card and found it gave him quick access to the system. Almost as soon as he registered at a North La Salle Street hotel the clerk made a reservation in Crawford's name for the following morning at Northeast's alcoholic treatment center. But, he soon learned, there is an even easier way to get into the center - if a person has that all-important green card.

Alcoholics in the area explained they don't have to wait for a desk clerk to send them to Northeast. They can just watch for James Zimmerman, an alcoholic "intake counselor" employed at the hospital, to come around in his van. One resident of the St. Regis Hotel, 516 N. Clark St., recalled that Zimmerman drove by recently, shouting to him, "Hey, you want to go on up to Northeast and see the doctor?" Henry Rohland, the desk clerk at the La Salle Plaza Hotel, 873 N. La Salle St., who arranged for Crawford's admittance, also knows of Zimmerman. "He makes the whole circuit in his truck," Rohland said. "Zimmerman comes around all the time and cons all these characters on the street. They come here, and he carts them off in his red truck. On weekends he uses the hospital van to haul guys away in." Tho alcoholics, ambulance drivers, and hospital employees are familiar with Zimmerman's round-ups, hospital officials expressed shock at his alleged activities.

"We have never heard anything about his picking up patients off the street and bringing them to the hospital," said Richard Troy, a hospital director, Chicago Park District general counsel, and the attorney who represented Mayor Daley's delegation in its seating battle at the 1972 Democratic National Convention. Only four months before Troy and other hospital officials were interviewed, Zimmerman testified about his activities in a federal hearing on a labor dispute with the hospital. He claimed to have an office in the La Salle Plaza Hotel paid for by the hospital and said, "I bring patients, or the potential patients, or out-patients, or whatever the alcoholic person is to the hospital." Rohland denied that Zimmerman had an office in the hotel.

Another activity that hospital administrators claim they are uninformed about concerns the Northmere Hotel, 4943 N. Kenmore Av., one of the hospital's prime sources of patients. The hospital recorded more than 100 patient admissions from the hotel in one six-month period, according to public aid records. A Northeast staff physician, Dr. Dan Stockhammer, holds regular office hours once a week at Northmere, charging public aid $7 a patient for an office visit. Stockhammer, who collected more than $40,000 last year in public aid payments, described his work at the hotel as a "closed clinic" for Northmere residents only. "It's just like if the Drake or the Palmer House hotel had a doctor only this is a lower social strata," he said. He sees several dozen patients on each visit and claims they are sent to the hospital of their choice when hospitalization is necessary.

But Charles Heilig, former Northeast Hospital Alcoholic Treatment program director, said he set up the program at the Northmere as an "after-care" service. He recalled that the hospital could "count on" three or four admissions from Northmere every Thursday evening following Stockhammer's visits. In fact, the hotel, populated mainly by residents on welfare, seems to operate much like a residential care home tho it has no license from the Chicago Board of Health. The hotel manager, Mary Ann Bilanzich, according to hotel residents, ambulance drivers, and hospital employees, keeps medicine behind the desk and doles it out daily to residents. "Mary Ann gives me my pill each morning," said one resident. "Mary Ann keeps our green cards behind the desk and our medicine," said another. "Mary Ann keeps short medical reports on all of us so she knows what our problem is," said a third. And Walter Ressetar, an ambulance driver who made frequent pick-ups at the hotel, said, "She had what you would describe as a medicine call. I've seen it many times."

Such handling of medications would be a violation of city and state regulations, according to a Board of Health spokesman. Miss Bilanzich denied that she kept any medications for hotel residents. On May 3, 1974, she pleaded guilty to federal charges of forgery and possession of stolen welfare checks and was placed on probation for a year. Northmere residents claim that she still keeps their welfare money, doling it out in $2-a-day allotments. And they say it is Miss Bilanzich who also decides when they should go to the hospital. "There's no way in the world that I would go to that hospital without Mary Ann's okay. I been at the Northmere seven years, but I never was in Northeast until I got to Northmere and met Mary Ann. I take an ambulance to the hospital and back," said James Leavell, 50, a frequent patient. "They treat people good at the hospital," said Leavell. "I been there several times."

Ted Pry, an owner of Rescue Ambulance Service, 4707 N. Harding Av., said his company stopped servicing the Northmere in April because Miss Bilanzich persistently called for ambulances when they weren't needed to take residents to Northeast hospital. "Anytime a person got drunk, it seemed like they'd call from the Northmere for an ambulance. A majority of them really didn't need an ambulance. They could have gotten there another way. We got so we had to tell them we were too busy doing emergency work." Rodney Murphy, a driver for Rescue, said calls came in almost once a night from the Northmere, and he was told to take residents to Northeast hospital 90 per cent of the time. "They could walk to the ambulance and didn't need us," he recalled. "I have taken people to hospital when I have been called and they only have a toothache. I pay taxes too, and I don't like it, but I have to do it."

Taxpayers are charged $45 plus $1.30 a mile for each ambulance ride. Ambulance service to Northeast is not limited to North Side hotels. "I call any ambulance that's available," said Wylie Russel, 37, a four-time visitor to Northeast who lives at 4518 S. Indiana Av., more than 14 miles from the hospital. "They take me to the hospital, and when I'm discharged, they take me home. As long as your green card is legitimate, you can go to that hospital as many times as you want. Why, I could call one right now and go there if they had an open bed." Tribune reporters posted outside the emergency entrance observed a steady stream of private ambulances arriving not only to deliver sick patients, some of them on stretchers, but also to pick up apparently healthy patients for a ride back home. Indeed, Tribune reporters interviewed dozens of Northeast's public aid patients who said they are routinely taken home in the comfort of a private ambulance even tho public aid regulations state that to use an ambulance service a patient must be too sick to go by public transportation.

A surveillance team watching the small parking area at the emergency room door one day saw it become clogged with private ambulances. Two patients walked nimbly across the lot from the emergency door threading their way thru the traffic jam to an Ambulance Service Corp. vehicle. The ambulance attendants dropped their passengers off at the Northmere Hotel. Max Rabin, owner of Ambulance Service, 14 E. Jackson Blvd., said the hospital called his company to take the patients home, claiming one was still dizzy from a head laceration and noting only that the other was hospitalized for "alcoholic rehabilitation. We were just told by the hospital to take them back," said Rabin. "They were sending them back by ambulance. That must be the hospital's procedure." Rabin billed the state $55 for each patient. A cab would have cost about $4 for both of them.

Reporter Crawford was picked up as an "emergency" case by La Salle Ambulance Service Corp., 2427 N. Clark St., at his hotel, the La Salle Plaza, and taken to Northeast, more than seven miles away. Public aid regulations require that in emergency cases the patient be taken to the nearest hospital. Crawford passed Henrotin Hospital, only a few blocks from his hotel, as well as three other hospitals near Lake Shore Drive. Dozens of other hospitals are closer than Northeast. The bill to public aid was $69. The ambulance company told public aid that Crawford suffered "acute abdominal pains, chest pains, and difficulty in breathing." In fact, Crawford walked easily from the hotel to the ambulance and sat for the entire ride talking with the attendant.

"What's wrong with you?" the attendant asked, poring over some forms. "I'm an alcoholic," Crawford replied. The attendant frowned and stared at the form. "What else is wrong with you?" he asked. Crawford repeated his answer. The attendant turned to the driver, Charles Booher, vice president of the company, with a perplexed look, appealing for guidance. "Uh, I also have slight stomach pains," Crawford volunteered, an answer that satisfied the attendant, Crawford never mentioned chest pains, the breathing problem, or the "acute" stomach pains that the company later reported to public aid. "They had to say that in order to get paid from the state as an emergency ride," observed Patrick Kain, assistant deputy director of medical programs at the Illinois Department of Public Aid. "We wouldn't approve a payment on an emergency call if the patient just had 'slight stomach pains.'"

The free ride to the hospital was arranged by Rohland, the desk clerk at the La Salle Plaza, when Crawford checked in the night before. Crawford had told Rohland he might be interested in going to Northeast. "Yeah, anytime you're feeling sick just let me know, and I'll call the hospital and make a reservation for you," Rohland replied. "You just give me that green card of yours, and I'll make the reservation right now. That way a nice clean bed will be waiting for you when you get up there." He picked up the telephone and dialed the admitting office at Northeast. "This is Hank from the La Salle Plaza. I would like to make a reservation for one Crawford, William, for 9:30 a.m. in the morning, green card number of 07 204 02 E93667. That's for tomorrow at 9:30 a.m. Thanks."

"Okay, Bill, you're all set," he said, placing the receiver down and putting the green card in a mailbox behind him. "Tomorrow either you come down here to the lobby, or I or the ambulance men will come up and get you," he continued. "Just sleep as long as you want, and when they arrive, we'll knock on your door." Rohland then offered him a bottle of cheap wine, "on the house." The next day, as promised, the ambulance arrived, and Crawford was admitted to Northeast without a hitch and without even seeing a doctor tho hospital officials deny that desk clerks can guarantee admission. "This hospital is not a hotel," June Reichert, a registered nurse who has handled admissions since January, said in an interview.

## 2.3   HEALTH POLITICS AND THE PUBLIC

### 2.3.1   Special Introductory Remarks

Since the early 1960s, as the costs of public welfare skyrocketed, an increasing undercurrent of agitation developed to include birth control services in the public health programs of Chicago and Cook County, and perhaps throughout the whole state of Illinois. In September 1962 a team of reporters from the *Chicago Daily News* decided that the birth control issue could no longer be contained to a whisper; that the public generally had a right to be informed. Staff Writer Lois Wille was assigned to do a series of articles presenting every point of view on the birth control issue. She immediately found it a tough problem getting sources to speak out. When the series was printed, it prompted numerous letters expressing vigorous differences of opinion - but unanimously commending the newspaper for its courage and its service to the public in bringing the topic into public discussion. A Pulitzer Prize jury recommended the exhibit of the *Chicago Daily News* for first place in its list, and the Advisory Board gave the 1963 Meritorious Public Service Prize to the newspaper "for calling public attention to the issue of providing birth control services in the public health programs in its area."

Since the early eighties a bold new science of the human mind called molecular psychiatry has been swiftly replacing classical psychiatric theories. Jon D. Franklin of the *Baltimore Sun*, an earlier follower of brain chemistry, learned that few people outside the scientific community had a clear understanding of the revolution that was taking place. He began assembling material for a series, which was a mammoth undertaking. Much of the material had appeared only in the scientific press and a good deal of it had never been printed anywhere. The writing alone consumed three months. An initial draft of 80,000 words was painstakingly reduced to 25,000 words appearing in a seven-part series of his paper. A Pulitzer Prize jury found the series to be "a distinguished example of a highly complex subject of significant new dimensions explaining with remarkable lucidity." Jon D. Franklin won the 1985 Pulitzer Prize for Explanatory Journalism for his series "The Mind Fixers", six years after winning a Pulitzer Feature Writing award.

## 2.3.2 Financing Measures of Birth Control Provisions

[Source: Lois Wille: How Milwaukee Met Birth Issue, in: *Chicago Daily News* (Chicago, Il.), 87th Year/No. 274, November 20, 1962, p. 8, cols. 3-8; reprinted by permission of the Chicago Sun-Times, Inc, Chicago, Il.]

Without religious warfare and public controversy, Milwaukee County has quietly initiated a tax-supported birth control service. Examinations, prescriptions and contraceptive supplies are available at Milwaukee's County General Hospital. But the program - expected to be discussed at the public hearings opening Tuesday of the Illinois Public Aid Commission - differs from the one now being considered by the IPAC in two significant aspects.

Only women living with their legal husbands are given birth control services, thus avoiding the charge that tax funds are used to "subsidize sin." (Under the plan proposed by IPAC Chairman Arnold Maremont, all women on relief would be eligible for the services. This would include Aid to Dependent Children recipients, 85 per cent of whom do not live with a legal spouse.) All low income families who rely on County General for their medical care can get birth control information - not just families on relief. (In Chicago's Cook County Hospital, women who ask for birth control services are now referred to privately operated Planned Parenthood clinics. The hospital itself does not treat them.)

The person credited with installing the birth control services at County General is Dr. Richard F. Mattingly, chief of obstetrics and gynecology at the hospital. Dr. Mattingly is chairman of obstetrics and gynecology at the School of Medicine at Marquette University, a Jesuit-backed school. Dr. Mattingly, a Catholic, fears that people will interpret the hospital's new attitude on birth control as a change in Catholic philosophy. "I definitely have not brought about, nor attempted to bring about, a change in Catholic attitude toward artificial birth control," he said. "If a woman comes to the hospital and asks for contraceptives, certainly I would not treat her, and other Catholic physicians would not. But, as a Catholic, I cannot impose my Catholic philosophy on others. Our non-Catholic residents at the hospital should have the opportunity to treat patients as they see fit."

Dr. Ervin Teplin, psychiatrist and former head of the Milwaukee Planned Parenthood Assn. medical advisory committee, speaks glowingly of Dr. Mattingly. "About five months ago, another physician and I explored the issue with him on a conscious, deliberate, open level. His approach is very objective. He took the job (at County General) with the express understanding he would not limit it to Catholic medical practice."

There have been no protests from Catholic organizations about the use of taxpayers' funds for a purpose they consider immoral, Dr. Mattingly said. Nor does he expect any. "All Catholics certainly are not in sympathy with this," he said. "But it has not been argued in public debate, and I definitely feel it will not be. There is a strong feeling among many Catholics that this is a breach of the use of public funds. On the other hand, there is a strong feeling among other groups that this is a very proper use of public funds, in view of the increasing burden on the taxpayer of public assistance programs."

Overshadowing these opposing opinions, according to Joseph Baldwin, director of the state's public assistance program in Milwaukee County, is this third view: "The position of the majority, including many in the Catholic Church, I believe, is that it would be a form of discrimination to deny the service to those who believe it is morally correct."

Milwaukee County is about 40 per cent Catholic, almost the same ratio as in Cook County. But in Cook County, Catholic family groups have strongly opposed use of public funds for birth control services for relief recipients. Why haven't Milwaukee Catholics protested? One reason for the lack of protest probably is the hospital's strictly enforced policy of not giving the information to unmarried women. In cases where women have lied about having husbands, nurses who found they were not legally married withdrew the contraceptive medication they had been given.

Mrs. John Sylvester, president of the Milwaukee Planned Parenthood Assn., offers another reason: "There never was a public statement announcing the service, so no groups felt compelled to denounce it," she said. "Sometimes, the more publicly you do things, the more furor is caused." There has been a puzzling lack of protest also over two other Wisconsin medical practices:

1. Throughout the rest of the state, where there is no public hospital to care for relief recipients, the state's public welfare department now picks up the doctor's bills for birth control services - exactly the plan proposed by IPAC Chairman Arnold Maremont. "The responsibility to seek this service rests with the individual relief recipient," said Baldwin. "The physician then bills us." And if she is unmarried? "We would refer

her," he said. "It is up to the doctor whether or not he would treat her." In Milwaukee County relief recipients are not referred to private doctors because they receive medical care exclusively at County General. This program also was not publicly announced - and not publicly protested.

**2.** Wisconsin has a eugenic sterilization law, and - in Milwaukee County, at least - a rather liberal policy of private sterilization operations for women who ask for them. One medical authority estimates that 250 women were sterilized last year in Milwaukee private hospitals, but no public funds were involved in these operations. Under the eugenic sterilization law, certain types of mentally retarded persons and some sex deviates can be sterilized by court order. "It used to be more or less routine at state hospitals," said Dr. Teplin. "Now, it is used very little - chiefly because of the concept that mental retardation is not necessarily inherited, so we have less right to make such a judgment."

Despite the absence of public fuss, Dr. Mattingly is somewhat uneasy about the birth control service at County General. Two things worry him: He is afraid that once the service becomes more widely known the caseload will be so great his staff won't be able to handle it. He also has doubts about the contraceptive pill. "We have found it is difficult to get women to come back for the physical examinations that are essential followups," he said.

## 2.3.3 The National Spreading of Depressive Sickness

[Source: Jon D. Franklin: Scientists expect cure soon for blue misery of depression, in: *The Evening Sun* (Baltimore, Md.), Vol. 149/No. 69, July 25, 1984, p. A 1, cols. 2-3; p. A 8, cols. 1-4; reprinted by permission of the A. S. Abel Company, Baltimore, Md.]

Perhaps 18 million Americans are victims of clinical depression. They are the "walking wounded" of the high-pressure modern world, and the blue misery that dogs them affects the rest of us as well. Depression puts a steady drain on national productivity and is a major spoiler of family life and social tranquility. But now scientists are making rapid progress in understanding the disease, and have already managed to trace it to a malfunction in two of the brain's chemical subsystems.

That discovery and a cascade of other findings about the nation's most common mental illness have poured from the new science of molecular psychology during the last few years. "There have been incredible breakthroughs in the understanding of depression," says Dr. Candace

Pert, one of the founders of the new science and a leading researcher at the National Institute of Mental Health in Bethesda. "The prospects for the future have never been so bright." Pert's enthusiasm echoes that of many neurochemists. And most believe the explosion of knowledge will translate directly into the creation of effective new drugs to combat depression.

Though no reputable scientist is willing to make specific predictions, most insiders interviewed by *The Evening Sun* say they would be surprised, even shocked, if such drugs didn't begin to appear within a decade. More effective drugs for depression would have a dramatic social and economic impact, not just on the victims and their families but also on the nation at large. The various identifiable types of "clinical depression," as distinguished from the day-to-day depression experienced by normal people in the face of real setbacks, is thought to affect about 8 percent of Americans. The diagnostic symptom is an overwhelming feeling of helplessness and a conviction that nothing the victim does will make any difference. Other symptoms include loss of interest in the outside world, malaise, feelings of self-hatred and a delusional expectation of punishment or impending tragedy.

But in the complexity of the human mind, those symptoms may be masked by other responses. What's more, the symptoms can jump from the mental to the overtly physical as the disease runs its course and the patient, full of self-hatred, fails to practice good hygiene. Whatever the manifestations, depression is among the most relentlessly painful of all known illnesses. Patients with over depression who also have suffered a notably painful physical condition, such as kidney colic, report that the psychic pain is far worse than the physical. Untreated victims of depression often end their agony with suicide, while others choose a slower form of self-destruction: drugs and alcohol. Experts believe that much addiction can be attributed to depression; the victim becomes addicted in a desperate quest to numb the psychic pain of an underlying depression.

If this is so, and there is substantial evidence to suggest it is, then the "pure" depressive patient represents only the tip of the iceberg and the disease really affects up to 20 percent of the population. This leads to an almost desperate need for antidepressants, but the search for those compounds has been severely limited. For one thing, no one knew the cause of depression. For another, depressive disease was known to exist only in humans, so potentially useful drugs couldn't be screened in animals. As a result, most of the currently available antidepressant drugs were discovered by accident. Since they can't be readily improved through animal tests they are often ineffective and retain serious, unpredictable and sometimes deadly side effects.

Today the single most effective therapy for severe depression remains electric shock treatment - an alternative that many consider unacceptable. Consequently millions of citizens with untreated depressive disease continue to function at home and work, but their performance in both arenas is often marginal. Their listlessness and lack of motivation, coupled with their use of alcohol and drugs, are thought to be a major cause of absenteeism and work accidents, and to constitute a steady drain on productivity. In addition, by contributing to the deterioration of family structures, depression entails an incalculable

# Michael Kuhar

At the Johns Hopkins Medical Institutions, high-tech brain scanning helps scientists map the receptor molecules that play a key role in the chemistry of thought.

social cost. "As we get new drugs for these things, it's going to have a tremendous economic impact," says Dr. Michael Kuhar, a neurochemist at Johns Hopkins University. "It's fantastic!"

Such effusive optimism from what is traditionally the most conservative quarter of biological science stems from the rapidly accelerating pace of discovery in the field. Depression, most molecular psychiatrists are now convinced, involves two specific subsystems in the brain. One of those systems consists of brain cells that communicate with one another via the chemical transmitter "norepinephrine." The other uses "serotonin" to carry its signals. Both are centrally involved in the lymbic system, where mood and emotion are processed. One of the clues that convince scientists they're on the right track involves the recent discovery of how the anti-drepressant drug imipramine works.

Imipramine, despite its side effects and the fact that it is not universally effective, is one of the best anti-depressants currently in use. But like other psychotropic, or mind-altering, drugs, it was discovered by accident and no one knew why it worked. Now molecular psychiatrists have found that it exerts its influence by snapping into a previously unknown receptor in the emotional part of the brain. Because of its shape, the imipramine molecule activates that natural receptor very much the same way the shape of a morphine molecule activates the receptor for enkephalin, a pain suppressant produced by the brain. Morphine, of course, directly interferes with a major neurotransmitter system, the normal function of which is to establish a pain threshold. As that threshold rises, the morphine user gets a "high".

Imipramine exerts a much more subtle and specific modulating effect. The receptor it activates apparently controls fine-tuning in the seratonin system, which is responsible in part for the maintenance of mood equilibrium. The imipramine triggers a metabolic chain reaction that lets the brain become more sensitive to its own seratonin. As it does so, the patient becomes less depressed. Another recent piece of evidence involves the discovery that imipramine receptors are also present on the surfaces of some blood cells, but there are abnormally fewer of them on the blood cells of depressed patients. "In conjunction with this," adds Pert, "there are studies that show that there's reduced seratonin in the brain and cerebral spinal fluid of people who die by suicide. So it's all wonderfully consistent. There's obviously something chemical going on."

Scientists are certain that that "something chemical" is, at least in part, genetic. Studies of identical twins reared in the same  household, for instance, have shown that if one twin becomes clinically depressed, the other has more than a 50-50 chance of developing the same illness. But with fraternal twins, whose genes are not identical, the pattern of

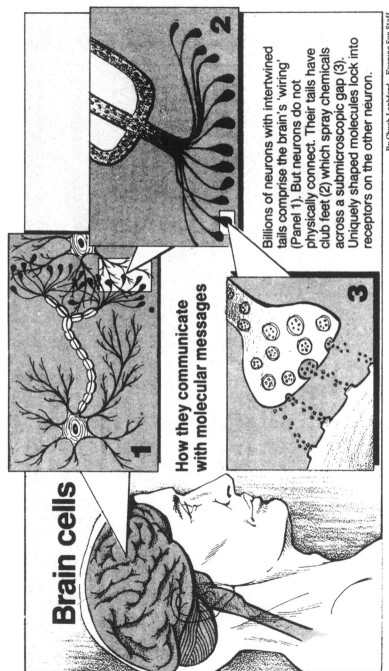

Brain cells

How they communicate with molecular messages

Billions of neurons with intertwined tails comprise the brain's 'wiring' (Panel 1). But neurons do not physically connect. Their tails have club feet (2) which spray chemicals across a submicroscopic gap (3). Uniquely shaped molecules lock into receptors on the other neuron.

By Chuck Lankford—Evening Sun Staff

shared depression is far less likely to develop. Significantly, alcoholism tends to run in the same families as depression. None of this is to say environment does not play a strong role. In fact, most experts believe that depression usually strikes people with a genetic vulnerability and who are also subjected to an environmental stress - the "double hit" theory.

Even so, it has recently been shown that, if the stress is intense enough, the environment alone is enough to induce depressive disease. In fact, environmental stress has been used to produce, for the first time, an animal model that can be used in laboratory experiments on depression. One of the experts in induced depression in animals is Dr. Fritz Henn, chief of psychiatry at the State University of New York at Stony Brook. On the basis of experimental work done at the University of Pennsylvania and elsewhere, he says, severe depression can now be triggered in any animal, "from rats to goldfish to humans." The method is simple, and involves what psychologists euphemistically term "exposure to adverse stimuli."

A rat, for instance, might be put in a cage with a metal floor and exposed to occasional, unpredictable electrical shocks to its feet. But it's not the shocks that induce depression. If there is a ledge the rat can jump onto when the jolts begin, the animal can endure the shock cage for extended periods of time while remaining psychologically normal. But if the shelf or other escape route is removed, and the rat is totally helpless, the effect is dramatically different. "When they can't predict when [the shocks] are going to come, and there's nothing they can do to stop them or escape from them... when they're waiting all the time to get hit... after a while... it looks as if [their minds] just shut down. They stop even trying to get away. They stop trying to do much of anything." Like depressed humans, the rats exhibit eating disorders and lose interest in sex. They have trouble sleeping, and it's more difficult for them to learn.

Depressed humans say they feel helpless, without any ability to influence what happens to them. The rats act, at least, as though they feel the same way. And, once depressed, they don't get over it. If they are put back in the shock cage, but are now provided with an escape route, they don't use it. They don't even seem to have the will to try; instead, they hunker down and accept the shocks almost as though they deserve them. "But when you treat them with a drug that's effective clinically [in humans]," Henn says, "something changes. Then they'll use the escape route." By killing the rats at various stages, dissecting their brains and recording the chemical changes, Henn's group made a remarkable discovery.

As the rats become depressed, predictable alterations occur in their brain receptors. Those changes occur at the same time the behavioral changes are taking place, and affect the brain in exactly those places where anatomists would expect them to. "We see these changes in certain receptor fields in the [emotional] system. The receptors become more or less dense...," Henn says. The principal alterations, he says, involve a subtype of norepinepherine receptors in one area and seratonin receptors in another. "And so both receptors seem to play a role," says Henn, "but they do it at different places. And they change as a result of experience... and they stay changed."

In itself, the development of an animal model for depression represents a significant breakthrough. As a result, drugs can be engineered specifically to activate or suppress the affected parts of the brain, and can then be tested and improved on live animals. "I'm very

# The utter agony of untreated clinical depression may result in suicide . . .

excited about this," says Henn. "[With the rat model] we can really take apart the neurochemical systems and see what's changing, and what's changing in conjunction with the behavioral charges. And we can then treat the animal with medications and we can reverse the behaviors. We can look and see what's changing." The result, he believes, will be to dramatically accelerate the development of new drugs to alleviate the agony and reduce the cost of human depression.

According to Dr. Fred Goodwin, chief scientist at the National Institute of Mental Health, it would be difficult to overestimate the importance of the exponential growth in our knowledge of depression and other mental diseases. He says a small foretaste of things to come can be found in the success story of lithium treatment for manic-depressive disease. Manic-depressive disease is a subtype of depression that strikes about 2 percent of the population. It is characterized by dramatic mood swings from profound depression to manic hyperactivity. During the 1960s it became a target disease for the development of the first rationally engineered psychotropic drug. Though that work predated the revolution in molecular psychology, the scientists were nonetheless successful.

Lithium was introduced in Europe during the late 1960s and proved dramatically effective in smoothing out the mood swings and restoring manic-depressive patients to good mental health. By 1974 it was in wide use in this country. By 1982 the federal government had computed that the introduction of lithium had saved the taxpayer what Goodwin calls "a very conservative $18 billion." That figure, Goodwin emphasizes, does not take into consideration the indirect social costs of the disease, which include diminished work productivity. Also, it did not consider the impact on the families and children of manic-depressive patients. As molecular psychology becomes an increasingly exact science, Goodwin says, he expects to see the development of new, more specific drugs with fewer side effects to replace currently available anti-depressants. He also expects to see new drugs that will be effective for the 15 percent of manic-depressive patients who do not respond to lithium, and in the larger group of patients who don't respond at all to current anti-depressant therapy. Such drugs could dwarf the social and economic savings attributed to lithium.

If the theories that link depression to drug addiction are correct, and new anti-depressant therapy can be translated into better drug treatment, the revolution in molecular psychology will directly affect perhaps 20 percent of the population. "There's no question," says Henn of Stony Brook, "that addiction is far and away the most serious and most costly mental health problem in the country. A study that was just completed at NIH documents that. Just walking away, alcoholism is the single most serious mental health problem we have. If we can find out what that is, and do something about it, the impact in terms of savings to the country would just be enormous. Absolutely enormous." Not since the public health revolution in the 1800s, and the eradication of filth-borne diseases, have the stakes been higher. And depression research represents but one battlefront in the molecular psychology revolution.

# 3

# VICTIMS OF DRUG ABUSE OR MISTREATMENT

## 3.1 TESTS OF MEDICAMENTS AND DESTINIES OF PATIENTS

### 3.1.1 Special Introductory Remarks

In March, 1959, the *Atlanta Constitution* reported that experimental drugs for the mentally ill were being administered to patients at the Milledgeville State Hospital without consent from or knowledge of the patients or their relatives. The research fund, sponsored by drug firms, was controlled exclusively by the research doctor, who made a profit from it. The fund was not a subject to state audit. The state was shocked, and the medical profession immediately moved to challenge the stories. Finally the Medical Association of Georgia nominated the series, written by Jack Nelson, for a Pulitzer Prize in Journalism. His "courageous coverage... led directly to the most far reaching reforms in the field of mental health in the state's history," the accompanying letter states and continues: "Nelson's reporting told the story in such clear and unmistakable fashion that the public quickly grasped the true facts as they never had before... Backed up by excellent editorial comment and cartoons..., Nelson continued to cover the fast developing story in the face of rising criticism from employees and citizens in Milledgeville, from some state officials, and from a few individual physicians. On more than one occasion he received threats of violence and once he was actually attacked." In 1960, the Pulitzer Prize for Reporting, Edition Time, went to Nelson "for the excellent reporting... on mental institutions in Georgia."

A similar drug scandal surfaced a decade later in the state of Alabama. Harold E. Martin of the *Montgomery Advertiser* and *Alabama Journal* disclosed that a so-called drug research corporation began intensive testing of new drugs for all major pharmaceutical firms by using prisoners as test persons. The firm had complete and unlimited access to inmates for testing purposes. The inmates were not given physicals before the tests, proper medical histories were not taken, and no one explained the dangers of side effects to the inmates as required by the protocols. The prisoners gave false medical histories and would not report side-effects or reactions to the drugs for fear of being taken off the program and losing their income. For describing and analyzing the complex issue Harold E. Martin earned the 1970 Local Investigative Specialized Pulitzer Reporting award "for his exposé of a commercial scheme for using Alabama prisoners for drug experimentation...".

## 3.1.2 Tests with Mentally Ill People

[Source: Jack Nelson: Unapproved Drugs Given Mental Cases, in: *The Atlanta Constitution* (Atlanta, Ga.), Vol. XCI/No. 221, March 5, 1959, p. 1, col. 3; p. 12, cols. 3-8; reprinted by permission of the Atlanta Journal and the Atlanta Constitution, Atlanta, Ga.]

A Milledgeville State Hospital doctor has been using experimental, unapproved drugs on mental patients here under research programs financed by drug firms. The drugs have been used without permission or knowledge of relatives of many of the patients. Dr. Zeb L. Burrell Jr. has been conducting the research programs with no accounting of the funds to the state hospital. Alan Kemper, director of the State Welfare Department, and Dr. T. G. Peacock, hospital superintendent, said they fully approved of the programs as carried out by Dr. Burrell.

### $30,000 GRANT

In an interview, Dr. Burrell said he had received about $30,000 in grants from six drug firms since July 1956. He said he had realized "some personal income" from the program. He estimated the income amounted to "a 15 per cent supplement" to his annual state salary. The hospital's audit for the year ending June 30, 1958, showed Burrell's salary was $8,835. Hospital laboratory facilities and employees have been used in carrying on the research program. Dr. Burrell estimated that he had administered unapproved drugs to about 300 persons, about half of whom are hospital employees or their dependents.

### STILL UNDER TEST

The drugs administered under the research programs are not approved by the Federal Drug Administration but are still being tested to determine if they meet all requirements. Such drugs are known as numbered drugs, have no names, and are identified by assigned numbers. They are named only when approved and put on the market. Kemper and Peacock said that when patients are admitted to the hospital, their next of kin or guardians sign a form approving use of treatment the hospital considers beneficial to the patients. They said they consider this gives the hospital permission to use the unapproved drugs. Dr. Burrell said the matter of getting permission of patients' relatives or guardians before use of unapproved drugs is still "open to question" as far as the American Medical Assn.'s Council on Ethics is concerned.

## DOCTOR DEMURS

He said he knew of only one doctor on the hospital staff who had refused to administer the unapproved drugs. He said he and the doctor had "personal" differences that caused the doctor to object to the program. The Atlanta Constitution has an affidavit from Dr. Thomas B. Phinizy, senior physician at the hospital, who said he had refused to administer numbered drugs ordered by Dr. Burrell for three different patients. "I never administer numbered drugs because I don't approve of experimenting on human beings," Dr. Phinizy declared. "Dr. Burrell did not have permission to administer numbered drugs to these three patients." Dr. Phinizy has received signed statements from relatives of three patients certifying they did not want the unapproved drugs used on the patients. The statements are dated March 2, 1959.

## LETTER CITED

An Atlanta woman wrote Dr. Phinizy: "I have not given permission for him (her husband) to be given any kind of experimental medicine. Dr. Phinizy, I want Mr. _____ to have everything that is known to help him, but he has enough trouble now that is known without experimenting on him. I'm so glad you gave me the opportunity to refuse this medicine." Dr. Joe D. Combs, clinical director of the hospital's white women's division, signed an affidavit saying Dr. Burrell approached him and requested that a numbered drug, P-607, be administered to schizophrenic patients. "This drug actually was prepared for treatment of diabetes," Dr. Combs said. "But Dr. Burrell wanted to experiment with schizophrenic patients to determine if the drug was a satisfactory substitute for insulin coma therapy. Injection of insulin lowers the blood level drastically and puts the patient in a coma.

"I told Dr. Burrell that it was a matter that addressed itself to him and the doctor in charge of the building, Dr. Mary Hires. Dr. Hires later told me that she administered some P-607 to some patients according to Dr. Burrell's directions, but she said she did it on a limited scale and had now stopped administering it at all. She said she had been uneasy about using the drug." Dr. Burrell said that in some cases he used numbered drugs on patients who were unable to communicate with him. He said he did not get the permission of the relatives of some of them and added this would have been difficult to do because the relatives had not inquired about the patients in three years or more. Dr. Burrell was asked if all the employees on whom he had used the numbered drugs were aware they were receiving unapproved drugs. "Some did know it and some didn't," he replied. "Most of the employees are familiar with me and have confidence in me. I could give them capsules of hay and they would take it knowing it was capsules of hay."

## SOME REQUESTED

Some employees have requested the use of experimental drugs, Dr. Burrell said. He explained that in some instances employees requested it because the particular medicine they had been using had not satisfied them. Dr. Burrell said he never received written permission from anyone concerning the use of numbered drugs. He said that on occasions, relatives of patients would read of new medical discoveries and would ask that experimental drugs be used. As an example, he said, "a woman would come in and say, 'Oh, if mama could try those pills for diabetes, I know it would help her.'" He said that only two or three patients had protested use of the numbered drugs. He said he immediately discontinued use of the drugs on them. He pointed out, however, that some of the patients who were given the drugs could not communicate with him.

## RELAYED TO FIRMS

Patients' reactions to the numbered drugs are recorded by Dr. Burrell under the research programs and are relayed to the drug firms. These reports are used by the firms as part of their information in trying to get the drugs approved by the FDA. Dr. Burrell said that the drug firms used the drugs on animals and on some humans before they are used in his research programs. He said the drug firms have "paid human guinea pigs" who are under contract to the firms. He said they are "double-edged" contracts which protect the persons by assuring them adequate medical treatment if they suffer bad side effects from the drugs and which protect the drug firms by stipulating they are not otherwise responsible for bad side effects. Dr. Burrell said that five of six drugs he has administered under the programs have since been approved and are now on the market. He said he expects the sixth to be approved soon.

## FORM IS SHOWN

He showed a reporter a form which he said he has to sign before he can be sent a shipment of numbered drugs through the mail. The form carries this declaration: "I have adequate facilities for the investigation to be conducted by me, and the above named drug will be used solely by me or under my direction for the investigation, unless and until an application becomes effective with respect to such drug under Section 505 of the Act." Dr. Burrell said that the reference to the application concerns the drug firm's application to get FDA approval of the drug. Dr.

Burrell said checks for the fund are made out to "Milledgeville State Hospital Research Fund" and are deposited in an account in that name in a Milledgeville bank. He said he would be glad to make a public accounting of the funds if Kemper requested it.

Dr. Burrell said he personally signs all checks on the fund. He said he had asked Dr. Peacock if he wanted to countersign them, but that Dr.

From: *The Atlanta Journal* and *The Atlanta Constitution*, March 8, 1959, p. E 6.

Peacock said he approved of the way the fund was being handled and did not think it was necessary to countersign the checks. Kemper, asked if he thought there should be a public accounting of the funds, replied: "My point is that if the patients are benefiting and drug companies are satisfied, and it does not cost the taxpayers any money, then I'm satisfied." Dr. Peacock said he saw no need for a public accounting of the funds and added, "I think that the man is entitled to a personal profit if he goes out and gets the money and it is for a specific purpose and he uses it for that purpose. Any accounting for it would be up to the drug firm." Kemper, Peacock and Burrell all agreed that the hospital had benefited by the research programs.

### 3.1.3 Experiments with Numerous Prisoners

[Source: Harold E. Martin: Pill Program Slows Prison Work, in: *The Montgomery Advertiser* (Montgomery, Al.), 142nd Year/No. 21, January 24, 1969, p. 4, col. 3; reprinted by permission of the Advertiser Company, Montgomery, Al.]

Convicts who are willing to volunteer for the experimental drug program at Kilby and Draper are excused from work or allowed to show up for work sick, sedated, or under instructions not to do any strenuous work. "The availability of prisoners for work on the farm has been cut at least thirty per cent as a result of the drug program," a prison official told *The Advertiser*.

"Inmates who are enrolled in the vocational schools have been warned," said another official, "that they will be dropped from the training program if they volunteer for the 'pill program'." "This became necessary," he added, "because the inmates were missing too much work, or were too sick to work when they did come." Operation of the Alabama Prison System is being hampered by the drug program to such an extent that the training and welfare of prisoners and the state's interests have become secondary to the profitable interests of Southern Food and Drugs, Inc., and what Corrections Board member Dr. Max McLaughlin of Mobile calls "advancement of drug therapy ... with all citizens reaping the humanitarian and health benefits therefrom." And all at the taxpayers expense!

The drug experimentation program, operated by Dr. A. R. Stough and Kilby prison physician Dr. Irl Long, has complete authority to send a list of prisoners who have volunteered for a certain drug program to prison officials, stating that the designated inmates will be delivered at the laboratory at a specific time on a certain day. These instructions are followed without question. Many experimental programs are carried on at the same time. Some consist of prisoners receiving medication at certain times during the day and going on with their work. Other programs require the "stopping up" of prisoners. This is an "in-patient" experiment in which prisoners are kept in the hospital room of Southern Food and Drugs Research's laboratory for periods of three days, a week or longer.

An examination of some of the drug company protocols shows how the outpatient medication programs cut down on the efficiency of the workers under medication, and limits their activity. One drug experiment says that "subjects shall not be permitted to engage in strenuous employment during the days of and one day following drug administration." Another program involves 80 inmates for a period of five weeks in a study to determine the degree of sedation produced by various doses of medication. Although this is an outpatient study that supposedly does not interfere with work or training, the inmates were observed daily for, among other things, the degree of sedation they were under.

An experiment on 27 healthy males on nine one-day programs of medication, each followed by three days of no medication, calls for "rest periods and no medication of any kind on non-study days." Eighty volunteers on a four week program are "not to be assigned to a potentially hazardous occupation for the duration of the study period." This would include working around any machinery. Thirty healthy male volunteers on a 28-day medication program are to be checked daily for expected reactions of headaches, dizziness, palpitation, blurred vision, appetite, nausea, vomiting, diarrhea, constipation or abdominal pain. The "stopped up" programs relieve the prisoners of all duties, whether work assignments or training.

They are allowed to remain in the laboratory infirmary. Here they can watch television, play cards, or sleep. Some of these "in-patient" studies are of short duration and on Saturday and Sunday. Others are longer. For example, a study called for nine healthy male volunteers, age 20-30, weight 160-170, who will "be admitted to (the) metabolic ward for seven days." Another is a Kilby program that "stopped up" 20 inmates for six days, during which time they are released only for meals. All of this in a year in which the prisons have the most civilian employees per prisoner, and the highest operations appropriations since the legislature established the penitentiary system on January 26, 1839.

## 3.2   TAKING DRUGS AND MEDICAMENTAL ABUSE

### 3.2.1  Special Introductory Remarks

In the face of a distressing increase in illegal narcotics traffic to Southern California, the *Los Angeles Times* decided in the late fifties to take decisive, positive action. Aware that dope had been the subject of sensationalism without results, the newspaper assigned a member of its staff, Gene Sherman, to pressure the government into alleviating the menace at the source. Sherman's assignment was, in essence, to determine how serious the narcotic situation was, where the major narcotics influx originated and what could be done to dry up the source. Sherman spent seven months, three of them full-time, on the story. The result was a shocking eight-part series that appeared in the paper in 1959. A Pulitzer Prize jury praised the initiative of the newspaper "for a well-conceived, long-continued and thorough-going attack on narcotics traffic resulting in a start toward United States-Mexican collaboration in the control of the international movement of illegal drugs." For "the enterprising reporting of Gene Sherman," the newspaper earned the 1960 Pulitzer Meritorious Public Service award.

Since the early 1970s, the editors of *Newsday* expressed growing concern for the increasing use of heroin among young people in Nassau and Suffolk Counties. This increase was reflected in a rapidly escalating suburban crime rate and an overdose mortality rate which had reached a high of 33 persons in 1970. Several months of preliminary study by an investigative team of the paper indicated that substantial media coverage had been given to the effects of heroin addiction on the economy, society and the individual addict. But little was known about why heroin continued to flow freely into the United States and into the arms of addicts on Long Island and elsewhere. The team traveled through Asia and Europe. Several journalists became the first known correspondents to actually live in a Turkish opium-growing village. The result was a series of articles leading to far-reaching consequences. A Pulitzer Prize jury was impressed that the series "named international profiteers, U.S. dealers, and neighbourhood pushers" which "required unusual courage and discipline by the reporting team." The Pulitzer Board gave the 1974 Meritorious Public service award to *Newsday* for its series 'The Heroin Trail.'

### 3.2.2 Deal with Mexican Narcotics in America

[Source: Gene Sherman: Mexican Monkey on our back - Dope's Evil Roots Run Deep, Spread Like Cancer, in: *Los Angeles Times* (Los Angeles, Ca.), Vol. LXXVIII/No. 221, July 12, 1959, p. 1, cols. 1-8; p. A, cols. 1-2; reprinted by permission of the Times-Mirror Company, Los Angeles, Ca.]

It's a fourth or fifth class hotel on a scale that pegs a flophouse as sixth or seventh class. An antiquated, dingy but curiously successful place in the southeast section of Los Angeles. The owner is a man in his late years who enjoys a reputation as a shrewd business head. He dresses conservatively, speaks quietly and associates socially with average people who could be your neighbors. You may have passed the hotel without giving it a glance. By remote but not impossible coincidence, you may know the owner. His acquaintanceship includes folks like you. For years he has been one of the city's biggest wholesale narcotics dealers...

She's 17, blond, cute as a button. She has a winsome smile, an appealing way of tossing her pony tail and her clear, blue eyes dance with freshness. She laughs nervously as she talks with wistful pride about her sweetheart. She tries to hide her nervousness with compulsive gaiety in her chatter, but the twisting of her fragile fingers betrays it. The men listening to her are sympathetic. They have heard the story before. Many times. She's telling them how her high school friends gather at one another's house or in parked cars to smoke marijuana they buy from a man in his 20s who can be reached near the school...

A plant grows in a pot in a narcotics enforcement squad room. Its leaves fan into seven long, slender, serrated segments. A healthy, rather attractive specimen of marijuana seized a few hours ago in a back-yard from a juvenile boy with a long record of "blowing pot." The officer in charge looks at it glumly. Only one lousy plant. This year, due primarily to favorable climatic conditions, the marijuana crop in Mexico is excellent. And the shipments into Los Angeles are so conveniently packaged. Manicured, cleaned, pressed into bricks and wrapped in cellophane. No fuss, not bother - just kicks...

In a plush office in Washington a high State Department official, flanked by two aides, talks guardedly about the narcotics traffic from Mexico. He has torn time from a schedule crowded with matters of high international significance to entertain a few academic questions about the accessibility of Mexican narcotics to Southern California. It is a touchy subject. He does not wish to be quoted. U.S. relations with Mexico are friendly, can we afford to jeopardize them for purely local interest? Isn't the narcotics problem really our own, to be solved by enforcement? Privately and off the record, the official speaks strongly about the situation. He would like to see sellers of illegal narcotics - especially to minors - sentenced to death...

A man who has spent most of his federal enforcement career battling narcotics twists a glass of water idly on the luncheon table. He knows as much about the subject as anyone who has spent years in close contact with it. But he is the kind of a man whose wisdom springs from the realization of how much he does not know. As do most men who deal personally with illicit narcotics on a working level, he waves aside the label of "expert." His job, in concert with other officers from five agencies (federal, state, city police, sheriff's office, district attorney's office) is to stop dope traffic. What he and his brother officers do makes the administrators experts. "You're confused and floundering?" he repeats. "Let me tell you something - Everyone in this business, including the heads of all agencies, is just as confused. They're all floundering."

## PROBLEM IS SERIOUS

The truth of that statement becomes increasingly evident the longer one delves into the problem and the more he talks with persons concerned with it. Eventually he becomes absolutely positive of only one fact: There is a serious illicit narcotics problem. Even attempting to prove the problem, let alone finding its root, is an indefinite undertaking. Statistics, in the opinion of informed officials, are at best indications, irritatingly inconclusive. This is patent in their confusing variance, according to the source. Ask any agent how many addicts there are in Los Angeles and he'll confess to only a guess. Ask how many dope peddlers ply their infamous trade and the answer also is a guess.

## NO ONE KNOWS

Only the most naive interrogator would ask how much heroin or marijuana comes into the city, state or country. No one knows. They can only add up the amounts seized from time to time. The Federal Bureau of Narcotics estimates there are 6,214 addicts in California, or 13% of the total in the country. That's the official figure for congressional assimilation and it's ludicrously precise. But local enforcement agencies laugh at the estimate. The number of addicts in Southern California alone is estimated by different sources at from 10,000 to 40,000 - but how can you really tell?

## FILTHY BUSINESS

Millions of words have been written on the dope peril by both irresponsible and conscientious pens. The problem has been magnified and dramatized beyond all reason and - even more surprising - has been minimized to trivia. Because it is a shadowy business and the filthiest, most reprehensible of rackets, it is a subject with which writers of fact and fiction can command attention and politicians can decry with great, passive righteousness. This is not to belittle the serious attempts to attack the problem which have resulted in medical treatment and legislation to reduce addiction and illicit peddling.

It simply is to point out that the subject of narcotics is so foreign, mysterious and far-removed from the average, normal person, so cloaked in mystery and lacking clear definition that it readily can be adopted as an issue by those who wish to shock, sensationalize or promote without too much fear of contradiction. In a way, it's like the automobile traffic problem. Everybody is against it and views it with horror, but nobody agrees what to do about it. Except eliminate it, some way. The stories in this series of articles are the result of weeks of association with narcotics enforcement officers on all levels, peddlers, addicts, informants and doctors.

## DISCUSSION SERIES

The purpose was to get some firsthand idea of how the problem affects this community, which is either the first or second area in addict population, depending on which authority you talk to. New York shares the infamy. Because of the nature of the subject, this series will be more in the form of a discussion than a report. The hope is it will convince you as citizens and parents there truly is a serious social cancer in the community and that it is folly to ignore it. Like the cancer it is, the illicit narcotics problem spreads with deadly, insidious certainty from its origin. Nationally, the origin may be Communist China, Europe or the Middle East. In Los Angeles, it primarily is Mexico.

### 3.2.3  The Death Rate of Heroin Addicts

[Source: Anthony Marro: Most Were White, Male and Single, in: *Newsday* (Long Island, N.Y.), Vol. 33/No. 177, March 2, 1973, p. 6, cols. 1-3; p. 7, col. 1; reprinted by permission of Newsday, Inc., Long Island, N.Y.]

They die in the darkness of their bedrooms or in cars parked in the night, on old mattresses in cellars or on living room sofas, with needles and syringes found near their bodies. They are found beside remote roadways by passersby - or by their parents in their own homes. They are the victims at the end of the heroin trail. The trail ended for 25 men and women on Long Island last year, whose deaths were directly related to the use of heroin. Another 22 died as a result of methadone ingestion, in many cases taken in combination with other drugs. Eight other deaths were related to heroin indirectly - victims of hepatitis, pneumonia, pulmonary disorders and infection, all with histories of chronic heroin use.

Who are the ultimate victims?

• They lived in neighborhoods throughout Nassau and Suffolk, in more than a score of villages and communities.

• Most were in their early 20s.

• Most were white, single and male.

• Most were employed or were students.

• Few were street addicts - jobless, desperately poor, frequently arrested.

• Most died in their homes or the homes of their parents.

• A few were veterans of the war in Vietnam.

• Many  kept their drug involvement a secret from friends and family.

• In almost all cases, the exact cause of death remained unknown - autopsies generally fail to reveal definitively if the victim is a regular, occasional or infrequent user. The postmortems also do not determine whether death resulted from an overdose of heroin, from an allergic reaction to the quinine or other foreign substances with which heroin is diluted or from the combination of drugs found in their body. In most cases, the medical examiner's report uses the phrase "acute narcotism" or "opiate intoxication."

• For almost all, death shocked their families and friends.

In 1972, traces of morphine - from which heroin is synthesized - were found in the bodies of 25 victims on Long Island. Of the 25, not more than two came from any single community. Twenty were white; 23 were male; 17 were single; 24 were employed or were students; 17 died at home. Most of the victims lived with their parents. Four others died at the home of friends. One died in a hospital. Two were found in parked cars. One body was found lying on a roadside in Lake Success. A resident of Queens, he was the only non-Long Island resident on the list of 25 fatalities.

The average age of the victims was just under 23. All but 10 were between the ages of 20 and 25. There was a 17-year-old who was found dead in the bathroom of his parents' home in Dix Hills. He was the youngest and one of five teenagers. Another five were between the ages of 28 and 33. Of the 25 victims, all but one was listed as employed or as a student by the country medical examiners. Their jobs were typical of suburban lower-middle-income employment: Four were laborers, two were clerks, one was a truck driver and another a barber. There were a gym instructor and a computer programer, a maintenance man and a mechanic, a waiter, a restaurant helper and a delivery man. Five were students.

The list of fatalities probably does not reflect who is using heroin on Long Island - only those who are using it fatally. For example, only one of the fatalities occurred in Hempstead - a 28-year-old woman who was separated from her husband. She was white. No deaths among Freeport or Roosevelt residents were recorded on the heroin list. There was one Westbury death. Yet both experienced addicts and drug treatment professionals expressed the view that the greatest numbers of addicts on Long Island were in the communities of Hempstead, Freeport, Westbury and Roosevelt - communities with sizable black populations.

Twenty-two men and women died on Long Island as a result of methadone intoxication or from the effects of methadone in combination with other drugs, such as barbiturates, alcohol and tranquilizers. Methadone, developed as a socially acceptable alternative for the heroin addict, is now readily available on the streets of Long Island. For the heroin addict, it can provide a few days of relief while he raises money to support his habit. But for the non-addict or the occasional heroin user, the illicitly purchased drug can be deadly. Of the methadone victims, 15 were between the ages of 20 and 29. Only two were over 30. Five were teenagers. The youngest was 15, a Roosevelt boy who had just returned home from the New York State's Division of Youth training school for boys at Warwick, N.Y. His mother said later: "My son learned about heroin there."

Nineteen of the 22 were Long Island residents. One came from Queens, another from the Bronx, another was listed as address unknown. The 19 Long Island residents came from 16 different communities. Only three communities - Southampton, Bay Shore and Elmont - had more than one resident on the methadone death list. Nineteen of the victims were white. There were two black victims from Nassau - a tool-and-die maker from Elmont and the 15-year-old from Roosevelt. In Suffolk, one of the 13 methadone victims was black - an 18-year-old student from Wyandanch.

As in the case of the heroin death list, male victims predominated. Seventeen of the 22 were men. Sixteen were single, two were divorced, two were married. Two of the women were separated from their husbands. The other three women on the list were single. In both counties, a majority of the methadone fatalities involved multiple drug use - methadone in combination with alcohol, tranquilizers and/or barbiturates. As in the case of the morphine death list, the majority of victims - 15 of 22 - were found in their homes or were taken from their homes to local hospitals where they were dead on arrival.

The first narcotics-related death on Long Island in 1972 was recorded in Nassau on Jan. 7. The body of an 18-year-old was found in an upstairs bedroom of his mother's home in Massapequa. He had served five months in Nassau County Jail in 1971 on a marijuana possession charge, and was released six months before his death. For a while he worked as a maintenance man in a cemetery that fall. He had no plans for the future. In the autopsy, traces of both morphine and methadone were found. He was the youngest victim on Nassau's morphine-related death list. He set a pattern for the heroin-related deaths: He was young, white, male, single, lived at home - and died at home. The combination of drugs found in his body was part of another pattern. Of the 25 victims in the morphine category, methadone was found in the bodies of five.

The first Suffolk County resident on the 1972 narcotics-related death list was married, and his wife was aware that he was addicted. Once, with his wife's help, he locked himself in a bedroom in their Copiague home, in an attempt to kick the heroin habit. "He was really trying to stop," his wife said later. Most of those who die - in either morphine- or methadone-related cases - could not be considered street addicts, according to officials of Nassau's homicide squad, which investigates all drug related deaths in the county. The victims are usually working people and are not the most frequent users. Those who are likely to survive are the users with a higher tolerance for the drug, who probably buy better-quality heroin and have better, more dependable connections, who are more experienced and more canny.

It is rare that the dosage taken by a heroin victim is officially recorded. In 1972, only one such statistic appeared on the medical examiner's public record. It was in the case of a 24-year-old gym instructor in a New York health spa, who was found dead in the bathroom of his Elmont home Feb. 22. He was found by his wife. An eyedropper and needle were found beside the body. Later an autopsy revealed the presence of morphine and quinine in his body. When the contents of the syringe found in the bathroom were analyzed, it proved to be 24 per cent heroin - a deadly "hot shot," as the potent dose is called in the vernacular of the addict. According to police, most addicts shoot a heroin mixture of about three per cent.

He was one of a number of victims whose bodies were found in the bathrooms of their homes. "It's the one room that has a lock on it, that's all," a former addict explained. In one such case, a fatality might have been avoided. On March 8, a young man was found unconscious in the bathroom of his Rockville Centre home with a syringe beside his body. His mother, however, did not call for help immediately. She felt her son would "sleep it off," the medical examiner's report stated later. Six hours later, on the morning of March 9, the police were called - but it was too late.

The body of one 22-year-old man was found in the hallway just outside the bathroom in his mother's Woodmere home. He was, according to the medical examiner's report, "a known narcotics user." On the sink, police discovered three empty glassine bags, a bottle cap used to cook heroin into soluble solution and a tourniquet. Traces of heroin were later found in the glassine bags. A syringe and needle were tucked between his arm and chest when his body was discovered by his mother on the afternoon of May 30 - Memorial Day. As usual, the medical examiner's report listed cause of death only as "opiate derivative intoxication."

According to Nassau medical examiner Dr. Leslie Lukash, "It is usually impossible to determine if a heroin death was caused by the potency of the drug or by an allergic reaction to the foreign substance with which the drug was cut." There is also a possibility, experts have suggested recently, that what had been called "overdose" fatalities in the past might have resulted from heroin in combination with other drugs such as alcohol or barbiturates. The combination of such depressants with heroin, also a depressant, could damage the respiratory system and cause fatal brain damage.

In almost all cases, autopsies fail to reveal definitively whether

LONG ISLAND

THE HEROIN TRAIL

the victim was a regular, occasional or infrequent user. However, a large number of victims had the scars of old needle tracks on their arms and legs. Many of the victims also had telltale tattoos on their arms - a familiar technique of the practiced addict to hide the traces of needle marks from family and police. In a few cases, there was evidence that the victim was no longer a regular user of heroin. One 23-year-old woman, for example, had been involved in drugs several years ago, according to her family. But she had given it up, they said. In the early morning hours of May 1, she died in a friend's car on the way home to her parents' Westbury residence. She had injected a fatal dose of heroin, despite the warnings of her companion. Later, he told police: "She had tried to stay clean... this was the first time in a long time."

Morphine was detected in the autopsy performed in her case. However, in some cases, only quinine is traced. In the case of one man, methadone and quinine were detected in the postmortem. And while death was attributed to methadone intoxication and pneumonia, the presence of quinine indicated a possibility that heroin might also have been used before the fatal methadone dose. The victim, who was living with a girl friend in East Rockaway, had been a varsity football player at Sewanhaka High in the late 1960s, and according to a classmate and fellow heroin user, began to purchase heroin when he was 17 in Elmont. "There was a red house near the Belmont track. You'd park a car and honk the horn. A guy would come out and you could buy $5 bags," he said. They would have cost $2 in Harlem, he added. The Elmont classmate, now a professional staffer with a New York anti-drug program, did not know if his friend had been a regular user at the time of his death.

But the medical examiner's office reported that a fresh needle mark and several tattoos were found on the victim's arms when he was brought to a Nassau hospital, where he died June 18. In both Nassau and Suffolk, methadone deaths have been on the rise. In Nassau, nine deaths were recorded in 1972 in which methadone was detected in the autopsy, plus five of the morphine cases in which methadone was also traced in the postmortem. In 1971, the methadone death figure in Nassau was four. In Suffolk, 1972 methadone deaths totaled 13, compared to two in 1971. In New York City, the number of methadone-related deaths increased in 1972, too. Only one death on Long Island was related to legalized methadone programs. A 25-year-old woman was found dead in her North Babylon apartment June 17.

On the county-sponsored methadone maintenance program for several months, she had also been taking barbiturates and tranquilizers just before her death. The drugs were taken to ward off the pain of a leg inflammation, her roommate said at the time. She had been warned against the multiple drug usage by the methadone clinic - and her death was directly attributed to the combination of methadone with barbiturates and tranquilizers. In Suffolk, at least eight of the 13 deaths attributed to methadone in 1972 also showed use of alcohol, barbiturates or tranquilizers before the fatal dosage was taken. In at least four of Nassau's nine methadone deaths, traces of barbiturates, speed or tranquilizers were also found.

In addition to the 25 victims whose deaths were associated with morphine and the 22 fatalities linked to methadone, there were eight other deaths on Long Island that were placed in a possibly heroin-related category. One was the death of a 22-year-old woman, a maid who lived in Hempstead. She died at the Nassau County Medical Center Oct. 15. Cause of death was listed as an infection, stemming from abscesses in her left arm, caused by repeated injections, which spread to her chest. She was a known heroin user, according to the medical examiner's report, and was thus added to the narcotics-related death list.

Seven other victims died of hepatitis, pulmonary edema and pneumonia, but since they had histories of chronic narcotism, their names were also added to the narcotics-related list of fatalities. In addition to these 55 victims in Nassau and Suffolk, there were seven others on the narcotics-related list in Nassau. Two of these deaths were attributed to cocaine intoxication and one was a barbiturate suicide, but was placed on the narcotics list because codeine was also found in the body. Three of the remaining deaths were attributed to pneumonia and one to an auto accident. In these four cases, methadone was indirectly connected with the deaths. The placement of these deaths on the narcotics-related death list might be debated, especially in one of the pneumonia cases.

It involved a 71-year-old who had become addicted to morphine while under a doctor's care in an earlier illness. At the time of his death, he was under methadone treatment to combat his morphine addiction. A separate list of victims of barbiturate overdose is also kept by the Nassau medical examiner's office. There were 35 barbiturate deaths in 1972, including 16 that were listed as suicide. However, the number of deaths involving methadone and barbiturates was markedly increased in 1972 over the previous year on Long Island - while heroin-related deaths remained at approximately the same level in 1972. Increasing methadone and multiple drug use may foreshadow a new blight for American communities, as the fight to stem the flow of heroin continues.

## 3.3   TREATMENTS AND DEATH OF PATIENTS

### 3.3.1  Special Introductory Remarks

In 1934, a small Wisconsin newspaper, the *Sheboygan Press*, uncovered hospital misdeeds in its region. The resultant state-wide purging of state hospitals eliminated cruel, inhumane treatment of defenseless patients, took the hospital system out of politics and placed it on a civil-service basis. The newspaper and the reporter following the case, W. J. Bollenbeck, were almost solely responsible for the reforms of unbelievable hospital conditions. In one instance, a patient died due to brutal treatment by the attendants. The resultant state-wide investigation led to the dismissal of thirty employees of state hospitals for the insane, including a number of assistant superintendents, a large number of attendants and a recommendation to dismiss two superintendents. The nomination of the series for a Pulitzer Prize was accompanied by a letter from the Governor of Wisconsin stating that the articles contained "a brief but comprehensive summary of events which caused Wisconsin to clean up a deplorable hospital situation...". The *Sheboygan Press* was awarded a 1935 Pulitzer Public Service Honorable Mention Prize "for the proof of hospital misdeeds."

In the spring of 1976, two reporters from the *Philadelphia Inquirer* discovered that the Farview State Hospital, an obscure institution in a remote corner of Pennsylvania, was not really a hospital. In theory, Farview was a place where the criminally insane were kept from doing harm and, when possible, cured. But actually, it was the end of the line for tough inmates from the prison system. Reporters Acel Moore and Wendell Rawls Jr. first heard of Farview from a former inmate. They found out that the hospital offered no medical care, some of the patients were not mentally ill at all and others were retarded. For decades, the newspaper series revealed, Farview had been a place of murder, brutality, falsified medical records, and corruption. To the members of a

Pulitzer Prize jury the newspaper's "range and intensity of the investigations and the excellence of the writing were impressive," and the Board awarded the 1977 Pulitzer Local Investigative Specialized Reporting Prize to both reporters "for their reports on conditions in the Farview (Pa.) State Hospital for the mentally ill."

## 3.3.2 Suspicion of Homicide in a Hospital

[Source: W. J. Bollenbeck: Additional Proof of Hospital Misdeeds, in: *The Sheboygan Press* (Sheboygan, Wi.), Vol. XXVII/No. 53, February 19, 1934, p. 1, cols. 7-8; p. 14, cols. 4-5; reprinted by permission of the Press Publishing Company, Sheboygan, Wi.]

Additional proofs of ill-treatment and abuse of patients and inefficient and deplorable management of the Northern Hospital for the Insane at Winnebago are expected to be brought forth this week when the legislative interim committee on prison labor renews its probe. Senator M. G. Kelly, Fond du Lac, chairman, and Attorney Frank W. Cosgrove, committee counsel, began their preliminary work in connection with the continuation of the probe today and expect to have sufficient new evidence to report to the entire committee on Tuesday or Wednesday. This new proof of mismanagement and brutality will concern the definite leads furnished by Dr. J. A. McElligott, senior physician, and information sent voluntarily to the committee by former patients and employees.

The committee conducted hearings last Tuesday and Wednesday, and after hearing 18 witnesses, decided that the members had heard enough to convince them that Dr. Peter Bell, superintendent, should be suspended immediately, together with seven or eight additional attendants. They made their preliminary report to Gov. A. G. Schmedeman Friday afternoon and on being informed of the astounding and shocking revelations the governor urged the legislators not to drop the inquiry but to return and investigate further. In a public statement he recommended that the legislators investigate that institution and all similar ones conducted by the state.

### DR. LORENZ IN CHARGE

As the committee was in conference with the state's chief executive word was received that Dr. Bell had requested the board of control to relieve him of his duties pending the probe, and that the request had been granted. Dr. W. F. Lorenz, Madison, was sent there to take charge

# Brutality Is Charged At State Asylum

## Information Charging That Oscar Schrader Was Cruelly Beaten Before His Death Is Cause For An Investigation

C. E. Broughton, editor of The Sheboygan Press, today set in motion an investigation involving alleged brutal treatment of Oscar Schrader, Sheboygan man, which may have resulted in his death at the state hospital for the insane at Oshkosh, Friday morning.

Receiving information from a Winnebago county source to the effect that Mr. Schrader was cruelly beaten a few hours before his death, Mr. Broughton immediately placed the matter before Coroner C. N. Sonnenburg and District Attorney Charles A. Copp.

Following conferences with the Sheboygan county officials, Mrs. Schrader and Otto Kapschitzke, her brother-in-law, were interviewed, and it was ascertained from them that they had received similar information from another source.

Examination of the body of Mr. Schrader at the Ramm Funeral Home revealed that several bruises and scratches on his body seemed to substantiate much of the information received by Mr. Broughton and Mrs. Schrader.

### Autopsy Ordered

Immediately after these disclosures were made, Mrs. Schrader, at the suggestion of Mr. Broughton, District Attorney Copp and Coroner Sonnenburg, asked for an autopsy to determine the probable cause of death.

Funeral services were held this afternoon, after which the body was to be returned to the

Start of the newspaper's investigation at the end of January

Saturday morning. This action prevented the forced removal of the superintendent. The legislators were considerably chagrined at the statement of the board of control in its letter to Dr. Bell in which Col. Hannan assured him of his complete confidence in him, and that no official information of inefficiency or brutality had come to the board's offices.

That statement was regarded as contrary to the known facts as disclosed at great length in The Sheboygan Press, the Oshkosh Northwestern, the Milwaukee Sentinel and the Milwaukee Journal, all of which had correspondents at the legislative probe who gave columns of detailed reports of witnesses who had seen not only cruelties but also violent deaths. In addition, many newspaper editors of the state devoted columns to editorial discussion of the expose. The public assertion that the board of control has no knowledge of what went on is regarded as amazing here.

Several state officials contend that such an attempt at a "public whitewash" merely indicated that the control board does not know what has been going on under its supervision and that it was unwise and impolitic to make a pronouncement of that kind. Chairman Kelly is one of those who is confident that it will act as a "boomerang" when the official copy of the testimony is ready. One of the committee members was so incensed that he was ready to demand of Gov. Schmedeman that he remove all three members of the board of control, but was finally prevailed upon to await the outcome of the further probe.

## MORE INFORMATION

The continuation of the investigation is partly the result of the additional information obtained by Chairman Kelly and Attorney Cosgrove from Dr. McElligott, who was called here by the chairman late Thursday night when The Press representative learned that some new angles were obtainable. The senior physician revealed that he had repeatedly called Dr. Bell's attention to cruelties and cited half a dozen cases which the committee might look into. With the superintendent away this and other physicians, as well as employees and patients, are expected to feel more free to talk before the probers.

The committee will also look into the cause of two additional charges of deaths of patients resulting from abuse. One of these is the case of Henry Beumler, Sheboygan, who died on Jan. 14, 1933, and Hans Anderson, Racine, who passed away on Dec. 21, 1932. Witnesses charged that both had been put to death by rough handling instead of the reasons given in their death certificates. These disclosures came after it was quite clearly proved that Oscar Schrader, Sheboygan, had been choked to death by Norton Brown, an attendant, in the early morning hours of Jan. 26, 1934. Brown was arrested on a first degree manslaughter charge on Tuesday of last week and was held under $2,000 bail.

When his preliminary hearing came up before Judge Henry Hughes, Oshkosh, on Saturday, he was bound over for trial for next Friday and his bail was increased to $5,000. The charge was brought about by District Attorney R. C. Laus, Winnebago county. The defendant's attorney, L. W. Hull, claimed on Saturday that the complaint against Brown contained a technical fault and Judge Hughes set next Wednesday for a hearing on this point.

The bodies of Beumler and Anderson may be ordered exhumed to determine the cause of death. The result may be that two additional manslaughter charges will be brought. Allegations that a fourth inmate also met a violent death will be probed and if they are substantiated a fourth manslaughter charge may be lodged.

## MORE TO BE PROBED

The committee expects to make greater progress this week since those having information need not fear the superintendent any longer. Letters received by Senator Kelly and by The Press editor and others indicate that there is considerably more to be probed. In addition to the clear mistreatment of patients the committee will investigate the business administration of the institution. The members have heard reports that one or two officials have enjoyed flourishing bank accounts, and that some state property has been used for private purposes.

Others are that foods and materials have been sold to enable the sellers to purchase liquor, etc. An audit of the books will be conducted with Assemblyman Ray Novotny, Oshkosh, the governor's private institutional investigator, in charge. That probe was started today. Some of the new evidence alleged that a Fond du Lac patient had a fractured jaw and possible skull fractures when brought home to be buried; that another was not treated like a human being but like "cattle," that information coming from a former patient now living in Chicago. One man claims he was knocked "cold" within five minutes after his arrival, according to his letter from an Ohio city.

The committee will later prove conditions at the Central Hospital for the Insane at Waupun. One former patient claims that an inmate was literally boiled to death in a bath tub; another insists that he was forced to push a heavy lawn-mower when virtually dying from tuberculosis; that another who cut his neck was allowed to be treated by insane inmates; that a convict had access to prison keys, and that a kidnaper had access to prison keys. Gov. Schmedeman, sensing the injustices which seem to prevail at these state institutions and the public demand for a housecleaning, wherever needed, is firmly backing the committee.

From: *Sheboygan Press*, February 28, 1934, p. 1.

Before these investigations are completed some heads are sure to fall for the renewed probe will be thorough and complete and will shield no one.

### 3.3.3  Unelucidated Death Series in a Hospital

[Source: Acel Moore/Wendell Rawls Jr.: More deaths to be probed at Farview, in: *The Philadelphia Inquirer* (Philadelphia, Pa.), Vol. 295/No. 32, August 1, 1976, p. 1 B, cols. 5-6; p. 9 B, cols. 1-3; reprinted by permission of the Philadelphia Inquirer, Philadelphia, Pa.]

Wayne County coroner Robert Jennings said yesterday that he plans to exhume two more bodies of former patients at Farview State Hospital, bringing the total number of exhumations to four. The exhumations are part of a broadening probe of "suspicious deaths" at the facility for the criminally insane.

The body of Russell Sell, a 46-year-old Farview patient who died on Jan. 7, 1963, will be exhumed within the next 7 to 10 days, Jennings said. Jennings said that he received permission last week from Sell's family to exhume the body from a Lebanon County cemetery. Farview hospital officials listed the cause of Sell's death as acute coronary occlusion (blockade of a blood vessel in the heart). An autopsy held one day after his death showed that Sell had three broken ribs.

When the Pennsylvania State Police conducted an investigation into Sell's death in 1974, they were told by witnesses that Sell had died as a result of a severe beating administered by Farview guards six days before his death. The other body to be exhumed is that of John Rankin, who died at Farview on July 26, 1969, at age 45. The cause of his death was officially given as "generalized carcinomatosis carcinoma of the right lung" (lung cancer).

Witnesses have said that Rankin also died after a severe beating by guards. The state police are also looking into the circumstances surrounding Rankin's death. "As soon as they finished with the files on Rankin I will order that his body be exhumed," Jennings said.

Sell's death was one of the topics covered during two days of hearings last week in Harrisburg conducted by a special State Senate committee that is investigating several alleged murders, beatings and other abuses at Farview. The hearings were prompted by a series of stories in The Inquirer that detailed cases in which patients died after beatings.

'Oh, my God . . . Here comes my therapist.'

From: *The Philadelphia Inquirer*, June 29, 1976, p. 6 A.

Sell's sister, Mrs. Pearl Reinhart of New Oxford, Pa., testified on Thursday, the second day of hearings, that her brother had been beaten beyond recognition the last time she saw him five months before his death. Mrs. Reinhart was one of seven persons who testified before the six-member panel headed by Sen. Henry J. Cianfrani (D., Phila.).

Pennsylvania Secretary of Public Welfare Frank Beal, whose testimony opened the hearings, told the committee that drastic improvements had been made at Farview in the last two years and that more reforms were underway. Beal said that 95 percent of the abuses outlined by The Inquirer stories and other news reports had happened in the past.

Francis Truman, head of Farview guards, and John Naughton, a former guard at the state facility, also testified. Truman told the committee that he had never seen a patient beaten by guards. He told the committee that guards would often have to subdue patients who attacked guards.

Naughton, who worked at Farview for seven years before resigning in 1974, testified that guards, now known as "psychiatric security aides" were required to join in beating patients or risk ostracism by their colleagues and trouble with their superiors.

Cianfrani said at the conclusion of the hearings last week that his committee would resume the sessions after reviewing the mounds of records and documents that have been subpoenaed. He expected this task would take two to three weeks. He added that his committee plans to subpoena dozens of witnesses, including more Farview employees and officials and former patients.

Meanwhile, Jennings is involved in a legal showdown with Welfare Secretary Beal, whose department is responsible for the operation of Farview. Jennings attempted to subpoena Beal to testify at an inquest two weeks ago into the death of John Rank, 68, who choked to death while eating a ham sandwich last March 2. An autopsy showed a heavy dosage of chlorpromoazine (Thorazine), a sedative that sometimes inhibits swallowing, in Rank's body.

Beal fought the subpoena on the ground that the coroner had no right or order him to testify. The inquest has been delayed until the court decides on the legal argument between the two officials. Jennings is investigating five deaths at Farview, including Rank's. He had earlier exhumed the bodies of Thomas Garret, 37, a patient who died in 1960, and Robert (Stonewall) Jackson of Philadelphia, who died in 1966 at age 36.

The results of the autopsies on both are not yet available. In another development, Farview employees recently formed an ad-hoc committee and hired a Scranton lawyer, Peter O'Malley, to represent any employee who is called before the committee.

# 4

# SPECIAL CASES OF MEDICAL CARE

## 4.1   EMERGENCY TREATMENTS AND EXTREME CONDITIONS

### 4.1.1  Special Introductory Remarks

"There is an ancient journalistic myth, spread largely by the un-knowing," Hohenberg states, "that city editors are mean and thoughtless men." Paul Schoenstein of the *New York Journal-American* gave a full and complete answer to that myth in August, 1943. His story of a race against death, in which supply of the new drug Penicillin was secured and administered within a period of five and a half hours to save the life of a two-year old girl, was a sensation in New York City. The girl's father had telephoned the newspaper and said that his daughter had only seven hours to live unless she could get Penicillin. Schoenstein verified the father's statement that the child lay near death at Lutheran Hospital, suffering from a blood disease. Through a series of phone calls Schoen-stein learned that a drug company in New Jersey had a supply, and well-known physicians used their authority to order release of the drug for civilian use. The girl survived, and the whole story was released nation-wide by other newspapers and news agencies. For their undertaking, Schoenstein and Associates, among them Charles Davis, received the 1944 Pulitzer Reporting Prize since they "cooperated in the development and publication of a news story... which saved the life of a two-year old girl in the Lutheran Hospital of New York City by obtaining penicillin."

In November, 1944, the U.S. Navy announced it would begin flying whole human blood from San Francisco to the Pacific fighting front within a period of forty-eight hours. Reporter Jack S. McDowell of the *San Francisco Call-Bulletin* conceived of the idea of going to the Red Cross Blood Donor Center, donating a pint of his own blood, then flying in the same plane with that particular day's shipment across the Pacific to watch this same blood transfused into the veins of casualties in the combat zone. He achieved his goal, and upon his return, his newspaper published a series of illustrated stories which were also used by news agencies for national distribution. Blood donations increased sharply as a result of the stories. In 1945, McDowell received the Pulitzer Reporting Prize "for his campaign to encourage blood donations."

## 4.1.2   The Use of Antibiotics to Save a Life

[Source: Charles Davis: '7 Hours to Live-' Scarcest Drug Rushed to Baby, in: *New York Journal-American* (New York, N.Y.), No. 20,309, August 12, 1943, p. 1, cols. 1-2; p. 10, cols. 3-6; reprinted by permission of the Hearst Newspapers, New York, N.Y.]

A tiny white light flashed a summons on the New York Journal-American city desk switchboard. The time was 3:40 p.m. Wednesday. Remember this time. It is important. Remember, too, this wisp of a switchboard light. For it was to magnify itself magnificently to a beacon of mercy.

The city editor who answered the telephone heard these words: "Hello, is this the city editor? My little girl is in Lutheran Hospital. The doctors say she has only seven hours to live - unless she gets the new drug penicillin. It is her only hope. The doctors have used sufla drugs and everything else. I must find someone with enough to help her. Can you help me?"

The caller identified himself as Lawrence J. Malone, of 83-11 34th ave., Jackson Heights. The child who lay near death in the Lutheran Hospital of Manhattan, at 144th st. and Convent ave., was his daughter, Patricia, 2.

Wheels were set moving on the Journal-American city desk. They moved fast. In New York. In Washington. In Boston. In New Brunswick, N.J. They moved so a little child might have a long chance on life. These wheels moved with force. They did not stop until, five and a half hours later, a doctor plunged a needle in the tiny leg of Patricia Malone and let flow into her veins the magical penicillin.

At 8 a.m. today, little Patricia was still fighting for her life, with every passing hour increasing her chance of survival. Doctors observed one hopeful factor - the baby appeared to be quiet and comfortable today, in contrast to her restless condition yesterday.

This is a nation at war. Yet men of government, medicine, the press and the police of two States joined all their energies in an attempt to save one small life. The search for penicillin was not an easy one. For this drug, hailed by medical science as a miracle worker, is so scarce as to be almost unobtainable. Even our armed forces can obtain only a small percentage of the penicillin they need.

## GRIM DEADLINE

Two minutes after the father had appealed for help, the Journal-American city desk set to work on the job with determination. Newspapermen are used to deadlines. But this was a grim one... "only seven hours to live unless -" A call to Lutheran Hospital verified that the child barely lived, that she suffered from a dread blood disease, the staphlocci type of septicemia.

Sulfa drugs had been used. Two blood transfusions had been given. They had not helped. Penicillin was held out as her only hope. A call was put in for U.S. Surgeon Gen. Thomas Parran in Washington. New York drug firms were canvassed, and it was learned that E. R. Squibb & Sons were manufacturers of penicillin.

## SEARCH NARROWED

Halloran General Hospital, the Army Hospital on Staten Island, was called. After 20 minutes of telephoning, the search had narrowed - but it had also become more difficult. The call to Surgeon Gen. Parran had been referred to Dr. A. N. Richards, in charge of research in the Office of Scientific Development, Washington.

"The E. R. Squibb & Sons research laboratories at New Brunswick, N.J., have a supply of penicillin," said Dr. Richards, "I'll wire them a release order immediately." In the meantime, it was learned Dr. Chester Keefer, Boston surgeon and WPB member, had direct authority to order release of the precious drug for civilian use. He was called.

## PROMISED SUPPLY

Dr. Keefer communicated with Dr. Dante Collitti, staff surgeon at Lutheran Hospital, and discussed the bacteriological aspects of the child's case. "You will get the penicillin," Dr. Keefer promised Dr. Collitti. This was at 4 p.m. Doctors were amazed at the speed with which a source of penicillin had been discovered and red tape binding its release cut. Minutes passed and the hands of the clock continued their relentless swirl.

To expedite the release of the drug from the Squibb laboratories at New Brunswick, it was arranged for Dr. Keefer to telephone a release to H. A. Holiday, director of the Squibb firm, via the Journal-American switchboard. At 4:25 p.m., it was announced that Squibb and Sons would release the valuable drug. Now plans were set in motion to arrange for police of two States to escort the mercy shipment of penicillin from New Brunswick to the bedside of the dying girl.

The police commissioner unhesitatingly granted the request. Now the clock stood at 5:46 p.m. Dr. Collitti dashed from Lutheran Hospital into a waiting cab. At 6:30 p.m., Dr. Collitti met an anxious group of reporters at the entrance to the Holland Tunnel. Now began the race against death.

## RACE AGAINST DEATH

Traffic on the Pulaski Skyway across the Jersey meadows was heavy, but the car which carried the only hope of a little girl raced on furiously. A siren sent lumbering trucks and crawling cars to the side of the highway. It was 7:30 p.m. when the car of mercy drew to a stop at the entrance to the Squibb laboratories. Three guards waited here. One of them stepped to the running board of the car and asked: "Dr. Collitti? Here is the penicillin."

## FIGHTING CHANCE

Here, at last, was the much-sought miracle drug, the last remaining supply of penicillin in the Squibb laboratories, according to Holiday. Dr. Collitti fondly held the cardboard carton, inside of which lay the penicillin packed in dry ice. Then he remarked: "Now we have a fighting chance."

At this moment, a radio squad car of the New Brunswick Police Department screamed to a stop. In it were Patrolmen Asher Van Dorrn and James B. Grey. It did not take long to reach the traffic circle, not at 70 miles an hour. Trooper John Fitzsimmons of the New Jersey State Police station at New Brunswick was waiting there, behind the wheel of a trim, white sedan.

## DASH THROUGH TOWN

Down the broad highway sped the two cars, past trucks, past open-mouthed pedestrians and hundreds of homeward-bound defense workers. Through one town they raced, criss-crossing through two lanes of traffic, narrowly missing trucks and extended culverts. At 8:25 p.m., the two cars roared to a stop at the New Jersey entrance of the Holland Tunnel.

Tunnel police were expecting the mercy car and flashed word of its arrival to a New York City motorcycle policeman waiting at the other end of the tunnel. Five minutes through the tunnel, and then up into the dim-out of New York. This last stage of the trip was covered in record time - from Holland Tunnel to Lutheran Hospital in eight minutes. The speedometer registered a steady 65 miles an hour in the race up the West Side Highway.

## THANKS REPORTERS

Then off the West Side Highway at 125th st. and the race continued through Harlem to the hospital door. Just before the car pulled up to the hospital entrance, Dr. Collitti said: "You fellows have done some-

thing today that all the doctors in the world couldn't have done."
"Maybe," admitted one of the reporters, "but from now on, Doc, it's up to
you."

In the hospital lobby, Dr. Collitti was met by Dr. Michael
Garofalo, attending physician. Together they rushed to the hospital laboratory to prepare the drug for use. Approximately 30 minutes were required to "warm" the drug. Afterwards, reporters tiptoed into the fourth-
floor room of the unconscious child. She breathed in labor, but her tiny
features beneath a silky mop of brown hair showed no evidence of pain.

PARENTS WEEP FOR JOY

"She's a pretty sick little girl," one nurse whispered. At their
Jackson Heights home, little Patricia Malone's parents wept with joy.
"Thank God," murmured Lawrence Malone. "At least my little girl will
have a chance," sobbed Katherine Malone.

Patricia was stricken 10 days ago. At first her illness was thought
to be polymyelitis. Later it was diagnosed as rheumatic fever. But
treatment for this malady did not help. On Monday she was taken,
unconscious, to Lutheran Hospital. A blood culture was taken. It showed
presence of the deadly septicemia bacteria.

Patricia was born on July 25, 1941. She was the second daughter of
the Malones. The sister is Jeanne, 7, who is unaware that her baby sister
is battling for her life.

## 4.1.3 Transporting of Stored Blood to a Patient

[Source: Jack S. McDowell: Call-Bulletin man takes own, others' blood to
islands, in: *The Call-Bulletin* (San Francisco, Ca.), Vol. 176/No. 108, December
5, 1944, p. 1, cols. 1-2; p. 2, cols. 1-6; reprinted by permission of the Hearst
Newspapers, New York, N.Y.]

The maps say the sick and wounded GI's lying in the steaming
jungles of the Marianas are more than 6,000 miles away - a quarter of the
way around the world. But the maps must be wrong - because just 48
hours after flying over the Red Cross Blood Donor Center on Jones
street, where more than 100 other San Franciscans and I put blood from
our veins into little pint bottles, I stepped with this cargo of liquid life to
the airstrip of an advance American base within 1,500 miles of Tokyo.

REAL THRILL AT BASE HOSPITAL

With the speed and ingenuity of the Naval Air Transport Service I
was able to make Jules Verne look like a crawling piker, but the real

thrill came in a forward area hospital as I watched color return to the paled face of a critically-burned Sea Bee. In the bottle suspended above his hospital cot was part of 22-year old Chesla O'Brien of 3309 California street, the blood I saw drained from her arm as she lay on a cot adjacent to mine in the blood center at 2415 Jones street. My own pint was in the hopper somewhere else, but I was able to follow that of Miss O'Brien all the way across the Pacific to the advance blood bank at Guam and ultimately to the veins of Painter Second Class Willie R. Boyter, 34-year old Navy Sea Bee from Pine Bluff, Ark.

## SAILOR HERO SAVES PLANE

Boyter, a veteran of the D-day fighting in the Marianas, was thin and pale. He had charged up the beach of this particular island through the hell of Japanese mortar and artillery fire. His buddies dropped, dead or wounded, beside him as his outfit pushed through the withering fire. But Boyter came through the battle unhurt - only to fall victim to the accidental explosion of a drum of turpentine. Medical officers at the base paid tribute to the sailor as a real hero. "The drum of turpentine exploded and caught fire right near a plane," one officer said. "Boyter was intent on saving the plane, and he ran toward the burning drum with a stick. He stuck the stick into the drum and carried it away before it could ignite the plane. But when he lifted the drum, the flaming turpentine spilled all over his back, sides and legs. He suffered first, second and third degree burns."

## TELLS STORY TO BOYTER

As the Navy doctors rigged tubing from the bottle of Miss O'Brien's blood to Boyter's arms, I sat beside his cot. He turned a pair of brave blue eyes toward me and asked if I knew the donor. "I saw her at the blood center in San Francisco a couple of days ago," I told him. "She was in there at the same time I was." Boyter wanted to know more about the girl who had sent him part of herself to help him back to health - and the United States. She had donated blood three times, I told him. She just recently moved to San Francisco from Boston, and one of the first things she did was call the Blood Donor Center to make an appointment. She said that made her "feel like she really belonged to the community." She has just gone to work for the Pacific Telephone and Telegraph Company as a teletype operator. "When she was giving her blood, she told us she was happy to do it, that she wanted it to go to some man overseas, and you're the man," I told Boyter. A touch of color was coming back to the sailor's cheeks now and those clear blue eyes seemed to send more messages than the words from his lips.

## 'I CAN'T BELIEVE IT'

"You don't know how thankful I am," Boyter said, licking his dry lips in the tropical heat. "Will you take a message back to that little girl in San Francisco for me? Tell her something to make her feel good - tell her how much I appreciate her sending part of her own blood all the way over here to me." Those sky-blue eyes looked beyond me now - and beyond the long rows of white cots in the Quonset hut hospital ward. You could see they were focused on a thought - not on one of the grim reminders of war and suffering in the forward area hospital. "San Francisco... couple of days ago..." he spoke, shaking his head slightly. "I can't believe it. Say, will you tell that girl in San Francisco something else for me, too? Tell her I hope her blood gets me home to my wife quicker. I haven't seen her in twenty-two months." His wife, he said, is named Caroline, and she manages the coffee shop of the Hotel Pines back in Arkansas. Not long ago Sea Bee Boyter was on the critical list of the huge base hospital where I found him. Now, according to medical officers, he definitely is on the mend.

The dramatic operation of giving blood transfusions by remote control is as daring and ingenious as any story to come from the battlefronts of World War II. Blood plasma - the processed portion of human blood which may be kept indefinitely - has performed thousands upon thousands of miracles. Wounded men, suffering shock so severely that pulse and breathing are hardly discernible, are sitting up smoking cigarets an hour and a half after a dressing station plasma injection at the front. And the need for plasma is still great. Thousands of gallons of it must continue to flow into the laboratories if the Army and Navy medical men are to save the lives of these lads who fell fighting for us just forty-eight hours west of Jones street. But, because the tissue-building red corpuscles have been removed from plasma, another need was discovered. Whole blood from the veins of another human must be introduced into the body of the casualty.

## THE CALL FOR VOLUNTEERS

The problem was partially solved when service doctors called for volunteers. Medical officers, hospital corpsmen, soldiers, sailors and marines - even some wounded men themselves - reclined beside casualties in forward hospitals to send a pint of their blood through a small rubber tube into the arm of the wounded man. But the Pacific war grew larger and larger. There was the Coral Sea, Midway and Guadalcanal, Attu, Bouganville and New Guinea, Tarawa, Kwajalein, Guam, Tinian and Saipan. More young Americans fell under the hail of shrapnel, torpedoes and bullets thrown by the retreating but fighting enemy. More men in the field gave their blood to another who had a greater need for it. But to the medical experts in the field and in Washington, the picture was becoming all too clear. You couldn't fight a winning war by draining blood from the fighting men beyond the point of safety. There was no shortage of volunteers, however. But every transfusion tied up men and hospital space.

The Army and Navy medical chiefs knew the only solution was to send whole blood from the veins of people at home. But blood would spoil before it ever got near the battlefronts - even in ships containing modern refrigeration equipment. They called in the experts of the Naval Medical Research Institute at Bethesda, Md., and tossed the problem into their laps. The institute had licked knotty problems before, and soon the answer was delivered. The experts devised an inexpensive plywood box, lined with insulating fiber glass and containing aluminum bottle racks and an ice cylinder which will accommodate 19 pounds of ordinary ice. At the same time, across the world was being blazed one of the most vast and efficient air services in the world. It's official name is the Naval Air Transport Service, but to millions of men in uniform it is affectionately known as "NATS."

## SHIPMENTS LEAVE EVERY DAY

The institute provided the container, NATS promised the transportation, and the remaining question was: "Where is the blood coming from?" To cut the danger of spoilage to a minimum, the West Coast was chosen as the supply point, and a hurry up call came across the nation from the surgeons general of the Army and Navy to the Red Cross blood donor centers at San Francisco, Oakland and Los Angeles. Every day shipments of whole blood are leaving here by air. They are landing at forward area hospitals two days later. The ingenious plan is working, but the demand is for more, more, more.

The realization that the man at the front is receiving blood from San Francisco a scant 48 hours after the donor leaves the blood center here was challenging to the imagination. I thought other San Franciscans, too, might have trouble placing Guam and Leyte, Saipan and Tinian as close to their homes - on a basis of time - as Portland. So, along with dozens of others - most of them women and service men - I went to the blood donor center, contributed a pint of my blood into the batch that was to leave that night. Then I followed the shipment to the sick and wounded men who receive it.

## 4.2  SCIENTIFIC RESEARCH AND SYNDROMES

### 4.2.1  Special Introductory Remarks

In 1933, outstanding scientists of the nation united in painstaking search for the cause of St. Louis sleeping sickness epidemic. It was H. Ellwood Douglass of the *St. Louis Post-Dispatch* who received wide public attention for his excellent and accurate coverage of the problem. Although skeptical of the publicity surrounding the encephalitis research, the Surgeon General of the U.S. Public Health Service had nothing but praise for Douglass' coverage: "His discretion could always be relied upon. His accuracy was unique, considering the technical difficulties of recording events in a field strange to him." The Pulitzer Prize jury was also impressed by the Douglass entry and said: "His reports are distinguished by maintaining strict scientific accuracy while at the same time making their subject matter intelligible and interesting to laymen." The Advisory Board also thought that Douglass produced an outstanding piece of science journalism and awarded him a 1934 Local Reporting Honorable Mention Prize for his news reports of the 1933 Encephalitis Epidemic.

Several decades later, the media began focusing on the problems of aging. Margo Huston, a reporter of the *Milwaukee Journal*, disclosed case after case of neglect of old people, some of them in their 80s and 90s. In a series called "I'll Never Leave My Home, Would You?" she found that profit-making care agencies, in the words of John Hohenberg, "were doing little to help these tragic shut-ins, that cold-eyed bureaucrats simply didn't enforce protective laws, that available in-home care aside from nursing homes was scarce and ineffective. A shakeup in the state's home health care system and a move to expand Medicaid services followed," Hohenberg adds about the effects of the series. "Margo Huston took a subject of vital interest," a Pulitzer Prize jury wrote in its report, "that has been exhaustively reported in American newspapers. She made this difficult subject compelling and moving through outstanding writing and meticulous reporting." She won the 1977 Pulitzer Local General Spot News Reporting Prize "for her reports on the elderly and the process of aging."

## 4.2.2  Investigating the Causes of Sleeping Sickness

[Source: H. Ellwood Douglass: Outstanding Scientists of the Nation Unite in Painstaking Search for Cause of St. Louis Sleeping Sickness Epidemic, in: *St. Louis Post-Dispatch* (St. Louis, Mo.), Vol. 85/No. 357, August 28, 1933, p. 1 C, cols. 4-7; p. 3 C, col. 4; reprinted by permission of the Pulitzer Publishing Company, St. Louis, Mo.]

Never have physicians more violently gone against their own preaching - "lots of rest and nourishing food" - than in the quest for the cause of the "sleeping sickness" outbreak in St. Louis and St. Louis County. Outstanding Government experts, distinguished local practitioners, noted scientists on the research staffs of both the St. Louis medical schools, are eating and sleeping when, where and if they have time in their concerted drive on one of the least understood of all diseases.

A famous epidemiologist of the United States Public Health Service pauses in midflight between a pin-studded map and a stack of records, which he has been shuffling on a Health Department window sill rather than take time to clear a desk. "Tonight," he tells a health officer, "I'm going to look into the possibility of...". "But when are you going to sleep?" asks his associate. The scientist grins. He doesn't know and apparently doesn't care. "When do you sleep?" he asks.

FOUR HOURS FOR SLEEP

"I get mine between 2 and 6 in the morning," the other replies, as though doctor's orders were four hours instead of eight. He is an executive, officially concerned only with gathering in the various threads of specialized research. Every phase is ably handled by local, state and Federal experts in that particular line, but the executive rises at 6, sees patients at 7:30, has his secretary set out lunch, if any, in his office, spends the evening reading up on every related factor, and the late hours turning over and over in his mind every bit of evidence for and against each theory on the unknown factors of this disease.

And the important factors are unknown - cause, specific remedy or preventive, mode of transmission. There has been little past opportunity to search for them. Though encephalitis records cover centuries, the outbreak here seems to be a new form, unseen previously, except since 1871 in Japan. And most epidemics of encephalitis, even in more usual forms have included but a few scattered cases, compared with the greater disease epidemics. The St. Louis and St. Louis County outbreak is described at Washington as the worst ever reported in any one locality in any country. Yet it resulted in few more than 200 reported cases, city and county, and fewer than 30 deaths in a month. Only six deaths and 50 cases were of patients residing inside the city.

## COMPARISON WITH INFLUENZA

For comparison, the influenza epidemic in the winter of 1918-19 resulted in 34,855 cases and 2354 deaths in the city alone. City deaths exceeded the deaths in the current "sleeping sickness" outbreak in each month from October, 1918, to March, 1919. Influenza deaths in the city leaped from two in September to 462 in October, 651 in December and 901 in January. They declined almost as sharply to none in July, 1919. In the following winter 8222 influenza cases and 557 influenza deaths were reported in the city, and as late as the calendar year 1931 they ran to 247 cases and 57 deaths - a death rate in proportion to cases far above that so far recorded in the encephalitis outbreak.

Not only in material but also in research organization and that prime factor, an early start, say the scientists, this epidemic offers an opportunity they have not had before in sleeping sickness. When the first few county cases went to hospital late in July, an alert pathologist gave them special scrutiny. They showed some differences from the epidemic form of encephalitis previously seen here, but physicians saw other cases arrive, almost exactly alike, with growing concern. County hospital authorities decided the disease, for safety, should be handled like an epidemic. They sent the patients to Isolation Hospital, in the city. The superintendent there immediately notified Health Commissioner Bredeck, with the result that the first 25 cases had been fully investigated, and milk, drinking water or food had been ruled out of possible sources of infection before the first city case was reported.

Three days after the existence of an epidemic was reported, Dr. J. P. Leake, senior surgeon of the United States Public Health Service and its expert on this disease, arrived to learn that the most urgent phase of the search for a transmission agent - since transmission by food, milk or drinking water might reach thousands overnight - had been completed, and that steps had been taken to unite health officers of county, city and the East Side toward blocking the epidemic and determining its cause. Since then Dr. Leake has been joined by two associates, a noted pathologist and an expert on disease-bearing insects. They were Dr. Charles Armstrong, director of sleeping sickness research at

Washington, and a former president of the American Epidemiological Society, and Dr. L. L. Williams Jr., a physician specializing in mosquito control. The State epidemiologist, Dr. E. K. Musson, arrived with Dr. Leake, and other Public Health Service experts will be called on whenever the quest demands specialized knowledge in their particular lines.

University experts were formally drafted in the first organization meeting of the Metropolitan Health Council, but informally they had been neck-deep in the fight from its beginning. Faculty members on the staff of the St. Louis University group of hospitals are making clinical studies and supervising the collection of material for study in the hospital laboratories and the central epidemic laboratory at Washington University, where local and Government scientists are collaborating. Health Commissioner Bredeck doubts that the laboratory men slept at all the first few nights of the outbreak. Pausing for lunch, even a hurried sandwich, still is out of the question, though they have help now. Noted local scientists abandoned plans of forthcoming vacations or cut outings short to return and get in the search.

## FLIVVERS ALSO DO PART

Dramatic as is the quest in the laboratory, much of it, no less dramatic and no less strenuous, goes on outside. The unromantic flivver, columns of figures and pin-dotted maps have their part as well as test tube and microscope. Touching many unknown aspects of the disease, the investigations go forward along diverse and specialized lines. In the laboratory lies the hope of finding the cause, and with it the possibility of devising a remedy or a preventive.

No preventive is known, and treatment now consists in relieving effects of the disease and attempting to maintain life until the infection runs its course. Mainly outside the laboratory, in the study of the patients' history and the search of the community for factors known to have had a part in epidemics elsewhere, lies the hope of finding the mode of transmission. So far, say the investigators, the indications point to transmission by human carriers, who may or may not have had the disease.

## CASE HISTORY FIRST

Inevitably, then, the "microbe-hunt" has called in hospital interns, charged with keeping voluminous case records; technicians in hospital laboratories, hospital nurses and nurses outside running down case histories, distinguished local physicians, whose specialized knowledge the investigators have not hesitated to call on at need, and hundreds of private practitioners on the lookout for mild cases, considered an important factor in spreading the disease. The quest begins with the study in the hospital, or in the home where the private physician is summoned. Here the case history is obtained for one major line of the search, the field work, and material is obtained for the other major line, the laboratory.

Every health officer in the county, city and East Side gets an immediate report of the case. Trained investigators, three nurses under an expert medical social worker - who is an unpaid volunteer, by the way - pin up the residence location on a city or county map, itself a graphic picture of the course of the epidemic. One of them, gathering what information is available at the Health Department, goes to the home to check up on the patient's source of food, water and milk, contacts, direct or second hand, with other known patients, previous illness, surroundings, the screening of the house, sanitation and the topography of the neighborhood. Every local health department is using the same questionnaire and similar methods to facilitate accurate analysis.

This investigation goes into every probable source of infection. Supplementing that, Dr. Williams is to provide specialized information for an investigation into the possibility of spread by mosquitoes. Insects have never been found to have anything to do with this disease, but the investigators are overlooking nothing. Dr. Williams' phase of the search, beginning in the field, probably will lead him into the laboratory. Recalled from his vacation by Surgeon-General Hugh S. Cumming, he arrived last Friday.

His first step is a sort of bird's-eye survey of topography to map out features of significance in the habits of disease-bearing insects. His experience has equipped him to recognize at a glance the sort of terrain where they are likely to be found. In such surroundings he will search for the insects. Finding mosquitoes of species likely to carry disease, he will go into the laboratory to determine if they are actually infected. If he finds an infection in an insect, the investigation may entail the breeding of thousands of that species for microscopic examination and tests of ability to transmit the infection.

### VIRUS, NOT MICROBE, SOUGHT

In the precise language of the laboratory men, their quest is not a "microbe-hunt." The evidence they have on the cause of the disease points to a virus, containing no "microbe" large enough to be seen by the most powerful microscope. It is so conclusive that, with the sanction of the Metropolitan Health Council, they are discarding the "germ" hypothesis in this disease and concentrating on the search for a virus. But, nonetheless, so thorough is this investigation they are incidentally "culturing" specimens of blood, spinal fluid and brain tissue, to make sure beyond any doubt that no organism is present.

The search for a causative virus can proceed along only one line, the search for a susceptible animal in which the disease can be produced by inoculation with material obtained from the patient. The United States Public Health Service has authorized purchase of animals. Preparations of the material for inoculation are strained through porcelain laboratory filters to eliminate all bacteria. Different methods of preparation and different animals are tried. Monkeys, of a South American species susceptible to a somewhat similar disease, are under experiment now. Small pigs, rabbits and mice also are to be tested, and, if non "takes," the experiment will be extended to other animals.

## RECORDS OF ANIMALS

The animals are in the hands of an expert caretaker and in quarters unusually equipped for their care. They get attention comparable to that given a human patient. Records are made of every change in their condition. The object is to produce a mild attack of the disease in the animal. It has never been successfully inoculated in any animal. Once they have a "take," they have the virus and the problem is half solved. While the animal is in a active stage of the disease, the virus can be taken for further inoculations. When it recovers, serums can be prepared and tested for treating or preventing the disease in other animals. If a serum safe for human beings can be devised in safe dosages, the scientists can submit it for tests in treating cases or blocking the epidemic. But this is not all a "take" would mean. It would enable the health authorities immediately to determine the period between exposure and onset of illness - an unknown of obvious importance in the search for the source of infection.

## WORK IN MATHEMATICS

Toward the same end a complex mathematical study of dates of onset of all reported cases is being conducted by the vital statistician, a new position in the Health Department. The interval between successive "peaks of incidence" is expected to provide a valuable guide toward the incubation period of the disease. The trained analyst of figures has many other functions in the quest. At its beginning, Dr. Leake called on her to determine certain norms of seasonal disease prevalence here as a measuring stick for one phase of his investigation. Case histories and the reports of field workers are being tabulated for her analysis, and more than one phase of the laboratory work is expected to demand her experienced scrutiny.

Thus, in effect, every local resource in medicine and related sciences is called on in this dramatic search. Should the virus or a transmission agent be identified, scientists in all parts of the world would get into the investigation, to check and recheck the results toward establishing a dependable means of throttling the disease for all time.

### 4.2.3  Fighting against Mental Diseases of Old Age

[Source: Margo Huston: Is Senility Real or Just an Easy Answer?, in: *The Milwaukee Journal* (Milwaukee, Wi.), 94th Year/No. 261, November 4, 1976, Part 2, p. 6, cols. 1-4; reprinted by permission of the Journal/Sentinel, Inc., Milwaukee, Wi.]

It's 4:30 in the afternoon, happy hour in some places. A stylish college student and a wobbly old man are strolling down the driveway of the modest Shorewood home. An exuberant hello brings only a stare from the old gentleman, a motion toward the house from the young woman. But a knock at the door and a friendly hello bring the works. "Hello, hello, my dear," an elderly woman greets the stranger. "Won't you please come in? I'm so delighted."

In a manner as elegant as possible for an old woman wearing a stained robe, scruffy slippers and false teeth that click, Harriet ushers in the stranger, then disappears. Now she's back, then gone again - dashing from cupboard to cupboard, opening, shutting. Finally, like a leprechaun, she appears with two elegant brandy snifters, decorated with tiny shamrocks, and pours the V-O and the Irish Mist so that most of it lands in the snifters.

Of course, it's happy hour. Cocktails are served at the fine dining room table. Around the corner the TV is blaring, so no one could overhear the conversation, but still Harriet whispers. "Oh, I'm so glad you stopped by," she tells the stranger, tightly grasping her by the arm, "but where were you yesterday? Oh, I thought I'd lose my mind, for sure. It got so terrible I couldn't stand it. He wants this, he wants that, up and down, up and down, all night. I don't know what I'm going to do." The front door opens; it's the wobbly husband, 88, and the college student, who puts him to bed, then leaves for the night.

For seven years, Harriet hasn't known what to do, but until recently she had managed to cope - with lots of help from her neighbors. Now she has the help of an aide, suggested by her husband's doctor, and the aide's college age daughter. At $3,50 an hour, the aide gets about $1 more than she would make working for a home health agency and Harriet pays about $1 less than if she went through an agency. The aide works six to eight hours a day, five days a week, earning between $105 and $140 a week; her daughter picks up some evening and weekend hours.

It was when Harriet's husband had his second prostate operation that his world fell apart. He quit: Quit going to the bathroom by himself, quit moving, quit eating right, quit dressing himself and, what's hardest to take, he quit laughing and talking to the wife with whom he had shared his life. Her home is deteriorating and so are her bank account, her own health, her strength and patience to care for her invalid husband. The couple had no children, but to look in the back room, you'd never believe it: Self-portraits and cut and paste artwork from a dozen neighbor children brighten the bulletin board.

Now a nephew has power of attorney over what remains of her husband's earnings - those years of selling printer's ink and chewing tobacco throughout Wisconsin. "I'll die, if I have to put him in a home," she says, sad eyed. "I would love to keep living in my own home - if I possibly can. Would you please put that in the paper? That's what I really want."

## ATTENTION COMES FIRST

"Everyone wants to go to heaven, but no one wants to stop in a nursing home along the way," says Jack Fernan, executive director of the Residents (of nursing homes) Advocates Program and an investigator in the State Nursing Home Ombudsman Program. Many people wouldn't have to make that dreaded stop, Fernan says, if they got more attention. With the embryonic field of home health care on the verge of expansion, Fernan suggests, "I don't know whether people actually need attention more than health care. Maybe if we gave people attention before they started complaining, they wouldn't have so many aches and pains. Perhaps it's time to stop worrying about our mother's aching back and start worrying about her aching heart."

But attention doesn't mean smothering. It doesn't mean taking away even a smidgen of independence. A person who can lift a spoon to his mouth should be allowed to do it - even if he slobbers some. On this issue, Fernan is in agreement with doctors, nurses, social workers, researchers, aides and everyone else interviewed about alternatives to nursing homes. "It's appropriate NOT to do everything for everybody," he says. "The more we do for them, the more dependent they become, which makes them less independent and less able to care for themselves."

## HABIT OF HAMBURGER

A cane stabilizing her, Gladys stops in an Inner City alley and starts unwrapping a hamburger. Her wrinkled hands shake so much, you think for sure the purse will fall, or the cane, or the hamburger, or

Gladys. The Journal reporter and artist ask if they can talk with her to find out more about how old people live outside of nursing homes. Gladys says she'll oblige, and she leads the pair up the tipsy steps to the back door of her apartment. Holding the screen door open with her cane, she puts one shaky hand into the top of her purple pantsuit and down deep into her bosom. Of course, the key.

Peeking out from under 72 plants in this tiny apartment is the hospital bed where Gladys' husband died three years ago. "I wouldn't let him go to no nursing home," she declares, her voice vibrating. "He wouldn't have lived a month." Instead, he lived for years and she cared for him, on nice days pushing his wheelchair down to the lake and back (six miles up and down hills). "I just wanted him to enjoy himself," she says, drying her tears.

She wrestles a cigaret from her wrinkled pack. She can't grasp hold of the matches, so the artist reaches over to give her a light. Soon a long ash tumbles to the carpet in front of her overstuffed chair. Gladys' mother died when she was 2; she lived in foster homes, then married a Navy man and moved around the world. Soon another ash forms. This time, Gladys tries for the ashtray. "I won't go to a nursing home," she declares. "Because I want to be independent and take care of myself." Still, she doesn't feel too good. She holds her side, "That's hard as a rock. Just feel it. Put your hand there."

She gets up, takes the reporter's hand and places it on the - yes - on the rock. It's hard. "Caused by shingles going inside," she says. "It hurts. I've been so nervous, ever since my husband died. That's why I shake so much. It's no fun. I can't go out to eat. They have to cut my food, or I spill my coffee. And I don't do much cooking, not no more." So she eats cereal and coffee at home, and sometimes goes to McDonald's for a hamburger and apple pie. When we met her in the alley, she had already eaten the apple pie, because, "I was starving."

## NUTRITION CAN BE PROBLEM

If you've lost your teeth, your sense of taste and the friends you used to eat with, you've lost much of your incentive to eat. And so, many older people don't eat, says Carol Graham, supervisor of the Bureau of Public Health Nursing. And their problems grow. Lack of proper nutrition brings on a false senility syndrome, Mrs. Graham says, causing people to become disoriented and to be falsely labeled senile. Take a look at these case records from the Milwaukee Health Department:

"Neighbor states patient 'senile'... eats many carbohydrates, especially sugar, seldom bakes as used to...". - "Nothing to eat today. Food in home consists of two cans of soup in pantry. Hamburger, milk, and coleslaw was spoiled and public health nurse discarded these...". -

"Patient eats very little (malts, coffee, sweet rolls and an infrequent hamburger brought to her hotel room). Rambles. Confused. Extremely thin, gaunt. So far today, she has had coffee, malt, sweet roll...". - "Patient admitted she had no food in the house because of the lack of refrigeration. She had onions on the table and apparently subsisted on onion soup which she made daily." - "Nervous breakdown, malnutrition. Widow one year. Patient very thin, appetite poor... Public health nurse discussed eating small amounts, frequently..." Eleven months later: "Patient is walking more and eating better, will spend Thanksgiving with her daughter at the lake...".

Dr. Michael MacLean, who worked with the Health Department on research about the elderly and who now is a resident in internal medicine at Mount Sinai Medical Center, goes one tentative step further than nurse Graham. Calling his idea highly speculative, MacLean says chronic brain syndrome (senility) could be the common name used to describe many different conditions including depression, loss of sensory perception and poor nutrition. What was commonly called dropsy in the 18th century is now known as six different edemas, MacLean says, suggesting that physicians in the future will diagnose "senility" in its component parts.

Old people have many reasons to feel depressed, MacLean asserts: loss of friends, increased isolation, fear of dying, feelings of uselessness in a society that values productivity. Because of the depression, people may isolate themselves further or get angry with the world. MacLean worked on a study by the Mental Health Planning Council in Milwaukee County, which concluded in a preliminary report that mental health needs of older persons were largely neglected by noninstitutional programs. The study points to the need for intensive communitywide action here.

## ALL ALONE IN WORLD

Even now, Lillian, 85, is sitting up there in one of the city's high rises for the elderly. She never leaves her room. She could eat a good noon meal downstairs, but she just can't bring herself to go down there, and no meals are delivered to the apartments. Lillian doesn't cook. Nor do friends stop in. Nor does she visit anyone because she's afraid of fainting again, like that time they found her in the elevator and wanted to send her to a nursing home. "I'm tired," she says, looking it. But she perks up to add, "I was just as peppy as any old skater on ice till... till, I don't know."

Lillian lives on a county pension; she says she doesn't want any dole, but her caseworker persuaded her that since she has Supplemental Security Income and Medicaid coming, she might as well apply for them. "I like company," Lillian says. "I never was a loner, but I don't know, now I'm not always so pleasant. I don't always feel so good. So, of course, I get kind of lonesome." Another old woman, another soiled cotton housedress, another pair of sad eyes. "I'm really very happy here," she says, not looking it, "I don't have to do nothing. If I want to sit and twiddle my thumbs, I sit."

And that is exactly what Lillian, friendly, certainly courteous, did through the visit: twiddled her thumbs, wrists resting in her lap. Melancholy again, she says, "If you wanted to break down, you could break down." Now pouting, lower lip quivering, "Sometimes when I go to bed at night, there's tears come into my eyes. Tears roll out onto the pillowcase and I think about how I'm all alone in the world. All alone. Oh, I can't tell you how much it hurts. I can't tell you." But, Lillian, you just did.

## 4.3   BRAIN SURGERY AND TOXIC SHOCK SYNDROME

### 4.3.1  Special Introductory Remarks

The organ of the mind puzzled scientists and philosophers for centuries, but in the 1970s its mysteries began, slowly, to unfold. The attention of science turned inward to the elusive chemical and physical processes of intelligence and personality. There was hope that the grim disorders of the brain would soon be preventable, treatable, even curable. At the end of 1978, the *Baltimore Sun* started a series of articles at this most intimate of frontiers. In writing about a revolutionary brain operation, reporter Jon D. Franklin "tackled a real challenge", Sloan states and continues: "He had to explain an extraordinarily complicated medical procedure in layman's terms as well as sustain reader interest... He managed to do both admirably. Through skilful writing, Franklin captures the tension in the operating room while informing readers about the latest in medical technology. He also makes his subjects - the doctor and the patient - real for the reader." A Pulitzer Prize jury ranked Franklin's work first in its report, and the Board awarded him the 1979 Feature Writing Prize "for an account of brain surgery."

At the end of September 1982, Nan Robertson, member of the *New York Times*' living/style staff, published a moving cover story about her personal bout with toxic shock syndrome for her newspaper's magazine section. The story was not only a dramatic account of how she was stuck down by toxic shock syndrome on Thanksgiving in Illinois the year before, but it was also a profile of toxic shock itself - its cause, treatment and the research it had provoked - and how the reporter struggled with its permanent damaging effects. After having the end joints of eight fingers amputated and fearful that she would never write again, Nan Robertson underwent intensive therapy to re-learn how to live in New York City. Her article was enormously effective; it prompted significant donations to the hospital that treated her. The Newswomen's Club of New York unanimously voted to honor the reporter with a special award. "The essay capsulizes an incredible quantity of complex medical information in a highly readable fashion," a Pulitzer Prize jury stated in its report. Nan Robertson won the 1983 Pulitzer Prize for Feature Writing "for her memorable and medically detailed account of her struggle with toxic shock syndrome."

## 4.3.2 Reporting on a Dramatic Brain Operation

[Source: Jon D. Franklin: Frightening Journey Through Tunnels of The Brain, in: *The Evening Sun* (Baltimore, Md.), Vol. 138/No. 48, December 12, 1978, p. C 1, cols. 1-6; p. C 2, cols. 1-6; Vol. 138/No. 49, December 13, 1978, p. C 1, cols. 1-6; p. C 5, cols. 1-6; reprinted by permission of the A. S. Abel Company, Baltimore, Md.]

In the cold hours of a winter morning, Dr. Thomas Barbee Ducker, University Hospital's senior brain surgeon, rises before dawn. His wife serves him waffles but no coffee. Coffee makes his hands shake. Downtown, on the 12th floor of the hospital, Edna Kelly's husband tells her goodbye. For 57 years Mrs. Kelly shared her skull with the monster. No more. Today she is frightened but determined.

It is 6:30 a.m. "I'm not afraid to die," she said as this day approached. "I've lost part of my eyesight. I've gone through all the hemorrhages. A couple of years ago I lost my sense of smell, my taste, I started having seizures. I smell a strange odor and then I start strangling. It started affecting my legs, and I'm partially paralyzed. Three years ago a doctor told me all I had to look forward to was blindness, paralysis and a remote chance of death. Now I have aneurisms; this monster is causing that. I'm scared to death... but there isn't a day that goes by that I'm not in pain and I'm tired of it. I can't bear the pain. I wouldn't want to live like this much longer."

As Dr. Ducker leaves for work, Mrs. Ducker hands him a paper bag containing a peanut butter sandwich, a banana and two fig newtons. Downtown, in Mrs. Kelly's brain, a sedative takes effect. Mrs. Kelly was born with a tangled knot of abnormal blood vessels in the back of her brain. The malformation began small, but in time the vessels ballooned inside the confines of the skull, crowding the healthy brain tissue. Finally, in 1942, the malformation announced its presence when one of the abnormal arteries, stretched beyond capacity, burst. Mrs. Kelly grabbed her head and collapsed.

After that, the agony never stopped. Mrs. Kelly, at the time of her first intracranial bleed, was carrying her second child. Despite the pain, she raised her children and cared for her husband. The malformation continued to grow. She began calling it "the monster." Now, at 7:15 a.m. in Operating Room 11, a technician checks the brain surgery microscope and the circulating nurse lays out bandages and instruments. Mrs. Kelly lies still on a stainless steel table. A small sensor has been threaded through her veins and now hangs in the antechamber of her heart. Dr. Jane Matjasko, the anesthesiologist, connects the sensor to a 7-foot-high bank of electronic instruments. Waveforms begin to move rhythmically across a cathode ray tube.

With each heartbeat a loudspeaker produces an audible popping sound. The steady pop, pop, pop, pop isn't loud, but it dominates the operating room. Dr. Ducker enters the operating room and pauses before the X-ray films that hang on a lighted panel. He carried those brain images to Europe, Canada and Florida in search of advice, and he knows them by heart. Still, he studies them again, eyes focused on the two fragile aneurisms that swell above major arteries. Either may burst on contact. The one directly behind Mrs. Kelly's eyes is the most dangerous, but also the easiest to reach. That's first. The surgeon-in-training who will assist Dr. Ducker places Mrs. Kelly's head in a clamp and shaves her hair. Dr. Ducker checks his work. "We can't have a millimeter slip," he says, assuring himself that the three pins of the vice are locked firmly against the skull.

Mrs. Kelly, except for a 6-inch cresent of scalp, is draped with green sheets. A rubber-gloved palm goes out, and Doris Schwabland, the scrub nurse, lays a scalpel into it. Hemostats snap over the arteries of the scalp. Blood splatters onto Dr. Ducker's sterile paper booties. The heartbeat goes pop, pop, pop, 70 pops a minute, steady. It is 8:25 a.m. Today Dr. Ducker intends to remove the two aneurisms, which comprise the most immediate threat to Mrs. Kelly's life. Later, he will move directly on the monster. It is a risky operation, destined to take him to the hazardous frontiers of neurosurgery. Several experts told him he shouldn't do it at all, that he should let Mrs. Kelly die. But the consensus was he had no choice. The choice was Mrs. Kelly's. "There's one chance out of three that we'll end up with a hell of a mess or a dead patient," Dr. Ducker says. "I reviewed it in my own heart and with other people, and I thought about the patient. You weigh what happens if you do it against what happens if you don't do it. I convinced myself it should be done."

And Mrs. Kelly said yes. Now, the decision made, Dr. Ducker pulls back Mrs. Kelly's scalp to reveal the dull ivory of living bone. The chatter of the half-inch drill fills the room, drowning the rhythmic pop-pop-pop of the heart monitor. It is 9 o'clock when Dr. Ducker hands the 2-by-4-inch triangle of skull to the scrub nurse. The tough, rubbery covering of the brain is cut free, revealing the soft gray convolutions of the forebrain. "There it is," says the circulating nurse in a hushed voice. "That's what keeps you working." It is 9:20. Eventually, Dr. Ducker steps back, holding his gloved hands high to avoid contamination. While others move the microscope into place over the glistening brain, the neurosurgeon communes once more with the X-ray films.

The heart beats strong, 70 beats a minute, 70 beats a minute, 70 beats a minute. "We're gonna have a hard time today," the surgeon says, to the X-rays. Dr. Ducker presses his face against the microscope. His hand goes out for an electrified, tweezer-like instrument. The assistant moves in close, taking his position above the secondary eyepieces. Dr. Ducker's view is shared by a video camera. Across the room, a color television crackles, displaying a highly magnified landscape of the brain. The polished tips of the tweezers move into view. It is Dr. Ducker's intention to place tiny, spring-loaded alligator clips across the base of each aneurism. But first he must navigate a tortured path from his incision, above Mrs. Kelly's right eye, to the deeply buried Circle of Willis.

The journey will be immense. Under magnification, the landscape of the mind expands to the size of a room. Dr. Ducker's tiny, blunt-tipped instrument travels in millimeter leaps. His strategy is to push between the forebrain, where conscious thought occurs, and the thumb-like forward projection of the brain, called the temporal lobe, that extends beneath the temples. Carefully, Dr. Ducker pulls these two structures apart to form a deep channel. The journey begins at the bottom of this crevasse. The time is 9:36 a.m. The gray convolutions of the brain, wet with secretions, sparkle beneath the powerful operating theater spotlights. The microscopic landscape heaves and subsides in rhythm to the pop, pop, pop of the heart monitor.

Gently, gently, the blunt probe teases apart the tiny convolutions of gray matter, spreading a tiny tunnel, millimeter by gentle millimeter, into the glistening gray. Dr. Ducker's progress is impeded by scar tissue. Each time Mrs. Kelly's monster flooded her brain with blood, scars formed, welding the structures together. To make his tunnel, Dr. Ducker must tease them apart again. As the neurosurgeon works, he refers to Mrs. Kelly's monster as "the AVM," or arterial-veinous malformation. Normally, he says, arteries force high-pressure blood into muscle or organ tissue. After the living cells suck out the oxygen and nourishment, the blood drains into low-pressure veins, which carry it back to the heart and lungs.

But in the back of Mrs. Kelly's brain, one set of arteries pumps directly into veins, bypassing the tissue. Over the years the unnatural junction, not designed for such a rapid flow of blood, has swollen and leaked. Hence the scar tissue. Some scar welds are too tight, and the damaged tissue too weak, to endure the touch of metal. A tiny feeder artery breaks under the pressure of the steel probe. The television screen turns red. Quickly, Dr. Ducker catches the ragged end of the bleeder between the pincers and there is a crackling bzzzzzzzt as the electricity burns it shut. Suction clears the field of blood and again the scene is gray. The tweezers push on. "We're having trouble just getting in," Dr. Ducker tells the operating room team. Again a crimson flood wells up. Again Dr. Ducker burns the severed bleeder closed and suctions out the red. Far down the tiny tunnel, the white trunk of the optic nerve can be seen.

It is 9:54. Slowly, using the optic nerve as a guidepost, Dr. Ducker probes deeper and deeper into the gray. The heart monitor continues to pop, pop, pop with reassuring regularity, 70 beats a minute, 70 beats a minute. The neurosurgeon guides the tweezers directly to the pulsing carotid artery, one of the three main blood channels into the brain. The carotid twists and dances to the electronic pop, pop, popping of the monitor. Gently, ever gently, nudging aside the scarred brain tissue, Dr. Ducker moves along the carotid toward the Circle of Willis, near the floor of the skull. This loop of vessels is the staging area from which blood is distributed throughout the brain. Three major arteries feed it from below, one in the rear and the two carotids in the front.

The first aneurism lies ahead, still buried in gray matter, where the carotid meets the circle. The second aneurism is deeper yet in the brain, where the hindmost artery rises along the spine and joins the circle. Eyes pressed against the microscope, Dr. Ducker makes his tedious way along the carotid. "She's so scarred I can't identify anything," he complains through the mask. It is 10:01 a.m. The heart monitor pop, pop, pops with reassuring regularity. The probing tweezers are gentle, firm, deliberate, probing, probing, probing, slower than the hands of the clock. Repeatedly, vessels bleed and Dr. Ducker cauterizes them. The blood loss is mounting, and now the anesthesiologist hangs a transfusion bag above Mrs. Kelly's shrouded form.

Ten minutes pass. Twenty. Blood flows, the tweezers buzz, the suction hose hisses. The tunnel is small, almost filled by the shank of the instrument. The aneurism finally appears at the end of the tunnel, throbbing, visibly thin, a lumpy, overstretched bag, the color of rich cream, swelling out from the once-strong arterial wall, a tire about to blow out, a balloon ready to burst, a time-bomb the size of a pea. The aneurism isn't the monster itself, only the work of the monster which, growing malevolently, has disrupted the pressures and weakened arterial walls throughout the brain. But the monster itself, the X-rays say, lies far away. The probe nudges the aneurism, hesitantly, gently. "Sometimes you touch one," a nurse says. "And blooey, the wolf's at the door."

Patiently, Dr. Ducker separates the aneurism from the surrounding brain tissue. The tension is electric. No surgeon would dare go after the monster itself until this swelling timebomb is defused. Now. A nurse hands Dr. Ducker a long, delicate pair of pliers. A tiny, stainless steel clip, its jaws open wide, is positioned on the pliers' end. Presently the magnified clip moves into the field of view, light glinting from its polished surface. It is 10:40. For 11 minutes Dr. Ducker repeatedly attempts to work the clip over the neck of the balloon, but the device it too small. He calls for one with longer jaws. That clip moves into the microscopic tunnel. With infinite slowness, Dr. Ducker maneuvers it over the neck of the aneurism. Then, in a instant, the jaws close and the balloon collapses. "That's clipped," Dr. Ducker calls out. Smile wrinkles appear above his mask. The heart monitor goes pop, pop, pop, steady. It is 10:58. Dr. Ducker now begins following the Circle of Willis back into the brain, toward the second, and more difficult, aneurism that swells at the very rear of the circle, tight against the most sensitive and primative structure in the head. The brainstem. The brainstem controls vital processes, including breathing and heartbeat. The going becomes steadily more difficult and bloody. Millimeter, millimeter, treacherous millimeter the tweezers burrow a tunnel through Mrs. Kelly's mind. Blood flows, the tweezers buzz, the suction slurps. Push and probe. Cauterize. Suction. Push and probe. More blood. Then the tweezers lay quiet. "I don't recognize anything," the surgeon says. He pushes further and finds a landmark. Then, exhausted, Dr. Ducker disengages himself, backs away, sits down on a stool and stares straight ahead for a long moment. The brainstem is close, close. "This is a frightening place to be," whispers the doctor.

In the background the heart monitor goes pop, pop, pop, pop, 70 beats a minute, steady. The smell of ozone and burnt flesh hangs thick in the air. It is 11:05 a.m. It is 11.05 a.m., the Day of the Monster. Dr. Thomas Barbee Ducker peers into the neurosurgery microscope, navigating the tunnels of Mrs. Edna Kelly's mind. A bank of electronic equipment stands above the still patient. Monitor lights flash, oscilloscope waveforms build and break, dials jump and a loudspeaker announces each heartbeat, pop, pop, pop, 70 pops a minute, steady. The sound, though subdued, dominates the room. Since 8.25 a.m., when an incision was opened in the patient's scalp above the right eye, University Hospital's chief neurosurgeon has managed to find and clip off one of two deadly aneurisms.

Now as he searches for the second aneurism he momentarily loses his way in the glistening gray tissue. For 57 years the monster has dwelled in Mrs. Kelly's skull, periodically releasing drops of blood and torrents of agony, and in the process it altered the landscape of the brain. Dr. Ducker stops and ponders, makes a decision and pushes ahead, carefully, carefully, millimeter by treacherous millimeter. The operating room door opens and Dr. Michael Salcman, the assistant chief neurosurgeon, enters. He confers briefly with Dr. Ducker and then stands in front of the television monitor. Thoughtfully, he watches the small tweezer instrument, made huge by the microscope, probe along a throbbing, cream-colored blood vessel.

An aneurism on an artery is like the bump on a tire that is about to blow out, Dr. Salcman says. The weakened wall of the artery balloons outward under the relentless pressure of the heartbeat and, eventually, it bursts. That's death. He says the aneurisms appeared because of the monster, a large malformation of arteries and veins in the back of the brain. Eventually Dr. Ducker hopes to remove or block off that malformation, but today the objectives are limited to clipping the two aneurisms. Then, those hair-trigger killers out of the picture, he can plan a frontal assault on the monster itself. But that will be another day. This day the objectives are the aneurisms, one in front and one in back. The front one is finished. One down, one to go.

The second, however, is the toughest. It pulses dangerously deep, hard against the brain's most sensitive element, the brainstem. That ancient nub of circuitry, the reptilian brain, controls basic functions like breathing and heartbeat. "I call it the 'pilot light,'" says Dr. Salcman, "because if it goes out... that's it." Dr. Ducker has a different phrase. It is "a frightening place to be." Now, as the tweezer probe opens new tunnels toward the second aneurism, the screen of the television monitor fills with blood. Dr. Ducker responds quickly, snatching the broken end of the tiny artery with the tweezers. There is an electrical bzzzzzzt as he burns the bleeder closed. Progress stops while the red liquid is suctioned out. "It's nothing to worry about," he says. "It's not much, but when you're looking at one square centimeter, two ounces is a damn lake."

The lake drained, Dr. Ducker presses on, following the artery toward the brainstem. Gently, gently, gently, gently he pushes aside the gray coils. For a moment the optic nerve appears in the background, then vanishes. The going is even slower now. Dr. Ducker is reaching all the way into the center of the brain and his instruments are the length of chopsticks. The danger mounts because, here, many of the vessels feed the pilot light. The heartbeat goes pop, pop, pop, 70 beats a minute. Dr. Ducker is lost again in the maze of scars that have obscured the landmarks and welded the structures together. Dr. Salcman joins his boss at the microscope, peering through the assistant's eyepieces. They debate the options in low tones and technical terms. A decision is made and again the polished tweezers probe along the vessel. The scar tissues that impede the surgeon's progress offer testimony to the many times over Mrs. Kelly's lifespan that the monster has leaked blood into the brain, a reminder of the constant migraines that have tortured her constantly since 1942, of the pain she'd now rather die than further endure.

Back on course, Dr. Ducker pushes his tunnel ever deeper, gentle, gentle, gentle as the touch of sterile cotton. Finally the gray matter parts. The neurosurgeon freezes. Dead ahead the field is crossed by many huge, distended, ropelike veins. The neurosurgeon stares intently at the veins, surprised, chagrined, betrayed by the X-rays. The monster. The monster, by microscopic standards, lies far away, above and back, in the rear of the head. Dr. Ducker was to face the monster itself on another day, not now. Not here. But clearly these tangled veins, absent on the X-ray films but very real in Mrs. Kelly's brain, are tentacles of the monster.

Gingerly, the tweezers attempt to push around them. Pop, pop, pop.. pop... pop.... pop..... pop... "It's slowing," warns the anesthesiologist, alarmed. The tweezers pull away like fingers touching fire. .... pop... pop.. pop. pop, pop, pop. "It's coming back," says the anesthesiologist. The vessels control blood flow to the brainstem, the pilot light. Dr. Ducker tries to go around them a different way. Pop, pop, pop. pop.. pop... pop... And withdraws. Dr. Salcman stands before the television monitor, arms crossed, frowning. "She can't take much of that," the anesthesiologist says. "The heart will go into arrhythmia and that'll lead to a... call it a heart attack."

Dr. Ducker tries a still different route, probing clear of the area and returning at a different angle. Eventually, at the end of a long, throbbing tunnel of brain tissue, the sought-after aneurism appears. Pop, pop, pop. pop.. pop... pop... The instruments retract. "Damn," says the chief neurosurgeon, "I can only work here for a few minutes without the bottom falling out." The clock says 12.29. Already, the tissue swells visibly from the repeated attempts to burrow past the tentacles. Again the tweezers move forward in a different approach and the aneurism reappears. Dr. Ducker tries to reach it by inserting the aneurism clip through a long, narrow tunnel. But the pliers that hold the clip obscure the view.

Pop, pop. pop... pop.... pop..... The pliers retract. "We're on it and we know where we are," complains the neurosurgeon, frustration adding a metalic edge to his voice. "But we're going to have an awful time getting a clip in there. We're so close, but..." A resident who has been assisting Dr. Ducker collapses on a stool. He stares straight ahead, eyes unfocused, glazed. "Michael, scrub," Dr. Ducker says to Dr. Salcman. "See what you can do. I'm too cramped." While the circulating nurse massages Dr. Ducker's shoulder, Dr. Salcman attempts to reach the aneurism with the clip. Pop, pop, pop. pop.. pop... pop...

The clip withdraws. "That should be the aneurism right there," says Dr. Ducker, taking his place a the microscope again. "Why the hell can't we get to it? We've tried, 10 times." At 12.53, another approach. Pop, pop, pop. pop.. pop... pop... Again. It is 1.06. And again, and again, and again. Pop... pop... pop, pop, pop... pop... pop-pop-pop... The anesthesiologist looks up sharply at the dials. A nurse catches her breath and holds it. "Damn, damn, damn." Dr. Ducker backs away from the microscope, his gloved hands held before him. For a full minute, he's silent. "There's an old dictum in medicine," he finally says. "If you can't help, don't do any harm. Let nature take its course. We may have already hurt her. We've slowed down her heart. Too many times." The words carry defeat, exhaustion, anger.

Dr. Ducker stands again before the X-rays. His eyes focus on the rear aneurism, the second one, the one that thwarted him. He examines the film for signs, unseen before, of the monster's descending tentacles. He finds no such indications. Pop, pop, pop, goes the monitor, steady now, 70 beats a minute. "Mother nature," a resident surgeon growls, "is a mother." The retreat begins. Under Dr. Salcman's command, the team prepares to wire the chunk of skull back into place and close the incision. It ends quickly, without ceremony. Dr. Ducker's gloves snap sharply as a nurse pulls them off. It is 1.30. Dr. Ducker walks, alone, down the hall, brown paper bag in his hand. In the lounge he sits on the edge of a hard orange couch and unwraps the peanut butter sandwich. His eyes focus on the opposite wall. Back in the operating room the anesthesiologist shines a light into each of Mrs. Kelly's eyes. The right pupil, the one under the incision, is dilated and does not respond to the probing beam. It is a grim omen. If Mrs. Kelly recovers, says Dr. Ducker, he'll go ahead and try to deal with the monster itself. He'll try to block the arteries to it, maybe even take it out. That would be a tough operation, he says, without enthusiasm. "And it's providing that she's in good shape after this."

If she survives. If. If. "I'm not afraid to die," Mrs. Kelly had said. "I'm scared to death... but... I can't bear the pain. I wouldn't want to live like this much longer." Her brain was too scarred. The operation, tolerable in a younger person, was too much. Already, where the monster's tentacles hang before the brainstem, the tissue swells, pinching off the source of oxygen. Mrs. Kelly is dying. The clock in the lounge, near where Dr. Ducker sits, says 1.40. "It's hard even to tell what to do. We've been thinking about it for six weeks. But, you know, there are certain things... that's just as far as you can go. I just don't know..."

He lays the sandwich, the banana and the fig newtons on the table before him, neatly, the way the scrub nurse laid out instruments. "It was triple jeopardy," he says, finally, staring at his peanut butter sandwich the same way he stared at the X-rays. "It was triple jeopardy." It is 1.43, and it's over. Dr. Ducker bites, grimly, into the sandwich. The monster won.

### 4.3.3  Symptoms and Therapy of Toxic Shock Syndrome

[Source: Nan Robertson: Toxic Shock, in: *The New York Times Magazine* (New York, N.Y.), Vol. CXXXII/No. 45,441, September 19, 1982, Sect. 6, p. 30, cols. 1-2; p. 31, cols. 1-2; p. 32, cols. 1-2; p. 33, cols. 1-2; p. 109, cols. 3-5; p. 112, cols. 3-5; p. 116, cols. 3-4; p. 117, cols. 1-2; reprinted by permission of the New York Times Company, New York, N.Y.]

I went dancing the night before in a black velvet Paris gown, on one of those evenings that was the glamour of New York epitomized. I was blissfully asleep at 3 a.m. Twenty-four hours later, I lay dying, my fingers and legs darkening with gangrene. I was in shock, had no pulse and my blood pressure was lethally low. The doctors in the Rockford, Ill., emergency room where I had been taken did not know what was wrong with me. They thought at first that I might have consumed some poison that had formed in my food. My sister and brother-in-law, whom I had been visiting, could see them through the open emergency-room door: "They were scurrying around and telephoning, calling for help, because they knew they had something they couldn't handle, that they weren't familiar with," was the instinctive reaction of my brother-in-law, Warren Paetz.

I was awake and aware, although confused and disoriented. The pain in my muscles was excruciating. I could hear the people bent over me, blinding lights behind them, asking me how old I was, when I had stopped menstruating, and, over and over, what I had eaten for Thanksgiving dinner the previous afternoon, Thursday, Nov. 26, 1981, and what I had had the day before. The identical, delicious restaurant meal my mother, Eve, and I had consumed on Thursday centered on roast turkey with the classic Middle Western bread stuffing seasoned with sage that I had loved since childhood. I had eaten slowly, prudently, because I had had only three hours' sleep the night before, catching an early plane to Chicago to connect with a bus to Rockford, a city of 140,000 in northcentral Illinois where all my family lives. Immediately after finishing my Thanksgiving dinner, I threw it up. It was 4 p.m. at the Clock Tower Inn in Rockford. I thought excitement and fatigue had made me ill. Neither I nor my mother, a gutsy 90-year-old, was overly concerned.

That was how it began: almost discreetly. I felt drained; my legs were slightly numb. The manager, apologizing all the way, drove us back to my sister's house in the hotel van. I was put to bed in the downstairs den. I awoke, trancelike, in the middle of the night to find myself crawling and crashing up the stairs to the bathroom. The vomiting and diarrhea were cataclysmic. My only thought was to get to the bathtub to clean myself. I sat transfixed in my filthy nightgown in the empty tub, too weak to turn on the water. Warren and my sister, Jane, awakened by the noise of my passage, carried me back downstairs, with exclamations of horror and disgust at the mess I had created. Warren, an engineer who is strong on detail, remembers it as five minutes before 3 a.m. As I lay in the darkened den, I could hear their voices, wrangling. Jane said it must be the 24-hour flu: "Let's wait until morning and see how she is." Warren said: "No, I can't find a pulse. It's serious. I'm calling an ambulance. Nan, do you want to go to the hospital now?" "Yes," I said. His choice, of course, was Rockford Memorial - the status Protestant hospital in Rockford where my family's doctors practiced.

The ambulance came within a few minutes, in the wake of a sheriff's car and a fire truck. People in uniform spoke to me gently, gave me oxygen. Lying in the ambulance, I could feel it surging forward, then beginning to turn right, toward Rockford Memorial, 15 minutes across town. I heard an emergency medical technician, 18-year-old Anita Powell, cry out: "Left! Left! Go to St. Anthony! She has no pulse! Rockford Memorial is 15 minutes away - she'll be D.O.A. [dead on arrival] if we go there! St. Anthony is three minutes from here - she'll have a chance." "Do what she says," my sister told the driver. We turned left to St. Anthony Hospital, and my life may have been saved for the second time that night, following Warren's decision to call the ambulance. In the early hours of Friday, Nov. 27, the baffled young medical staff on holiday emergency-room duty telephoned several physicians. One of them was Dr. Thomas E. Root, an infectious-diseases consultant for the Rockford community. He arrived at 7:30 a.m. Dr. Root was informed about the vomiting, the diarrhea, the plummeting blood pressure. By then, a faint rash was also beginning to stipple my body. I did not develop the last of the disease's five classic acute symptoms - a fever of more than 102 degrees - until later. But Dr. Root is a brilliant diagnostician. And, incredibly, he and his colleagues had treated two similar cases within the previous year. "I think she has toxic shock syndrome," Dr. Root said to his colleagues. "Let's get going."

Most doctors have never seen, or have failed to recognize, a single case of this rare malady. Yet the St. Anthony doctors had treated two before me. The first, an 18-year-old who was hospitalized for six months in 1981, was left with total amnesia regarding the first weeks of her illness, but no other apparent damage. The second, a 17-year-old boy, who had a mild case, was out of the hospital within a week with no lasting damage. "The most striking thing about you was your terribly ill appearance," Dr. Root recalled later. "Your whole legs and arms were blue - not just the fingers and toes. But the central part of your body, the trunk and your face, were more an ashen color. You were in profound shock. Your blood was not being pumped to your extremities. There was just almost no circulation at all. Your eyes were red, another important clue. But you were 55 years old and you had not worn tampons since the onset of your menopause 11 years before." Nevertheless, Dr. Root made the diagnostic leap to toxic shock syndrome.

This is the story of how, almost miraculously and with brilliant care, I survived and prevailed over that grisly and still mysterious disease. Almost every major organ of my body, including my heart, lungs and liver, was deeply poisoned. I narrowly escaped brain damage and kidney collapse. The enzyme released into my bloodstream that reflected muscle destruction showed almost inconceivable damage - an abnormally high reading would have been anything over 100 units; I showed 21,000 units. At first, the Rockford doctors thought they would have to amputate my right leg and the toes of my left foot. Because of the treatment, my legs were saved. But the dry gangrene on eight fingers persisted. The end joints of my fingers were amputated. In all, three operations were performed. The first, at St. Anthony on Jan. 14, 1982, was delayed in a successful effort to save more of each digit. The other operations, involving corrective surgery, took place at University Hospital in New York at the end of April and again in May. The Illinois doctors theorized that gangrene had not affected my thumbs because the blood vessels in them were larger and nearer to a major artery.

This is also the story of how - with luck and expertise - this life-threatening disease can be avoided or detected, monitored, treated and destroyed before it reaches the acute stage. Yet few physicians know how to test for it or what to do about it once the strain of a common bacterium, Staphylococcus aureus, releases its toxins. Toxic shock syndrome strikes healthy people like a tidal wave, without warning. Only two weeks before in New York, my internist of 25 years had said, after my annual physical checkup, which included a gynecological examination: "If you didn't smoke, Nan, you'd be perfect." Later, other doctors told me that smoking constricts blood vessels, further impeding circulation and thereby worsening gangrene when it occurs. But, "Nobody should die of toxic shock syndrome," says Don Berreth, a spokesman for the United States Public Health Service's Centers for Disease Control in Atlanta, "provided one gets prompt treatment and appropriate supportive care." This view is shared by Dr. Kathryn N. Shands, the physician who until last June headed the Federal toxic shock syndrome task force at the C.D.C. and who has studied every case reported to it from January 1980 to last June.

Toxic shock is rooted in the public mind - and in the minds of many doctors as well - as a tampon-related disease. It is true that of menstruating cases, about two-thirds occur in women under the age of 25, almost all of whom are using tampons when the disease strikes. They are at very high risk. But about 15 percent of all cases are nonmenstruating women such as myself, men and children. In this group, there has been no recorded case of a recurrence of toxic shock. Dr. Shands warns, however, that a tristate study - conducted by the Wisconsin, Minnesota and Iowa departments of health - "showed that menstruating women who have had toxic shock syndrome and who have not been treated with an antistaphylococcal antibiotic and who continue to wear tampons have possibly as high as a 70 percent chance - horrifyingly high - of getting toxic shock again. Some people have had their second episode six months later; others as soon as one month later." The shockingly high rate of recurrence among menstruating women indicates that most doctors may misdiagnose toxic shock the first time around, or that sufferers may not seek medical aid if the case is relatively mild.

The disease was first given its present name in 1978 by Dr. James K. Todd, an associate professor of pediatrics at the University of Colorado and director of infectious diseases at Denver Children's Hospital. Writing in the British medical publication Lancet, Dr. Todd described seven cases of the devastating malady he called toxic shock syndrome and suggested that staphylococcus bacteria might be the cause. His patients were seven children from 8 to 17 years old: three were boys and four were girls of menstrual age. One boy died with "irreversible shock" on the fourth day after being hospitalized. One girl, aged 15, suffered amputation of the end joints on two toes. By June 1980, the national Centers for Disease Control had linked toxic shock with tampon use. The findings were based on a study it had conducted after surveys of victims of the disease by the Wisconsin state health department had suggested a correlation. Publicity about the disease ballooned, spreading alarm across the nation, particularly among the estimated 52 million American women who wear tampons.

Also that June, the C.D.C. toxic shock task force invited the major tampon manufacturers to Atlanta to brief them on the results of the studies. Shortly thereafter, the Federal Food and Drug Administration (F.D.A.) issued a ruling requesting tampon manufacturers to include warnings about their products. As part of its surveillance, the C.D.C. began to take cultures of women patients at family-planning clinics for Staphylococcus aureus - a procedure as simple as obtaining a pap smear to test for cervical cancer. It was found that 10 percent of the menstruating patients carried the bacterium in their vaginas, a statistic that still holds. "But it is not necessarily the particular strain that causes toxic shock syndrome," Dr. Shands pointed out in a recent telephone interview. Only "about 1 percent of all menstruating women," she said, "carry the poison-producing strain of the bacterium in their vaginas during their menstrual periods." Infectious-disease experts say that approximately 2 percent of the general population carry the poison-producing strain of Staphylococcus aureus in the mucous membranes of their noses.

In September 1980, the C.D.C. reported that of 50 toxic shock victims contacted who had become ill during the previous two months, 71 percent had used superabsorbent Rely tampons. Of the control group of 150 healthy women, 26 percent used Rely. From January through August of 1980, 299 cases had been reported. The death rate was 25 persons, or 8.4 percent. Late in September 1980, after the C.D.C. toxic shock task force had met with F.D.A. officials in Washington about the matter, Procter & Gamble announced it would withdraw its Rely tampons from the market. (Other superabsorbent tampons, however, are still being marketed.) The company is now facing about 400 lawsuits from the surviving victims, or the next of kin of those who died. The plaintiffs have won every one of the half-dozen or so cases that have come to trial, and last month Procter & Gamble settled out of court with a woman whose original trial was the first against the company. In October 1980, Procter & Gamble blitzed the country with advertisements encouraging women to stop using the superabsorbent Rely tampon. Then, both publicity and the number of reported cases among menstruating women fell precipitously in virtually all states. One of the few exceptions is Minnesota, where the health department has vigorously ridden herd on doctors and hospitals to count and report all toxic shock cases. There, the incidence has remained at about nine cases a year for every 100,000 menstruating women. The severity of the disease can range from mild to fatal: The death rate in cases *reported* in 1981 was 3.3 percent over all but the actual count is almost certainly higher, according to experts on the disease.

A National Academy of Sciences advisory panel also warned last June that toxic shock syndrome had not disappeared. Indeed, the academy's experts concluded, the disease is probably underreported by physicians who don't recognize the symptoms in victims or don't report the cases they do identify to state authorities. State health agencies, however, are still giving notice of about 30 to 50 cases a month to the Centers for Disease Control in Atlanta. Between 1970 and April 30, 1982, the Centers for Disease Control received word of 1,660 toxic shock cases, including 88 deaths. Although only 492 cases were reported in 1981, down from a high of 867 in 1980, the Institute of Medicine of the National Academy of Sciences estimated that the true number is about 10 times greater, or at least 4,500 a year. That estimate is based on figures from Minnesota. Last month, the Journal of the American Medical Association carried an article by three doctors from the Yale University School of Medicine that said a review of five toxic shock studies found flaws that could lead to biased conclusions against tampons.

However, an editorial in the same issue of the journal, while agreeing that there were deficiencies in the studies (the largest of which found tampon users were up to 18 times more likely than nonusers to develop the disease), said that "only substantial new research evidence evoking alternative explanations for the existing observations would be sufficient to negate the association between TSS in menstruating women and tampon use." In the cases of nonmenstruating victims, Staphylococcus aureus can enter the body through a postsurgical wound or boil; is found inside women who have recently given birth; or anywhere on the skin. According to Dr. Root, there is no evidence that it can be sexually transmitted. In my case, among many theories, a tiny sore on the vaginal wall "may have favored the staphylococcus getting there from somewhere on your skin and then growing," according to Dr. Root. The staph was also found in my colon and urinary tract.

*

I was one of the dangerously ill cases. For at least four days after toxic shock struck me, the Rockford doctors did not believe I would live. Dr. Edward Sharp, a leading surgeon at St. Anthony, who would later perform the first amputation of the ends of my fingers, alternately bullied and coaxed me to fight on, and was "amazed" that I survived. "If ever anybody had a good reason to die, you did," he said later. "Your age alone! If you had been a 15- or 20-year-old, it wouldn't be so unusual. Of course, this just means you're as tough as nails." It also meant the treatment was swift and superlative, once Dr. Root decided I had the syndrome. Afterward, Dr. Root recalled: "There are two aspects to the therapy. One is the right antibiotic to treat the staphylococcus germ. Almost all staph is resistant to penicillin now." So he prescribed beta-lactamase-resistant antibiotics to inhibit and wipe out Staphylococcus aureus and to prevent recurrences. Last June, the National Academy of Sciences' advisory panel on toxic shock emphasized, however, that, in the disease as it usually appears in menstruation, "evidence is not available to indicate that such treatment ameliorates symptoms or shortens the course of the acute illness." The two-pronged attack on the disease in my case began, as it would in all others, with "vigorous therapy for the cardiovascular collapse, the shock. And what that involves," Dr. Root said, "is massive amounts of intravenous fluid. Your body has to have a certain amount of fluid within the blood vessels, the heart, to be able to pump effectively."

The amount of fluid that flowed from wide-open bottles and flushed through me in the first 24 hours "would stagger the imagination of many physicians," Dr. Root declared. "You got approximately 24 liters, or quarts, of fluid. I think it was because of that 24 liters, 10 of which replaced fluid lost from vomiting and diarrhea before coming to the hospital, that your kidneys managed to make it through without being terribly damaged. You gained, with those fluids, about 40 pounds in the first day. Your body blew up." At one point, a nurse emerged from the intensive-care cubicle where I lay and blurted out to my sister and brother-in-law: "Your sister has become a conduit." "But if we hadn't kept that adequate volume of fluid in your blood, then the kidneys would have gone and we would have lost the whole ball game because everything would have collapsed," Dr. Root explained. "The single most important thing in your therapy, in my opinion, was the incredible volume of fluid we put into you, keeping some measure of circulation going. And then, as the effects of the poison weakened, that circulation eventually picked up and was enough to restore you back to normal."

I was left, however, with eight partially dead and gangrenous fingers; bilateral foot-drop, a form of paralysis in both feet caused by lack of blood flow resulting in damaged nerves, which can leave the patient with a permanent limp, and severely poison-damaged muscles all over my body. "Shock basically means that your legs and arms were getting no circulating blood anymore, that the amount of blood in your body was so depleted because, first of all, you'd lost volumes and volumes of fluid from your diarrhea and vomiting," Dr. Root told me. "Secondly, with toxic shock, the whole body is damaged, so that the blood vessels, instead of holding the fluid that's circulating through them, leak it, and the blood doesn't flow well; it gets too thick. Your body is made so that at all costs it preserves the blood flow into the brain and the kidneys and the heart. When you lose blood pressure, those organs get the blood flow and the legs and arms don't." About 12 hours into my hospitalization I slipped into a moderate coma, from which I did not emerge for two days. My brother-in-law went to the Rockford retirement home where my mother lives to tell her I might not make it. Forever gallant, she never showed me her grief and dread during the two months I was hospitalized in St. Anthony. Her tears were secret tears.

The day before I was transferred to the Institute of Rehabilitation Medicine in New York, my mother confessed, "I have cried more in the last eight weeks than I have in all my 90 years." In the first hours, a catheter was inserted into my heart so that the doctors could judge how much fluid to give me. Another tube ran from my trachea to a respirator to enable me to breathe. Within the week, in a profound gift of friendship, Pat Novak, a close friend since college days and a doctor's daughter, came out to Illinois from New Jersey to stay by my side until the worst was over. She kept a daily diary which she later sent to me. These were her first impressions: "I drove into St. Anthony Hospital and donned the gloves, mask, hat and apron required for the isolation unit. There, lost in a huge white bed, was a small face swathed in tape, with tubes from each nostril. Nan's sister, Jane, was there talking loudly, getting limited response from the brown eyes that opened occasionally as the head nodded, indicating a positive or negative response. A gurgling and hissing came from the respirator pumping oxygen directly into her lungs through the thick plastic tube in her nose. After asking permission of the nurses, I reached over to touch Nan. I stroked her tightly stockinged legs. Her eyes were wet with tears of welcome and gratitude. I saw the hands, fingers ending in charred and blackened tips, lifeless and distorted. Her arms were webbed in maroon rashes from her armpits to her wrists, sores and lesions and Band-Aids, wounds of the battle of the past few days."

Shirley Katzander, another dear old friend who had already become my "information central" back East, arrived from New York for a visit. "Your hands were a mummy's hands," she told me long afterward. "The fingers were black and shriveled, with small, perfect black nails. I almost fainted when I saw them. Thank God you were asleep when I walked in, and could not see my face." It was clear by then that the ends of my fingers would have to be amputated. Both thumbs had been spared from gangrene, which meant that I could possibly retain 40 percent of my hand function, using my thumbs and palms only. The day the surgeon told me he would have to amputate, I was filled with horror. I was certain I would never be able to write again. I was still on the respirator, and speechless. My friend and executive editor at The New York Times, Abe Rosenthal, telephoned. Pat Novak broke the news. Abe began to cry. When he had composed himself, he said something that carried me through many of the hardest days: "For Chrissake, tell Nan we don't love her for her typewriter; tell her we love her for her mind."

Then I was swept with rage, rage that fate had once again struck me down, after 10 dark, troubled years following the traumatic death of my husband, Stan Levey, at the age of 56. Through my long struggle and the help of others, I had finally emerged the previous summer onto what Winston Churchill had called the "broad, sunlit uplands" of life. But now, as soon as they took me off the respirator, I began to heap my anger onto my family, the doctors and nurses. I reviled everyone who entered the room. I became imperious, demanding, argumentative, impossible. One day, when my sister materialized at the foot of the bed, I looked at her with hatred. "Go home," I said, icily. For at least 10 days I was possessed by fury, at everyone. One morning I awoke and felt for the first time cleansed and filled with hope. "You have everything to live for," I told myself. That morning in late December 1981, my recovery truly began. It has been a long road back. Among my Illinois doctors, I shall always cherish Dr. Root, the first to diagnose me correctly, and with whom I later had many instructive and comforting talks, and Dr. Sharp, the surgeon who took a risk and decided to wait before operating on my fingers, putting me as soon as possible into physical therapy. I had dry gangrene, akin to frostbite gangrene, not the wet burn gangrene that gets infected and spreads and so must be removed immediately. Day after day until mid-January 1982, as I winced with pain, Dr. Sharp would rip away bits of the hard black sheaths around my fingers to find, triumphantly, healthy pink flesh beneath. Then the physical therapists would pull and bend the joints of my fingers to bring them back to life and flexibility. "We saved an inch of your fingers," he said later - which meant I retained a whole, middle joint on each of the eight affected digits.

Waiting to be operated on was agonizing. I longed for it to be over. Finally they had saved all the tissue they could. Dr. Sharp operated on Jan. 14, 1982, more than six weeks after the onset of toxic shock. I awoke from the anesthesia to find my hands suspended from bedside poles, swathed in bandages like boxing gloves. The healthy thumbs stuck out. Two days later, Dr. Sharp unwound the bandages. I was afraid. Then I forced myself to look at what my hands had become. I felt a surge of relief and surprise. I rotated the hands, front and back, and told the doctors with a smile: "I can live with this." My truncated fingers did not repel me. Nor did they shock my family and friends. "This is the worst they will ever look," Dr. Sharp said. Meantime, the doctors and therapists were fighting to save me from foot-drop paralysis. I began to stand and walk in orthopedic shoes, with steel braces up to my knees. I exercised my legs and arms and hands obsessively, in bed and out. Under the sheets, I wore cross-shaped board splints attached to what I called "bunny boots" on my feet. I loathed them because they prevented me from turning on my side to sleep. I kept removing them. "If you don't wear them," Dr. Sharp finally warned me, "you will be a cripple for life." I wore them, after first making an enormous fuss, and was soon walking short distances - without braces, unaided and with only a slight limp when I was tired. As yet another index of how catastrophic the sweep of toxic shock syndrome can be, I was treated by 14 doctors during the eight weeks at St. Anthony. They ranged from cardiologists and lung specialists to a podiatrist who cut thick crusts from my toes and the soles of my feet. The cost of eight week's hospitalization in Rockford was $35,000, not counting the doctor's fees. Ahead lay additional tens of thousands of dollars in New York, in hospital stays, additional surgery and daily outpatient therapy on my hands, which will continue for months to come.

On Jan. 26, 1982, my brother-in-law and sister put me on a plane, homeward-bound to New York. For weeks, I had wanted to return to the city that was the center of my life and my career, and by then, thanks to my Illinois doctors, I was well enough to make the trip. I had had the good fortune to be accepted by the Institute of Rehabilitation Medicine, of New York University Medical Center, on East 34th Street, commonly known as the Rusk Institute, after its founder, Dr. Howard A. Rusk, the great father of rehabilitation for the disabled. I went there by ambulance directly from the airport. It is a place with miracles in every room, with people in wheelchairs crowding the halls like the pilgrims at Lourdes. During 17 days there as an inpatient, the beneficiary of some of the most sophisticated physical and occupational therapy available anywhere, I progressed by quantum leaps. It seems incredible to me, considering the vast need, that there are only a half-dozen civilian rehabilitation centers associated with university hospitals in the United States, outside the Veterans Administration network. I was so rare, as the first and only case of toxic shock seen at the hospital despite its worldwide reputation, that the doctors and nurses looked at me as if I were a piece of the Ark.

"They will not believe your medical records from St. Anthony," Dr. Sharp had predicted, and he was right. Dr. Root had also delivered himself of a statement the day before my discharge from the Rockford hospital. "You now know more about toxic shock syndrome," said this expert, "than the majority of physicians in the United States."

For instance, the terrifyingly high rate of recurrence in menstruating victims - 70 percent - indicates that most doctors may misdiagnose toxic shock the first time around, or that the sufferers may not get to a doctor if the case is relatively mild. My gynecologist in New York, Dr. Howard Berk, who has seen several hospitalized toxic shock cases some time after acute onset, said he advises his patients "to call me immediately and urgently if they have sudden high fever, vomiting or diarrhea during their menstrual period - it could point to toxic shock syndrome." Although it is most unlikely that I will ever get the disease again, because I have not menstruated for more than 11 years, Dr. Berk is monitoring me carefully. He now examines me every three months; takes cultures of my nasal mucosa and vagina for Staphylococcus aureus, and immediately after my discharge from Rusk began a program of local estrogen therapy to strengthen the vaginal walls, thus preventing irritation. Publicity and the performance of the tampon manufacturers in warning users about toxic shock have been spotty since Procter & Gamble took superabsorbent Rely off the market late in 1980. A new F.D.A. ruling issued last June 22 - and effective in December - requires a warning on the outside of tampon boxes and a longer explanation of the association between toxic shock and tampons on a leaflet inside the package. Right now, the major manufacturers of superabsorbent tampons have warning notices on the boxes or on their inside instruction leaflets, or both.

This year, International Playtex Inc., which manufactures Playtex superabsorbent tampons, has been running a television commercial that begins: "Brenda Vaccaro for Playtex tampons. If I was a mother of a teen-ager, I'd tell her to buy Playtex tampons..." - thus aiming at the age group that is at the highest risk of getting toxic shock syndrome. When Walter W. Bregman, president of Playtex, U.S., was asked to comment on that television advertisement, he said: "The objective of the current Brenda Vaccaro commercial is to appeal and communicate to a variety of women, both in terms of age - in other words, those both older and younger than Brenda - and those with and without children. It is not intended to reach only teenagers, and, in fact, Burke day-after recall research indicates this commercial most effectively communicates to women 25 to 34 years of age." Government research has shown that a blood-filled tampon can provide a place for the growth of

Staphylococcus aureus. "What we think probably happens is that the staph either grow better in the presence of menstrual fluid and a tampon, or they produce toxin better in the presence of menstrual fluid and a tampon," said Dr. Shands of the C.D.C. toxic shock task force. The bacterium was not found on unused tampons, but could be grown on them. One study showed that the "supers" absorb more fluid, making the vaginal walls dryer and more subject to irritation. Dr. Shands pointed out that the risk of using superabsorbent tampons is greater than the risk of using less absorbent tampons. At least one case of toxic shock in women using sea sponges has also been recorded.

Testing for Staphylococcus aureus might be a good idea in my case, but not in many others, according to Dr. Kathryn Shands. "You could pick up Staph. aureus from someone else at any time," she said, by touching them or from particles of a sneeze. "In addition, you could pick it up and carry it in your nose, and you'd certainly never know it, and transfer it to your vagina at any time. So suppose you went to your gynecologist today and said, 'Please do a culture for Staph. aureus,' and he did and he said, 'It's negative. There's no Staph. aureus.' There's nothing to prevent your picking up Staph. aureus on Saturday." She went on: "So in order to have some reasonably high degree of certainty that you will not develop toxic shock syndrome with this menstrual period, you would have to go in the day before your menstrual period and every day during your period and have Staph. aureus cultures done. And you would have to do it for every menstrual period every month. Pretty expensive for you and pretty much a waste of time. And if you multiply it by the millions of menstruating women in the United States, it becomes a ridiculous exercise; the entire health budget could be used up doing just that." Asked if there is any way a young woman can eliminate the risk of coming down with toxic shock syndrome, Dr. Shands replied: "She could not use tampons." She hastened to add: "What we've tried to do is put the whole thing into perspective. You are more likely to be killed in a car accident than you are to get toxic shock syndrome. Not *die* from toxic shock syndrome, but *get* toxic shock syndrome. And yet people make the choice every day to drive cars. And if you want to take protective measures, you are far likelier to *die* from lung cancer from smoking cigarettes than you are to get toxic shock syndrome when using tampons."

From a doctor's point of view, such a perspective is no doubt reasonable. From my point of view, as I continue the tortuous process of regaining the use of my hands and right leg, such statistics seem irrelevant. The day after I was admitted to Rusk, Dr. Kristjan T. Ragnarsson, my chief physician there, did the first evaluation of me based on my Rockford medical records and his own hospital's neurological, muscle and mental tests. My first question on that day was: "Will I ever take notes again?" Dr. Ragnarsson nodded and said, "Yes." "Will I ever type again?" I persisted. His rosy face darkened. Then he smiled. "Oh, well, all you newspaper people are hunt-and-peck typists with two fingers, anyway," he responded. I said, "Dr. Ragnarsson, I have been a touch typist, using all 10 digits, since I was 18 years old." He looked somber again. I did not pursue my queries. For a long, long time, pain was my daily companion. The worst is now over, but Dr. Ragnarsson believes it could be one to two more years, or never, before normal sensation returns to my finger tips and my right foot. The recovery time depends on how far up toxic shock struck my limbs, since the nerve endings regenerate at the rate of about an inch a month. I have been an outpatient at Rusk five mornings a week since my discharge last Feb. 12.

On Feb. 13, back in my own apartment and alone after 10 and a half weeks of being hospitalized, I totally panicked for the first time. Because of the long Lincoln-Washington holiday weekend, I was not immediately able to arrange for a nurse's aide to help me readjust. I could not turn a single knob on any door, or any faucet, or the stereo or the television set. I could not wash myself, dress or undress myself, pull a zipper, button a button, tie shoelaces. Punching the telephone numbers with one thumb, I called Nancy Sureck, perhaps the most maternal of all my friends, awakening her and her husband, David. "Help," I said. Nancy was at my side within the hour, taking charge. The next week I hired a wonderful nurse's aide for the mornings; afternoons, I was at Rusk; evenings, a half-dozen close women friends took turns coming in to fix dinner and pop me into bed. Harriet Van Horne, another earth mother, always arrived, like Little Red Riding Hood, with a basket of exquisite home-cooked goodies. It was months before I could open a taxi door on my way to and from the outpatient hand clinic at Rusk. The cab-drivers of New York, with one exception, invariably sprang to my rescue with a gallantry that amazed, amused and touched me. I had decided to try a frontal, self-confident approach to all strangers in this tough city. I would hail a cab, hold up my hands, and say with a smile, "I have a bum hand - could you open the door for me?" Without an instant's hesitation, the drivers would leap around to the back door and open it with a flourish. As we approached our destination, I would hand them my wallet, tote bag or purse and they would hold up each bill and coin like a rosary or miraculous medal or baby to be blessed. "This is a dollar bill," they would say. "This is a quarter," and then return the rest of the money to its place. One driver said, "Even my wife won't trust me with her wallet," and another muttered, "Anyone takes advantage of you should be shot."

*The reporter's appeals for help in opening taxi doors were met by New York cabbies with a gallantry that amazed and touched her.*

Once, in bitter cold that turned my fingers purple because I could not bear yet to wear gloves or mittens, or stick my fingers in my pockets, I could not find an unoccupied taxi. An off-duty cabbie finally stopped in the rush-hour crush for my young, beautiful occupational therapist Gail Geronemus, while she explained why he should take me. As we reached one end of my block, we saw a fire engine blocking the other end. A policeman approached the taxi. "Back up," he commanded. "Hey, hey, this lady's come straight from surgery!" cried the driver, lying with that brilliant New York penchant for instant invention. "We've got to get her through to Number 44!" "Back up," the stone-faced cop repeated. The two men exchanged a stream of obscenities. When I had recovered from my laughter, I told the cabbie that I could make it to my apartment in the middle of the block. As usual, he hopped around to open the back door. I got to my lobby, and burst into tears of fatigue and relief. The one and only stinker cabbie was an elderly man who refused to roll down his window or open the back door for me. I finally asked a woman on the street corner to help; she complied with alacrity and without asking why. "You roll down the window, you get a gun to your head," the driver said.

When I had settled inside, he snarled, "You got only one bum hand, why didn't you open the door with the other?" I shrieked back: "Because all the fingers on both my hands have been amputated!" He almost dissolved into a heap of ashes. "I'm sorry, lady," he said, while a surge of gratifying catharsis rolled through me. I reflected later that I had finally expressed my deepest, pent-up resentments for the first time since my rages in St. Anthony.

Every day of my recovery has brought its frustrations and disasters - and its triumphs. On March 25 at the Rusk Institute's hand clinic, Gail, my occupational therapist, said, seemingly casually: "Why don't you try out our electric typewriter?" I was stunned with the enormity of her suggestion. I had thought it would be months before I would be able to attempt such a thing. I went to the typewriter. With incredible slowness and apprehension, I pecked out "Now is the time..." As the letters appeared on the paper, I began to sob. Gail and Ellen Ring, my physical therapist, rushed to my side. "Are you in pain?" they chorused. "These are tears of joy," I said. Almost six weeks after I had begun outpatient therapy at Rusk, Gail wrote this evaluation of me: "Patient tends to protect her hypersensitive stumps by using her palms and thumbs instead of her fingers. She self-splints her hands [holds wrists, hands and fingers rigidly upright] by using her palms and thumbs instead of her fingers to complete various tasks." The tasks I could not properly perform then included picking up coins and unscrewing jar lids.

But, day by day, my occupational and physical therapists were bringing my hands back to life and function. Traumatized by toxic shock, gangrene and then surgery, my finger tips - the most sensitive part of the body, I had been told - had stiffened straight out, the opposite of a stroke victim's fingers that often curl into claws. As an outpatient, I began to wear custom-made "splints," which consisted of castlike wrist braces, leather nooses for each finger and rubber bands that passively pulled my fingers down into fists so that I could grasp objects. These splints perform much like braces on a child's teeth, without active effort on the wearer's part. There were endless, excruciatingly boring but vital exercises at home. At the clinic, I pawed through coffee cans heaped with raw rice, kidney beans, macaroni and gravel to toughen my finger ends: this invariably set my teeth on edge. I hated the touch of metal of any kind, such as the nails I had to pick up and put in holes. But there is no way to win at physical therapy without working through pain to healing. "There are the survivors, and there are those who would rather take 50 pills and just slip under," a nurse at Rusk told me. "All human beings divide into those two groups. I have even seen babies who do not want to live - who literally pined away and died."

By early May, I was able to open taxi doors with two hands, and the door knob crisis was over. I was buttoning my blouses and dresses in a trice with a button hook, and awkwardly cutting the top off my breakfast soft-boiled egg with a knife encased in a tube of foam that provides a wider gripping surface. By mid-June, I could punch a push-button telephone with my index finger. (I am still having trouble cutting meat.) By late July, my therapists were "thrilled" with my progress in hand strength, dexterity and range of motion. Just as important, Dr. Barry M. Zide, a skilled young plastic surgeon at University Hospital, with which Rusk is associated, liberated me from much of my pain in two operations on my fingers last April 29 and May 26. One of my doctors at Rusk had run into Dr. Zide, a kind of Alan Alda in "M*A*S*H" - witty, irreverent and all heart as well as talent - in a hospital corridor just after failing, as had two other doctors, to remove the Illinois surgical stitches from my fingertips without causing me agony. "No problem," said Dr. Zide. "I'll throw a nerve block in her wrists." The next day, painlessly, he took the sutures out, and I fell in love with yet another doctor.

He then told me to brace myself for more surgery. With a sinking heart, I heard him say: "I can see by the way your nails are coming in that you are set up for chronic infection as soon as the nails grow back. In addition, the unpadded skin at the finger tips will never withstand the constant trauma of daily living. The bone below this thin skin is surely going to become exposed and infected." First on the left hand in April and then on the right in May, Dr. Zide amputated up to half an inch of some of the fingers, removing the nailbeds and infected bone. The thicker, more resilient skin on the palm side of my fingers was then draped over the newly shaped bone. Within a week, I was making tremendous progress in the use of my hands and becoming increasingly independent in every facet of my daily life. My story is almost over except for one crucial detail: My deepest fear did not materialize. I have typed the thousands of words of this article, slowly and with difficulty, once again able to practice my craft as a reporter. I have written it - at last - with my own hands.

# 5

# *DESTINIES OF PROMINENT NATIONAL FIGURES*

## 5.1 PROBLEMS OF DISABLED PEOPLE AND THE PUBLIC

### 5.1.1 Special Introductory Remarks

When a right-to-life lawyer went to court to force surgery for a severely handicapped baby at Stony Brook University Hospital in October, 1983, a *Newsday* reporter team treated the story as a national medical, political and ethical problem. Kathleen Kerr was among the eleven journalists covering the issue, and she wrote the opening article of a series on the so-called Baby Jane Doe case. Although the *Newsday* entry was only second choice on a Pulitzer Prize jury report it was praised as "imaginative, enlightening, sensitive and clear." The Advisory Board thought it deserved highest honors and gave the General or Spot News Reporting award to a team of reporters from *Newsday*, Long Island, N.Y., "for their enterprising and comprehensive coverage of the Baby Jane Doe case and its far-reaching social and political implications."

Two years later the *Baltimore Sun* submitted an entry for the Pulitzer Prize competition with a story of courage and triumph in the face of adversity. Calvin Stanley, a fourth-grader at Cross Country Elementary School in Baltimore was champion of the story: he rode a bike, watched television, played video games and did just about everything other ten-year-old boys did, except see. Journalist Alice Steinbach covered the story as a feature reporter for the *Sunday Sun*. According to the Pulitzer Prize jury report, she brought the readers "into the special world of a ten-years old who has been blind since birth... It is a something sad but always hopeful story, told with compassion and grace." The Advisory Board was also impressed by the Steinbach entry and awarded her with the 1985 Pulitzer Prize for Feature writing "for her account of a blind boy's world, 'A Boy of Unusual Vision.'"

## 5.1.2  The Case of the Birth-Defected Baby Jane Doe

[Source: Kathleen Kerr: The Case of Baby Jane Doe - An Issue of Law and Ethics, in: *Newsday* (Long Island, N.Y.), Vol. 44/No. 54, October 26, 1983, part II, p. 4, cols. 1-4; p. 5, cols. 1-4; reprinted by permission of Newsday, Inc., Long Island, N.Y.]

For two painful weeks, the parents of Baby Jane Doe have waited as lawyers and physicians engaged in public debate and private soul-searching in an attempt to determine the fate of the 15-day-old girl, who suffers from multiple severe birth defects. Today in Albany - amidst the majesty of oaken walls, choice Mexican onyx, and rich, red leather - the state's highest court, the seven-member Court of Appeals, will hear arguments on whether or not to order surgery for the infant against her parents' wishes. The case has caught national attention as attorneys, sociologists and theologians struggle with the moral and ethical implications of court-ordered medical care.

On Oct. 11, Baby Jane Doe was born at St. Charles Hospital in Port Jefferson with spina bifida, a condition in which the spinal column is open; hydrocephaly, excess fluid on the brain, and microcephaly, an abnormally small head. Doctors predicted that she would be severely retarded and suffer numerous other medical problems, but they said she could live as long as 20 years if the spine condition was corrected through surgery and the fluid was drained from her brain.

The parents decided against the surgery. But attorney Lawrence Washburn, who said he had received a confidential tip about the situation from a representative of Birthright in Smithtown, a group that monitors such cases, filed a petition in State Supreme Court seeking to mandate the operation.

In a hearing last week, Dr. George Newman, a neurologist from University Hospital at the State University at Stony Brook, where the infant was transferred shortly after birth, told State Supreme Court Justice Melvyn Tanenbaum that the infant would probably die within two years without the surgery. Newman and Dr. Albert Butler, chief of neuro-surgery at University Hospital, both testified that the parents' decision to simply provide nutrition, medication, and special coverings for the open-spine condition was an acceptable alternate treatment to surgery.

Nevertheless, Tanenbaum last Thursday ordered that the surgery be performed. But one day later, the Appellate Division of State Supreme Court ruled unanimously that the parents - whose identities have been kept secret by the court - had acted responsibly in choosing an alternative to surgery. Now William Weber - the Suffolk County lawyer who had been acting as court-appointed guardian for Baby Jane Doe -

has brought the case to the Court of Appeals in still another effort to have surgery performed on the infant.

There are those who say that there are moral, sociological and ethical questions that transcend the issue of whether or not Baby Jane Doe should have surgery. And there are also those who say that determining medical decisions in court is an intrusion into family life. On one side are the groups that argue that life should be preserved at any cost; on the other side are those who say that the quality of that life is a consideration.

The Rev. John Paris, a Catholic theologian, teaches medical ethics at the University of Massachusetts and Tufts University. Yesterday, he called the intervention by outsiders into the Baby Doe case "an outrage. What we have here is a self-appointed petitioner seeking a guardian for the child," said Paris, referring to Washburn's petitioning the court for a guardian for Baby Jane, even though medical authorities did not disagree with the parents' choice of treatment.

"Doctors do have a role in these cases - these decisions do not belong exclusively to the parents," Paris said. "Parents might and do make mistakes. Since the child can't speak for herself, a surrogate should speak for her, and the surrogate should be the parents unless there is evidence of neglect." Paris emphasized that cases like Baby Jane Doe's involve moral issues and do not simply involve technical, medical questions. He stressed the importance of considering each case separately. "The treatment decision for children should be the same as for any other human being," said Paris. "They have every right to treatment."

This is not the first time that the question of treatment has been an issue before the courts. In a case that Baby Jane Doe's guardian referred to in his plea for Tanenbaum to order surgery, Bronx State Supreme Court Justice Martin B. Stecher ordered that surgery be performed on an infant born with spina bifida at Misericordia Hospital in the Bronx. The parents of Lena Vataj would not permit the surgery and a hospital official, Frank Cicero, asked the court to intervene.

Lena Vataj, 4, is alive today and has no medical or psychological problems, a close relative said yesterday. "She is normal," said the relative, who asked for anonymity. "I don't know what would have happened if they didn't do the surgery." But Lena suffered only from spina bifida and not the multiple neurological and physiological problems that afflict Baby Jane Doe. In ruling in favor of Baby Jane's parents' decision to withhold surgery, the Appellate Division cited the 1978 Hofbauer case, in which the court ruled that 8-year-old Joseph Hofbauer would not have to undergo radiation therapy and chemotherapy as treatments for Hodgkin's disease.

The court ruled that the parents' decision to take the boy to Jamaica for laetrile treatments constituted a suitable medical alternative. Joseph ultimately died from his cancer. In fact, Charles Newell, the appeals lawyer for Baby Jane's parents, told the Appellate Division he "was hanging his hat on Hofbauer." And Paul Gianelli, another attorney for the parents, said yesterday that he and Newell would rely on the Hofbauer case again today in their arguments.

The first widely publicized case of this kind occurred in Indiana in 1981, when a retarded baby died after his parents withheld food and asked physicians not to perform surgery. In that case, the State Supreme Court ruled against a county prosecutor who sought an order to force care. Later, President Reagan ordered the U.S. Department of Health and Human Services to notify hospitals of a law forbidding the withholding of treatment. His order was later overturned by the courts.

Life is the key issue as far as George Annas, professor of health law at the Boston University School of Law, is concerned. "It's almost always better to be alive than dead," said Annas. But he also cautioned about the importance of examining individual cases carefully. "Hofbauer's a pretty weird case," said Annas. "Our question is whether one treatment [such as the alternatives to surgery proposed for Baby Jane Doe] is really nontreatment." Annas explained that in some cases an alternative to surgery is an acceptable treatment, but he cautioned that experts must be sure that the alternative treatment is not, in fact, simply no treatment.

And Annas emphasized the importance of the 1981 Storer case. In that case the State Court of Appeals ruled that a 52-year-old retarded man with terminal bladder cancer should have received blood transfusions despite his mother's objections. But John Storer died before the court made its determination. "It is necessary to focus on the quality of life for the child," said Annas. "Is it [the condition] treatable - that's the issue. You've got to make sure there is an alternate treatment and, if it's not working, that they will go ahead and apply surgery."

The Appellate Division's decision did not deal with the question of what to do should the alternate treatment chosen for Baby Jane Doe fail. And there are those who believe that beyond the ethical questions, beyond the moral questions, there is a constitutional question - civil rights for the handicapped. "It appears the possible retardation of the child is the reason why she is not receiving surgical treatment," said Burke Balch, counsel for Americans United for Life, a coalition of groups that support the handicapped.

"We regard this as a civil-rights issue for disabled Americans and their rights under the 14th Amendment to the equal protection of the law," said Balch. "The child is entitled to the same treatment for her handicap that a nonretarded person would receive." But Thomas Murray, a social psychologist and ethicist at The Institute of Society, Ethics and the Life Sciences at Hastings-on-Hudson, cautioned against legal and medical interference in family decisions.

"It seems we should not do violence to the autonomy of the family since none of us can make a better decision than the family," Murray said. "This is a medical decision, but it's also a moral decision." Murray said that parents should be the final judges when medical authorities cannot decide what treatment is best for an infant whose life hangs in the balance. "It is not for the doctor, not for some lobbying group," Murray said. "It should be left to the parents."

### 5.1.3  The Story of the Blind Boy Calvin Stanley

[Source: Alice Steinbach: A Boy of Unusual Vision, in: *The Sun* (Baltimore, Md.), Vol. 84/No. 22, May 27, 1984, magazine section, p. 12, cols. 1-2; p. 14, cols. 1-2; p. 17, cols. 1-3; p. 18, col. 3; p. 19, cols. 1-3; p. 20, cols. 1-3; reprinted by permission of the A. S. Abel Company, Baltimore, Md.]

First, the eyes: They are large and blue, a light, opaque blue, the color of a robin's egg. And if, on a sunny spring day, you look straight into these eyes - eyes that cannot look back at you - the sharp, April light turns them pale, like the thin blue of a high, cloudless sky. Ten-year-old Calvin Stanley, the owner of these eyes and a boy who has been blind since birth, likes this description and asks to hear it twice. He listens as only he can listen, then: "Orange used to be my favorite color but now it's blue," he announces. Pause. The eyes flutter between the short, thick lashes. "I know there's light blue and there's dark blue, but what does sky-blue look like?" he wants to know. And if you watch his face as he listens to your description, you get a sense of a picture being clicked firmly into place behind the pale eyes.

He is a boy who has a lot of pictures stored in his head, retrievable images which have been fashioned for him by the people who love him - by family and friends and teachers who have painstakingly and patiently gone about creating a special world for Calvin's inner eye to inhabit. Picture of a rainbow: "It's a lot of beautiful colors, one next to the other. Shaped like a bow. In the sky. Right across." Picture of lightning, which frightens Calvin: "My mother says lightning looks like a Christmas tree - the way it blinks on and off across the sky," he says, offering a comforting description that would make a poet proud. "Child," his mother once told him, "one day I won't be here and I won't be around to pick you up when you fall - nobody will be around all the time to pick you up - so you have to try to be something on your own. You have to learn how to deal with this. And to do that, you have to learn how to think."

There was never a moment when Ethel Stanley said to herself, "My son is blind and this is how I'm going to handle it." Calvin's mother: "When Calvin was little, he was so inquisitive. He wanted to see everything, he wanted to touch everything. I had to show him every little thing there is. A spoon, a fork. I let him play with them, just hold them. The pots, the pans. *Everything.* I showed him the sharp edges of the table. 'You cannot touch this; it will hurt you.' And I showed him what would hurt. He still bumped into it anyway, but he knew what he wasn't supposed to do and what he could do. And he knew that nothing in his room - *nothing* - could hurt him. And when he started walking and we went out together - I guess he was about 2 - I never said anything to him about what to do. When we got to the curbs, Calvin knew that when I stopped, he should step down and when I stopped again, he should step up. I never said anything, that's just the way we did it. And it became a pattern."

Calvin remembers when he began to realize that something about him was "different": "I just figured it out myself. I think I was about 4. I would pick things up and I couldn't see them. Other people would say they could see things and I couldn't." And his mother remembers the day her son asked her why he was blind and other people weren't. "He must have been about 4 or 5. I explained to him what happened, that he was born that way and that it was nobody's fault and he didn't have to blame himself. He asked. 'Why me?' And I said 'I don't know why, Calvin. Maybe there's a special plan for you in your life and there's a reason for this. But this is the way you're going to be and you can deal with it." Then she sat her son down and told him this: "You're *seeing*, Calvin. You're just using your hands instead of your eyes. But you're seeing. And, remember, there is *nothing* you can't do."

It's spring vacation and Calvin is out in the alley behind his house riding his bike, a serious-looking, black and silver two-wheeler. "Stay behind me," he shouts to his friend Kellie Bass, who's furiously pedaling her bike down the one-block stretch of alley where Calvin is allowed to bicycle. Now: Try to imagine riding a bike without being able to see where you're going. Without even knowing what an "alley" looks like. Try to imagine how you navigate a space that has no visual boundaries, that exists only in your head. And then try to imagine what Calvin is feeling as he pedals his bike in that space whooping for joy as the air rushes past him on either side. And although Calvin can't see the signs of spring sprouting all around him in the neighboring backyards - the porch furniture and barbecue equipment being brought out of storage, the grass growing emerald green from the April rains, the forsythia exploding yellow over the fences - still, there are signs of another sort which guide him along his route: Past the German shepherd who always barks at him, telling Calvin that he's three houses away from his home; then past the purple hyacinths, five gardens away, throwing out their fragrance (later it will be the scent of the lilacs which guide him); past the large diagonal crack which lifts the front wheel of his bike up and then down, telling him he's reached his boundary and should turn back - past all these familiar signs Calvin rides his bike on a warm spring day. Ethel Stanley: "At 6, one of his cousins got a new bike and Calvin said 'I want to learn how to ride a two-wheeler bike.' So we got him one. His father let him help put it together. You know, whatever Calvin gets he's going to go all over it with those hands and he knows every part of that bike and what it's called. He learned to ride it the first day, but I couldn't watch. His father stayed outside with him." Calvin: "I just got mad. I got tired of riding a little bike. At first I used to zig-zag, go all over. My cousin would hold on to the bike and then let me go. I fell a lot in the beginning. But a lot of people fall when they first start."

There's a baseball game about to start in Calvin's backyard and Mrs. Stanley is pitching to her son. Nine-year-old Kellie, on first base, has taken off her fake fur coat so she can get a little more steam into her game and the other team member, Monet Clark, 6, is catching. It is also Monet's job to alert Calvin, who's at bat, when to swing. "Hit it, Calvin," she yells. "Swing!" He does and the sound of the ball making solid contact with the bat sends Calvin running off to first base, his hands groping in front of his body. His mother walks over to stand next to him at first base and unconsciously her hands go to his head, stroking his hair in a soft, protective movement. "Remember," the mother had said to her son six years earlier, "there's *nothing* you can't do."

Calvin's father, 37-year-old Calvin Stanley, Jr., a Baltimore city policeman, has taught his son how to ride a bike and how to shift gears in the family's Volkswagen and how to put toys together. They go to the movies together and they tell each other they're handsome. The Father: "You know, there's nothing much I've missed with him. Because he does everything. Except see. He goes swimming out in the pool in the back yard. Some of the other kids are afraid of the water but he jumps right in, puts his head under. If it were me I wouldn't be as brave as he is. I probably wouldn't go anywhere. If it were me I'd probably stay in this house most of the time. But he's always ready to go, always on the telephone, ready to do something. But he gets sad, too. You can just look at him sometimes and tell he's real sad." The son: "You know what makes me sad? 'Charlotte's Web.' It's my favorite story. I listen to the record at night. I like Charlotte, the spider. The way she talks. And, you know, she really loved Wilbur, the pig. He was her best friend." Calvin's voice is full of warmth and wonder as he talks about E. B. White's tale of the spider who befriended a pig and later sacrificed herself for him. "It's a story about friendship. It's telling us how good friends are supposed to be. Like Charlotte and Wilbur," he says, turning away from you suddenly to wipe his eyes. "And when Charlotte dies, it makes me real sad. I always feel like I've lost a friend. That's why I try not to listen to that part. I just move the needle forward."

Something else makes Calvin sad: "I'd like to see what my mother looks like," he says, looking up quickly and swallowing hard. "What does she look like? People tell me she's pretty." The mother: "One day Calvin wanted me to tell him how I looked. He was about 6. They were doing something in school for Mother's Day and the kids were drawing pictures of their mothers. He wanted to know what I looked like and that upset me because I didn't know how to tell him. I thought, 'How am I going to explain this to him so he will really know what I look like?' So I tried to explain to him about facial features, noses and I just used touch. I took his hand and I tried to explain about skin, let him touch his, and then mine. And I think that was the moment when Calvin really *knew* he was blind, because he said, 'I won't ever be able to see your face... or Daddy's face," she says softly, covering her eyes with her hands, but not in time to stop the tears. "That's the only time I've ever let it bother me that much." But Mrs. Stanley knew what to tell her only child: "I said, 'Calvin, you *can* see my face. You can see it with your hands and by listening to my voice and you can tell more about me that way than somebody who can use his eyes."

Provident Hospital, November 15, 1973: That's where Calvin Stanley III was born, and his father remembers it this way: "I saw him in the hospital before my wife did, and I knew immediately that something was wrong with his eyes. But I didn't know what." The mother remembers it this way: "When I woke up after the caesarian, I had a temperature and couldn't see Calvin except through the window of the nursery. The next day a doctor came around to see me and said that he had cataracts and asked me if I had a pediatrician. From what I knew, cataracts could be removed so I thought, 'Well, he'll be fine.' I wasn't too worried. Then when his pediatrician came and examined him, he told me he thought it was congenital glaucoma." Only once did Mrs. Stanley give in to despair. "When they knew for certain it was glaucoma and told me that the cure rate was very poor because they so seldom have infants born with glaucoma, I felt awful. I blamed myself. I knew I must have done something wrong when I was pregnant. Then I blamed my husband," she says, looking up from her hands which are folded in her lap, "but I never told him that." Pause. "And he probably blamed me."

No, says her husband, "I never really blamed her. I blamed myself. I felt it was a payback. That if you do something wrong to somebody else, in some way you get paid back for it. I figured maybe I did something wrong, but I couldn't figure out what I did that was that bad and why Calvin had to pay for it." Mrs. Stanley remembers that the doctors explained to them that the glaucoma was not because of anything either of them had done before or during the pregnancy and "that 'congenital' simply means 'at birth.'" They took Calvin to a New York surgeon who specialized in congenital glaucoma. There were seven operations and the doctors held out some hope for some vision, but by age 3 there was no improvement and the Stanleys were told that everything that could be done for Calvin had been done. "You know, in the back of my mind, I think I always knew he would never see," Mrs. Stanley says, "and that I had to reach out to him in different ways. The toys I bought him were always toys that made a noise, had sound, something that Calvin could enjoy. But it didn't dawn on me until after he was in school that I had been doing that - buying him toys that would stimulate him."

Thirty-three year old Ethel Stanley, a handsome, strong-looking woman with a radiant smile, is the oldest of seven children and grew up looking after her younger brothers and sisters while her mother worked. "She was a wonderful mother," Mrs. Stanley recalls. "Yes, she had to work, but when she was there, she was with you every minute and those minutes were worth a whole day. She always had time to listen to you." Somewhere - perhaps from her own childhood experiences - Mrs. Stanley, who has not worked since Calvin was born, acquired the ability to nurture and teach and poured her mothering love into Calvin. And it shows. He moves in the sighted world with trust and faith and the unshakable confidence of a child whose mother has always been there for him. "If you don't understand something, ask," she tells Calvin again and again, in her open, forthright way. "Just ask." When it was time to explain to Calvin the sexual differences between boys and girls, this is what Mrs. Stanley said: "When he was about 7 I told him that when you're conceived you have both sexes. It's not decided right away whether you're going to be a boy or a girl. And he couldn't believe it. He said, 'Golly, suppose somebody gets stuck?' I thought, 'Please, just let me get this out of the way first.' And I tried to explain to him what a woman's sexual organs look like. I tried to trace it on the table with his fingers. I said, well you know what yours look like, don't you? And told

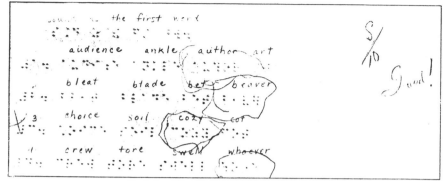

Calvin Stanley is a fourth-grader
at Cross Country Elementary School. He rides a bike,
watches TV, plays video games and does just about
everything other 10-year-old boys do.
Except see.

Top of page, a vocabulary quiz in braille. Above, Calvin (left) in Miss Jackson's reading class.

him what they're called, the medical names. 'Don't use names if you don't know what they mean. Ask. Ask.'"

"When he was little he wanted to be Stevie Wonder," says Calvin's father, laughing. "He started playing the piano and he got pretty good at it. Now he wants to be a computer programmer and design programs for the blind." Calvin's neatly ordered bedroom is outfitted with all the comforts you would find in the room of many 10-year-old, middle-class boys: a television set (black and white, he tells you), an Atari game with a box of cartridges (his favorite is "Phoenix"), a braille Monopoly set, records, tapes and programmed talking robots. "I watch wrestling on TV every Saturday," he says. "I wrestle with my friends. It's fun." He moves around his room confidently and easily. "I know this house like a book." Still, some things are hard for him to remember since, in his case, much of what he remembers has to be imagined visually first. Like the size and color of his room. "I think it's kind of big," he says of the small room. "And it's green," he says of the deep rose-colored walls. And while Calvin doesn't need to turn the light on in his room he does like to have some kind of sound going constantly. *Loud* sound. "It's 3 o'clock," he says, as the theme music from a TV show blares out into his room. "Turn that TV down," says his mother, evenly. "You're not *deaf*, you know."

From the beginning, Ethel and Calvin Stanley were determined their blind son would go to public school. "We were living in Baltimore county when it was time for Calvin to start school and they told me I would have to pay a tuition for him to go to public school, and that really upset me," Mrs. Stanley says. "I had words with some of the big honchos out there. I knew they had programs in schools for children with vision problems and I thought public education should be free. We decided we would move to Baltimore city if we had to, and I got hold of a woman in the mayor's office. And that woman was the one who opened all the doors for us. She was getting ready to retire but she said she wasn't going to retire until she got this straight for Calvin. I don't know how she did it. But she did." Now in the fourth grade, Calvin has been attending the Cross Country Elementary School since kindergarten. He is one of six blind students in Baltimore city who are fully mainstreamed which, in this context, means they attend public school with sighted students in a regular classroom. Four of these students are at Cross Country Elementary School. If Calvin stays in public school through the 12th grade, he will be the first blind student to be completely educated within the regular public school system.

Two p.m., Vivian Jackson's class, Room 207. What Calvin can't see: He can't see the small, pretty girl sitting opposite him, the one who is wearing little rows of red, yellow and blue barrettes shaped like airplanes in her braided hair. He can't see the line of small, green plants growing in yellow pots all along the sunny window sill. And he can't see Mrs. Jackson in her rose-pink suit and pink enameled earrings shaped like little swans. ("Were they really shaped like little swans?" he will ask later.) But Calvin can feel the warm spring breeze - invisible to *everyone's* eyes, not just his - blowing in through the window and he can hear the tapping of a young oak tree's branches against the window. He can hear Mrs. Jackson's pleasant, musical voice and, later, if you ask him what she looks like, he will say, "She's nice." But best of all, Calvin can read and spell and do fractions and follow the classroom work in his specially prepared braille books. He is smart and he can do everything the rest of his class can do. Except see. "What's the next word, Calvin?" Mrs. Jackson asks. "Eleven," he says, reading from his braille textbook. "Now tell us how to spell it - without looking back at the book!" she says quickly, causing Calvin's fingers to fly away from the forbidden word. "E-l-e-v-e-n," he spells out easily.

It all seems so simple, the ease with which Calvin follows along, the manner in which his blindness has been accommodated. But it's deceptively simple. The amount of work that has gone into getting Calvin to this point - the number of teachers, vision specialists and mobility instructors, and the array of special equipment - is staggering. Patience and empathy from his teachers have played a large role, too. For instance, there's Dorothy Lloyd, the specialist who is teaching Calvin the slow and very difficult method of using an Optacon, a device which allows a blind person to read a printed page by touch by converting printed letters into a tactile representation. And there's Charleye Dyer, who's teaching Calvin things like "mobility" and "independent travel skills," which includes such tasks as using a cane and getting on and off buses. Of course, what Miss Dyer is really teaching Calvin is freedom; the ability to move about independently and without fear in the larger world. There's also Lois Sivits who, among other things, teaches Calvin braille and is his favorite teacher. And, to add to a list which is endless, there's the music teacher who comes in 30 minutes early each Tuesday to give him a piano lesson, and his home room teacher, Mrs. Jackson, who is as finely tuned to Calvin's cues as a player in a musical duet would be to her partner.

An important part of Calvin's school experience has been his contact with sighted children. "When he first started school," his mother recalls, "some of the kids would tease him about his eyes. 'Oh, they're so big and you can't see.' But I just told him, 'Not any time in your life will everybody around you like you - whether you can see or not. They're just children and they don't know they're being cruel. And I'm sure it's not the last time someone will be cruel to you. But it's all up to you because you have to go to school and you'll have to deal with it.'" Calvin's teachers say he's well liked, and watching him on the playground and in class you get the impression that the only thing that singles him out from the other kids is that someone in his class is always there to take his hand if he needs help. "I'd say he's really well accepted," says his mobility teacher, Miss Dyer, "and that he's got a couple of very special friends." Eight-year-old Brian Butler is one of these special friends. "My *best* friend," says Calvin proudly, introducing you to a studious-looking boy whose eyes are alert and serious behind his glasses. The two boys are not in the same class, but they ride home together on the bus every day. Here's Brian explaining why he likes Calvin so much: "He's funny and he makes me laugh. And I like him because he always makes me feel better when I don't feel good." And, he says, his friendship with Calvin is no different from any other good friendship. Except for one thing: "If Calvin's going to bump into a wall or something, I tell him, 'Look out,'" says Brian, sounding as though it were the most natural thing in the world to do when walking with a friend. "Charlotte would have done it for Wilbur," is the way Calvin sizes up Brian's help, evoking once more that story about "how friendship ought to be."

A certain moment: Calvin is working one-on-one with Lois Sivits, a teacher who is responsible for the braille skills which the four blind children at Cross Country must have in order to do all the work necessary in their regular classes. He is very relaxed with Miss Sivits, who is gentle, patient, smart and, like Calvin, blind. Unlike Calvin, she was not able to go to public school but was sent away at age 6, after many operations on her eyes, to a residential school - the Western Pennsylvania School for the Blind. And although it was 48 years ago that Lois Sivits was sent away from her family to attend the school for the blind, she remembers - as though it were 48 minutes ago - how that blind, 6-year-old girl felt about the experience: "Oh, I was so *very* homesick. I had a very hard time being separated from my family. It took me three years before I began getting used to it. But I knew I had to stay there. I would have given anything to be able to stay at home and go to a public school like Calvin," says the small, kind-looking woman with very still hands.

Now, the moment: Calvin is standing in front of the window, the light pouring in from behind him. He is listening to a talking clock which tells him, "It's 11:52 a.m." Miss Sivits stands about 3 feet away from him, also in front of the window, holding a huge braille dictionary in her hands, fingers flying across the page as she silently reads from it. And for a few moments, there they are, as if frozen in a tableau, the two of them standing in darkness against the light, each lost for a moment in a private world that is composed only of sound and touch. There was another moment, years ago, when Calvin's mother and father knew that the operations had not helped, that their son was probably never going to see. "Well," said the father, trying to comfort the mother, "we'll do what we have to do and Calvin will be fine." He is. And so are they.

## 5.2   TOP POLITICIANS AND THEIR DISEASES

### 5.2.1   Special Introductory Remarks

For generations, the health condition of top political figures have been of great public interest. James Reston, chief Washington correspondent of the *New York Times* in the 1950s, covered such problems among other topics from the Nation's Capital. In a series of analytical commentaries during 1956, Reston discussed the Presidential election and its consequences. At this time President Eisenhower, having just recovered from a heart attack, was contemplating running for a second term and in so doing established a reputation for being honestly open with his health problems. A Pulitzer Prize jury thought that Reston's writing on this topic was "especially clear, vigorous, informative...". The Advisory Board awarded the 1957 Pulitzer Prize for National Reporting to Reston "for his distinguished national correspondence, including both news dispatches and interpretive reporting, an outstanding example of which was this five-part analysis of the effect of President Eisenhower's illness on the functioning of the Executive Branch of the Federal Government."

One of the major American news events of 1972, and to some extent the turning point in the presidential race, was the withdrawal of Democratic vice-presidential nominee Thomas Eagleton following public disclosure of his treatment for a mental disorder. This was an event unprecedented in American political history. And, unlike other significant news events of the year, it was uncovered solely by the press, therefore fulfilling its obligation to inform. A complete explanation of the inquiry by Robert S. Boyd and Clark Hoyt, reporters for *Knight Newspapers*, was part of an exhibit presented to the Pulitzer Prize jurors. In its report the jury considered the piece "was an example of outstanding reporting work in ferreting out difficult-to-get medical information and that it was done in the best tradition of responsible journalism." Boyd and Hoyt earned the 1973 Pulitzer National Reporting

Prize "for their disclosure of Senator Eagleton's history of psychiatric therapy...".


## 5.2.2  President Dwight D. Eisenhower's Heart Condition

[Source: James Reston: The Presidency - A Study of Effect of Eisenhower Illness On Functioning of the Executive Branch, in: *The New York Times* (New York, N.Y.), Vol. CV/No. 35,940, June 18, 1956, p. 12, cols. 2-3; reprinted by permission of the New York Times Company, New York, N.Y.]

The illness of President Eisenhower has focused attention here not only on the personal well-being of the President but also on the workings of the institution of the Presidency during his absence from the White House. The two illnesses in the last nine months have coincided with two important events that influence all interpretations of the subject. These are:

The Presidential election, in which Republicans are trying to retain and the Democrats to regain control of the White House. The atomic revolution, which has confronted all major governments with major adjustments in their policies, and a new political and economic offensive by the Communist powers for control of the uncommitted or neutral nations. These two events, involving not only the political control of the most powerful nation in the free world but the balance of power in the world struggle with Communism, have sharpened and distorted all comments on the subject and raised a number of specific questions.

TWO CONTRADICTORY ANSWERS

Have the President's illnesses affected the efficient conduct of the nation's business? Has the Eisenhower staff system strengthened the institution of the Presidency to the point where it can make up for his prolonged absences from the White House? So far, the public has been given two contradictory and politically inspired answers to these questions. They are:

1. The official Administration answer is that the President's illnesses have not affected the efficient operation of the executive. But this answer contains an obvious contradiction. When the President was well, his closest associates made a great deal, and justifiably, of the profound effect of his character and personality on Administration leadership, particularly in the deliberations of the National Security Council, the Cabinet and the Tuesday morning meeting with Republican legislative leaders. When the President was unable through illness to

carry on these personal and institutional meetings, however, the same officials maintained that the President's absence did not affect the Administration's efficient conduct of business.

2. The Democratic line has been equally contradictory. The Democrats have tended to argue from the first that General Eisenhower was an absentee President a good deal of the time, even when he was well, and that he relied almost wholly on his White House staff and Cabinet. But when he was taken out of action, they rejected the argument that the Cabinet could carry on effectively and contended that his loss tended to cripple the Government.

## PRESIDENCY STRENGTHENED

No reporter can say with assurance where the truth lies between these two points of view, especially since the Administration is not in a mood to cooperate with anybody trying to get at the facts. But some points are fairly obvious, among them the following: This Administration has strengthened the institution of the Presidency by more effective staff work in the White House office headed by former Gov. Sherman Adams of New Hampshire; in the National Security Council, which is a Cabinet committee recommending coordinated security decisions to the President on the basis of carefully prepared staff papers, and in the Cabinet, which now deals primarily with domestic questions and has, at last, an operating Cabinet secretariat.

In the first 115 weeks of this Administration, the National Security Council met 115 times, usually for about two hours each time, with the President in the chair. During that period before the President's heart attack it was reduced to writing basic security policies that undoubtedly continue to provide policy guidance to the Administration leaders during the President's absence. From the start, the President gave extraordinary power to Governor Adams to bring questions to the point of decision, just as he had given unusual power to his wartime chief of staff, Gen. Walter Bedell Smith, and his North Atlantic Treaty Organization and his Chief of Staff, Gen. Al Gruenther.

He gave similar latitude to his Cabinet members, just as he gave wide latitude to his theatre commanders in the war. Meanwhile, an elaborate system of secretaries, special assistants and administrative aides was established to try to keep up with the rapid growth of the President's responsibilities. A competent Staff Secretary, Col. Andrew J. Goodpaster, was appointed to supervise the paper work and maintain personal contact for the President with the Pentagon.

## THE NEW AND THE OLD

It is generally agreed here that these things were all to the good, that they were necessary and useful refinements of the system that was originally put into operation at the White House in the late Forties after years of prodding by the late James Forrestal. A sharp distinction should be made, however, between the operation of this system on the administration of established policies, which the President had personally reviewed and settled, and the effectiveness of the system in producing new policies or modifications of old policies when the President is absent.

The Cabinet can carry on, for example, the established policy of this Administration toward Latin America or Japan or Canada. Everybody knows what it is: the policies have been reduced to writing and kept up to date. It is the range of new problems - created by the new weapons, the new post-Stalin, post-hydrogen bomb policies in Moscow and Peiping, the rising strength and importance of the neutral nations and the new political and legislative factors on Capitol Hill - that highlights the absence of the President. What happens when a fundamental question such as United States disarmament policy has to be hammered out without the personal participation of the President?

What happens when sincere differences between the Army, Navy and Air Force over their missions and their development and use of the new atomic weapons and guided missiles reaches such a point that official documents are leaked out of the Pentagon to bring public opinion into the dispute? Is it reasonable to suppose that the President's personal intervention was not missed last Tuesday in the White House when the legislative leaders came to discuss the $1,100,000,000 cut made by the House of Representatives in the Administration's foreign aid program?

## QUESTIONS ARE POSED

What happens when the evidence piles up that the country is still unconvinced about the importance of a foreign aid and liberal foreign trade policy that the President himself regards as vital to the success of his whole "cold war" policy? Who is to straighten out the confusion over the Administration's policy toward the neutrals when Secretary Dulles says precisely the opposite from General Eisenhower and then merely proclaims that there is no difference? What is there in the impressive big black policy books that the Cabinet members take to the National Security Council about the reorganization and redirection of the North Atlantic Treaty Organization? The answer to all these questions is that they remain to be settled, that they have been in need of prolonged discussion and revision for many months and that the illnesses of the President have had a profound effect in delaying necessary decisions. This Administration, bound together by loyalty to the President, has been far less guilty than any of its Democratic predecessors in the last generation of squabbling in public. But it does not follow from this that its leaders are agreed on what to do about many of these questions.

On the contrary, there are basic differences about the new disarmament policy now under discussion, about the whole question of foreign trade and foreign aid, about the attitude the United States should take toward the new Soviet policy of subversion, capital development and political resiliency, and about the meaning of the Soviet military manpower reduction. Ever since the Geneva conference, where agreement was reached not to use the ultimate weapons to settle the "cold war," it has been almost unanimously agreed among foreign policy experts here that the United States had to review its propaganda effort, its diplomacy and its foreign economic policy if it were to avoid a steady deterioration of the free world's position.

## NEED FOR REVISION DENIED

For months it was denied that any need for revision existed. From early August until late in September, the President was in Denver on vacation. Thereafter, he suffered his first illness and did not get back to his full duties until Jan. 9. Meanwhile, there was divided counsel within the Administration about how to respond to the new Soviet economic and political offensive. The "spirit of Geneva" had faded and the Communist arms deal with Egypt had been completed but it was not until Jan. 19 that the President called his principal aides to the White House study to try to settle the differences over the foreign aid budget. And then this was compromised in the budget and a decision made to have Joseph Doge, the President's foreign economic adviser, study the meaning of the whole Soviet economic drive.

Some progress was beginning to be made on disarmament policy, East-West contacts policy and one or two others, when the President suffered his second illness. The backlog of unsettled questions and the divisions in the Government, therefore, remain. The price of these divisions and of the President's absences has not been catastrophic or irretrievable. It cannot be said that any fundamental change has taken place in the world balance of power during these nine months, though the entrance and growing influence of the Soviets in the Eastern Mediterranean is a historical and disturbing fact. The price, however, has been delay and a sense of uncertainty about the leadership of the United States. The Administration has reacted by saying that America's prestige is higher than at any time since the war, that European union is closer than ever in history, and that the Government, despite the President's illness, has lost none of its effectiveness.

All a reporter can do is to check these observations with responsible officials and diplomats. What he finds is simply that they do not believe it. In fact, they seem to be more conscious of the value of the President's leadership than many of his associates. They think, in short, that the President is sorely missed, that his relations with Congress and with other governments have deteriorated and that no amount of staff work or orderly committee analysis makes up for the unremitting leadership of the President in the White House.

## 5.2.3 Psychiatric Treatment of Missouri Senator Tom Eagleton

[Source: Robert S. Boyd/Clark Hoyt: Eagleton Reveals Past Mental Care; McGovern Rejects His Offer to Quit - Hospitalized Three Times From '60-'66, in: *The Miami Herald* (Miami, Fl.), 62nd Year/No. 240, July 26, 1972, p. 1, cols. 7-8; p. 17, cols. 1-7; reprinted by permission of the Miami Herald Publishing Company, Miami, Fl.]

Thomas Eagleton acknowledged Tuesday that he has twice undergone electroshock therapy for psychiatric problems and had offered privately over the weekend to withdraw as George McGovern's Democratic running mate. The revelations came as a result of a week-long inquiry by Knight Newspapers into the 42-year-old Missouri senator's medical history.

In an exclusive interview with Knight reporters Tuesday, Eagleton said McGovern refused his offer to withdraw. "He flatly said it wasn't in his mind," Eagleton said, after disclosing that he had been hospitalized three times - in 1960, 1964 and 1966 - for "nervous exhaustion and depression."

At a news conference after a two-hour meeting with Eagleton in his Sylvan Lake log cabin retreat near here, McGovern declared: "I think Tom Eagleton is fully qualified to be vice president of the United States and if necessary to take over the presidency on a moment's notice." Eagleton told the news conference: "I am satisfied that my health is sound and I've learned the lessons of the past."

Later, appearing relaxed and at ease as he was being driven to the airport at Rapid City, S.D., for a chartered flight to California, Eagleton told Knight Newspapers that he was immensely relieved to be unburdened of his longtime secret. "I've been living with it for 12 years... It's been a millstone around my neck," he said, puffing on a cigaret and peering out at the lush green hills. "I always knew it was going to come out someday."

Eagleton conceded that his staff deliberately misled Missouri newsmen in 1966 by hinting that he was being treated for a "gastric disturbance" at Johns Hopkins University Hospital in Baltimore, Md., when in fact he was receiving shock therapy at the Mayo Clinic in Rochester, Minn. "I never was at Johns Hopkins," he said, "it was a ploy... a mild attempt to be diversionary." The Missouri senator disclosed his treatments Tuesday after Knight Newspapers had uncovered evidence in his home town, St. Louis, and elsewhere that he had been hospitalized several times after heavy campaigning. Eagleton has had a meteoric political career that began in 1956 when he was elected as the youngest city prosecutor in St. Louis history. Eagleton had not told McGovern the full details of his past mental troubles until Knight Newspapers informed the presidential nominee's staff of what it had learned. Based on that information, the McGovern organization summoned Eagleton's records from the Renard Psychiatric Division of Barnes Hospital in St. Louis and from the Mayo Clinic.

Eagleton, however, refused formal request to permit reporters to examine the records. "Medical reports are matters between one doctor and another doctor," he said. "They are not written for lay public... They are all mumbo-jumbo." He also refused to authorize the physician who treated him to make a public evaluation of his past condition. "I'm not going through ancient history," he told Knight Newspapers. "As far as I'm concerned, the case is closed on that."

–United Press International Telephoto

**Sen. Eagleton Explains Health Problems**
*... news conference held in Custer, S.D.*

At the news conference, with

McGovern standing by his side, Eagleton said that "on three occasions in my life I have gone voluntarily to the hospital as a result of nervous exhaustion and fatigue... I'm a rather intense and hard-driving person... and as a young man I drove myself too far." He told the news conference that the first incident came in December 1960, shortly after he was elected attorney general of Missouri, at 31, the youngest in the state's history. Feeling very tired and depressed, Eagleton said, he was admitted to Barnes Hospital for four weeks lasting into early January 1961. During that period, he said, he received electroshock therapy at his doctor's suggestion.

After his second statewide campaign in 1964, when he was elected Missouri's lieutenant governor, Eagleton said, he again felt it necessary to seek medical attention and was hospitalized for four days between Christmas and New Year's at the Mayo Clinic. He received a full physical examination but was not given shock treatment on that occasion he said. In late September or early October 1966, Eagleton said, he returned to Mayo and underwent shock therapy again. It was "one of the accepted methods of treating depression" in the 1960s, he told Knight Newspapers, although it is rarely used for that purpose now. "My doctor asked me if I was willing to have shock treatments. I said, 'You're the doctor.' He said it was worth trying, so I had it." Although suicidal tendencies sometimes develop in cases of severe depression, Eagleton said he had never become so depressed that he considered it.

He said, one of the symptoms of his depression was that he would grow "irascible" with his children. "If Terry (his son, now 13) dropped a fork on the floor, I'd get irritable." His symptoms also included a "nervous stomach," Eagleton said, "not too different from the fellow in the Alka-Seltzer ad who says 'I can't believe I ate the whole thing.'" He does not have an ulcer, the senator said. Eagleton said his psychiatrist warned him. "I'd better learn to pace myself... to avoid excessive campaigning from sunup to sundown seven days a week." He added that he took the advice to heart. "I have every confidence that at age 42 I have learned to pace myself. I've learned the limits of my powers of endurance... I'll give it (the 1972 campaign) all I have, but on a measured basis."

In his first statewide campaign, he said, he had to handle all the chores normally shouldered by political assistants. He even had to drive his own car across the state, often arriving at his last stop at 2 or 3 a.m. "I pushed myself terribly, terribly hard," he said. "Now I've learned to be a better relaxer... I can go to Bethany Beach (near Washington) and take some good books. I'll sit on the beach and relax. I'll have a nice lunch and dinner and do nothing. I couldn't do that in 1960. I had to be moving. As I get older I've learned to roll with the punches. I don't blow my cork at a negative editorial now the way I used to. As a younger person I was less resilient." Eagleton said he takes tranquilizers when he becomes overtired "but not on a regular, routine basis." He said he didn't know the name of the drug, but it is "a little blue pill." Even when he was depressed he had no trouble making rational decisions, Eagleton said.

Eagleton had some difficulty explaining why he didn't tell McGovern about his medical history sooner. He said he and his wife, Barbara, discussed the possibility of his being picked for vice president as they were on the way to the Democratic convention in Miami Beach. He said she asked him whether he was satisfied that his health was strong enough for the stresses of the campaign and the vice presidency. He told her yes. Then, he said, they discussed whether he would be asked about his psychiatric treatment. "I told her I fully expect to be asked and am prepared to answer," he said. However, when McGovern telephoned Eagleton to sound him out on being his running mate and asked if there was "any problem in the past" that Eagleton thought was significant, Eagleton said no.

On Tuesday, McGovern said he thought that to be a true answer because the disorders occurred years ago and had not recurred. "It was a very brief conversation," Eagleton told Knight Newspapers Tuesday. "I didn't think that this was a disqualifying factor and I still don't... Maybe the public will... We'll just have to wait and see." Aides to McGovern said Tuesday that they had heard rumors the night before Eagleton was nominated, that Eagleton had a history of alcoholism and nervous disorders. Richard Dougherty, McGovern's press secretary, said an informal investigation was made but no confirmation was found. Consequently, Dougherty said, McGovern's aides decided not to even ask Eagleton about the rumors because they appeared to be so far-fetched.

Eagleton denied persistent rumors - which have dogged him throughout his adult career - that he has a drinking problem. "Alcohol is not involved in any way, iota, or shape whatsoever," he declared emphatically. "There is no trace, no hint, not one iota of alcoholism as part of the actual facts." Repeated inquiries by Knight reporters also turned up no evidence that Eagleton has a problem with liquor. The Senator said he received a preliminary physical examination last Friday and a further exam Monday at Bethesda Naval Hospital after Knight Newspapers began making the inquiries about his health. The doctors examined "everything from toenails to dandruff," he said, and told him "I am two pounds overweight and have half a hemorrhoid."

Eagleton said he flew to South Dakota from Washington convinced he had to make public his medical pasts and prepared to resign as vice presidential nominee if necessary. "I said to Sen. McGovern that I wanted to make this accounting today - and in all candor, if this would in any way embarrass him or compromise his chances, I would withdraw," the Missouri senator said. But although McGovern's staff discussed the possibility of having to request Eagleton's resignation, McGovern himself decided to stand squarely behind his running mate. McGovern maintained that Eagleton would have been his choice even if he had known beforehand of Eagleton's medical past. "I wouldn't have hesitated one minute had I known everything Sen. Eagleton has just said here today," McGovern declared.

The inquiry began after a nervous-sounding man telephoned a Knight editor at The Detroit Free Press and said he had information that Eagleton had been given shock treatments at Renard Psychiatric Division in the early 1960s. The caller said he was a supporter of McGovern and Eagleton and wanted to warn them that Republicans knew Eagleton's history and might use it against him in the campaign. A Knight reporter already in St. Louis to do research for a profile of Eagleton was dispatched to check the caller's information with a physician named by the caller. The physician declined to talk but also did not deny that Eagleton underwent the therapy.

Other sources, including a leading St. Louis Democratic official and a top Republican who is an official of the Committee for the Reelection of the President, said they believed Eagleton had been treated for nervous exhaustion at the Menninger Clinic in Topeka, Kan., in early 1965 and again in 1967. It turned out that they had the wrong place and their dates were slightly off, but in the end Eagleton confirmed the essence of their information. As other evidence of Eagleton's medical history began piling up, Knight reporters prepared a detailed summary memo and gave a copy to McGovern's political director, Frank Mankiewicz, who showed it to McGovern and Eagleton. Along with the memo, Knight reporters asked for an interview with Eagleton and access to his doctor's medical records. The first request was granted, the latter two were denied.

It was this inquiry, Eagleton said Tuesday, that finally moved him to make public what he had hidden for a dozen years. "One has a private life that should be just that," he said. "Even if you're in politics, you would like to have some kind of private life. But now that I'm in the national fishbowl, my private life is almost nil. I'm not saddened by that. It's natural." The Eagleton campaign plane left South Dakota after the press conference, bound for California and, ultimately, Hawaii. Met at the airport by reporters, Eagleton steadfastly refused to answer further questions about the South Dakota press conference.

## 5.3 AMERICAN CELEBRITIES AND THEIR SUDDEN DEATH

### 5.3.1 Special Introductory Remarks

On a night in early March, 1960, Leonard Warren, leading baritone of the Metropolitan Opera, suffered a heart attack on stage during a performance, and was pronounced dead in a few minutes. Since no staff reporter of the *New York Herald-Tribune* was available, Sanche de Gramont, a night rewrite man, was sent to the Met, a block from the office. At that time Leonard Warren had been taken into seclusion and no one had positive word of his condition. The *Herald-Tribune's* journalist studied Warren's file in the archive for basic facts, learned from members of the cast and the audience the circumstances of the collapse and when a physician announced the death, de Gramont was instructed by the city desk to return and write the story. His manuscript was ready just before the deadline of the late city edition and ran on page one. A Pulitzer Prize jury was impressed by de Gramont's article "written under pressure of deadline," and the Board awarded him the 1961 Reporting - Edition Time Prize "for his moving account of the death of Leonard Warren on the Metropolitan Opera stage."

For approximately ten hours on November 22, 1963 - first in Dallas, Texas, then in Washington, D.C. - Merriman Smith of *United Press International* stood close to a series of shocking and grievous events. In covering the assassination of President John F. Kennedy, Smith, a UPI White House reporter for more than two decades, had his greatest test of professional skill and physical endurance within a stressing couple of hours. He was on the scene for every momentous turn of events that day, working under incredible and unremitting competitive pressures. His dramatic account was, in the eyes of a Pulitzer Prize jury, "clearly the stand-out entry among the seventy-one exhibits entered in this category. In the jury's opinion, it ranks as a distinguished piece of reporting and writing in the best tradition of Joseph Pulitzer. At a time when confusion swept through Dallas, ... Mr. Smith detached himself from the distractions of the fast-breaking events to write a calm, deeply moving account that portrayed the impact of the President's assassination." For his "outstanding coverage" of the event Smith earned the 1964 Pulitzer National Reporting award.

## 5.3.2 Opera Baritone Leonard Warren's Heart Attack

[Source: Sanche de Gramont: Leonard Warren Dies at the Met. Audience Aghast as Baritone Is Stricken on Stage, in: *New York Herald-Tribune* (New York, N.Y.), Vol. CXIX/No. 41,366, March 5, 1960, p. 1, cols. 5-7; p. 4, cols. 4-6; reprinted by permission of the International Herald-Tribune Corporation, New York, N.Y.]

Leonard Warren, leading baritone of the Metropolitan Opera, died last night on the stage where he had sung for more than twenty years. The forty-nine-year-old singer collapsed as he was ending the second act of Verdi's "La Forza del Destino." He fell forward as he was making his exit at 10:05 p.m., and twenty-five minutes later the house physician pronounced him dead, victim of a heart attack.

There was an awesome moment as the singer fell. The rest of the cast remained paralyzed. Finally someone in the capacity audience called out "For God's sake, ring down the curtain." The curtain came down, ambulances were called, and a member of the cast tried mouth-to-mouth respiration. A priest arrived to administer the last rites to the singer, who was a recent convert to Roman Catholicism.

Members of the staff who came from the stage weeping announced that the opera star was dead. The news was met with hushed consternation by many in the opera house who had come backstage after the curtain was lowered. In the audience were many critics who came to hear Mr. Warren and Renata Tebaldi, making her first appearance this year. Mr. Warren was

LAST ROLE—Leonard Warren as Don Carlo in "La Forza del Destino."

acknowledged to be the world's best dramatic baritone. He had a repertoire of twenty-six operatic roles.

A member of the Metropolitan staff said Mr. Warren had appeared in perfect health when he came to sing last night. At the time he collapsed, Mr. Warren had just finished the aria "O fatal pages of my destiny." He was singing the role of Don Carlo in the opera, set in Italy and Spain, and was dressed in the colorful uniform of a Spanish grenadier. The opera has a tragic ending in which Don Carlo is killed by an erstwhile friend.

The surgeon, in the opera, played by Roald Reitan, a baritone, sings to Mr. Warren: "E salvo (He's well)." Mr. Warren responds: "E salvo, e salvo, O Gioia (He's saved, he's saved, O joy)." He turned to his left, and prepared to make his exit, which ends the act, and collapsed. Some thought he had tripped. The conductor, Thomas Shippers, froze. Mr. Reitan raced to Mr. Warren's side as the curtain fell. He was followed by Richard Tucker, who was playing Don Alvaro and was watching from the wings. Mr. Tucker said: "Lennie, Lennie, what is it?" They turned him over.

## WIFE IN AUDIENCE

The singer's wife, Mrs. Agatha Leifflen Warren, was watching from a parterre box with her brother, Roy Leifflen, a Washington attorney, and Msgr. Edwin Broderick, of St. Patrick's Cathedral, a friend of the Warrens. Mrs. Warren saw Mr. Warren's face and gasped. Msgr. Broderick went backstage. Dr. Adrian W. Zorgniotti, the house physician, also went backstage.

Mr. Warren remained unconscious. The physician said he thought the singer suffered a massive cerebral vascular hemorrhage. His respiration stopped two or three minutes after he collapsed. He was pronounced dead at 10:15 p.m. Half an hour after Mr. Warren collapsed the warning buzzer sounded in the foyers and lobbies of the packed house. The audience returned to its seats.

The audience chattered until the house lights dimmed and a moment later the spotlight hit the curtain and Rudolf Bing, general manager of the Metropolitan Opera, stepped out. With his hands clasped in front of him he announced: "It is one of the saddest days - " At this point the audience broke into shouts of "Oh No. Oh No."

## TRIBUTE BY BING

Mr. Bing continued, "I ask you to stand. ..." The audience again moaned and whispers went through the audience, "He's gone, He's gone." "... In tribute," Mr. Bing continued, "to one of our greatest performers, he died as I am sure he would have wanted to die. He died in the middle of a performance."

## "CANNOT CONTINUE"

"I'm sure you will agree that under these circumstances we cannot possibly continue." Mr. Bing made an about-face and returned backstage. The audience left the theater in visible shock and disbelief. Ambulances from at least three hospitals and oxygen from a police emergency squad arrived at the opera too late to help.

## AUDIENCE STUNNED

The audience emptied into Broadway and stopped momentarily in front of the ambulance pulled up in front of the W. 40th St. exit, its red light flashing. Police blocked the backstage entrance. In the theater, musicians talked quietly among themselves, recalling the singer's career.

Mr. Bing called the singer's last performance "one of his greatest." A spokesman for the Metropolitan Opera said it was believed to be the first time in the opera house's existence that a star had been fatally stricken on stage in the middle of a role.

Mr. Warren was taken to the dressing room he occupied for many years, and from there to the Abbey Funeral Home, 66th St. and Lexington Ave. Mr. Warren made his debut at the Metropolitan on Jan. 13, 1939. He was to sing another Verdi role, "Simon Boccanegra," in Philadelphia Tuesday, and had been scheduled for the title part in the company's first production of Verdi's "Nabucco" for the Metropolitan's fall season.

## IN 600 PERFORMANCES

Mr. Warren had sung a total of more than 600 performances of twenty-two roles, more than a fifth of them as Rigoletto. Like most top-flight singers, he was temperamental. He told other singers how to sing, conductors how to conduct, directors how to direct, photographers how to make pictures, recording engineers how to record and costumers how to costume.

He was forgiven for all this because many regarded him as the greatest baritone in Italian repertory, a "human bellows mounted on matchsticks." He had a fifty-one-inch chest (unexpanded), a size 17½ collar, a massive head, almost six feet of height and well over 200 pounds of weight - all supported on thin legs. At the time he was engaged by the Metropolitan he had seen only one opera in his life, "La Traviata," when he was twenty-two. He had no definite idea of making a career in music, and began his career in his father's fur business.

In 1935, he went to Radio City Music Hall, went backstage, asked for an audition and got it and a job. He stayed at Radio City for three years, spending all of the time in the chorus. He never got a chance for a solo turn. Mr. Warren went to the Met by way of the "Auditions of the Air" in 1938, when he was dared into entering by fellow chorus

Mr. Warren in the title
role of "Macbeth."

Mr. Warren as Count di
Luna in "Il Trovatore."

members at Radio City. When he auditioned for Wilfrid Pelletier, the conductor thought a ringer had been brought in. He did not have a single operatic role at that time, and he went to Italy to prepare some repertoire. Working under Giuseppe Pais and Ricardo Piccozi in Rome and Milan, he learned seven roles in seven months.

Mr. Warren was born in the Bronx, and attended Public School 11 and Evander Childs High School. For a year he studied business at night at Columbia University, preparatory to entering his father's fur brokerage business. As a hobby he began studying music at the Greenwich House Music School, and sang lustily while counting muskrats and minks in his father's establishment. After his audition with the Radio City Music Hall, he studied voice production with Sidney Dietch.

Besides the Metropolitan Opera, Mr. Warren appeared with the San Francisco Opera, the Chicago Opera and the Cincinnati Summer Opera, and sang concerts extensively throughout North and South America. He also appeared often on major radio and television programs, including "Voice of Firestone" and "Toast of the Town." His extensive list of recordings for RCA Victor included a wide variety of music from "Falstaff" to sea chanties and Kipling ballads.

### 5.3.3  President John F. Kennedy's Assassination

[Source: Merriman Smith: Veteran Reporter's Eyewitness Account Of Assassination. 'One Sees History Explode Before One's Eyes...', in: *The Dallas Times Herald* (Dallas, Tx.), No. 293, November 23, 1963, p. 2 A, cols. 1-4; reprinted by permission of United Press International, Washington, D.C.]

It was a balmy, sunny noon as we motored through downtown Dallas behind President Kennedy. The procession cleared the center of the business district and turned into a handsome highway that wound through what appeared to be a park. I was riding in the so-called White House press "pool" car, a telephone company vehicle equipped with a mobile radio-telephone. I was in the front seat between a driver from the telephone company and Malcolm Kilduff, acting White House press secretary for the President's Texas tour. Three other pool reporters were wedged into the back seat.

Suddenly we heard three loud, almost painfully loud, cracks. The first sounded as if it might have been a large firecracker. But the second and third blasts were unmistakable. Gunfire. The President's car, possibly as much as 150 or 200 yards ahead, seemed to falter briefly. We saw a flurry of activity in the Secret Service followup car behind the chief executive's limousine. Next in line was the car bearing Vice President Lyndon B. Johnson. Behind that, another followup car bearing agents assigned to the vice president's protection. We were behind that car.

#### SECONDS LIKE A LIFETIME

Our car stood still for probably only a few seconds, but it seemed like a lifetime. One sees history explode before one's eyes and for even the most trained observer there is a limit to what one can comprehend. I looked ahead at the President's car but could not see him or his companion, Gov. John B. Connally of Texas. Both men had been riding on the right side of the limousine from Washington. I thought I saw a flash of pink which would have been Mrs. Jacqueline Kennedy. Everybody in our car began shouting at the driver to pull up closer to the President's car.

But at this moment, we saw the big limousine and a motorcycle escort roar away at high speed. We screamed at our driver, "Get going, get going." We careened around the Johnson car and its escort and set out down the highway, barely able to keep in sight of the President's car and the accompanying Secret Service followup car. They vanished around a curve. When we cleared the same curve we could see where we were heading - Parkland Hospital, a large brick structure to the left of the arterial highway. We skidded around a sharp left turn and spilled out of the pool car as it entered the hospital driveway.

## PRESIDENT FACE DOWN

I ran to the side of the limousine. The President was face down on the back seat. Mrs. Kennedy made a cradle of her arms around the President's head and bent over him as if she were whispering to him. Gov. Connally was on his back on the floor of the car, his head and shoulders resting in the arms of his wife, Nellie, who kept shaking her head and shaking with dry sobs. Blood oozed from the front of the governor's suit. I could not see the President's wound. But I could see blood spattered around the interior of the rear seat and a dark stain spreading down the right side of the President's dark gray suit.

From the telephone car, I had radioed the Dallas bureau of UPI that three shots had been fired at the Kennedy motorcade. Seeing the bloody scene in the rear of the car at the hospital entrance, I knew I had to get to a telephone immediately. Clint Hill, the Secret Service agent in charge of the detail assigned to Mrs. Kennedy, was leaning over into the rear of the car. "How badly was he hit, Clint?" I asked. "He's dead," Hill replied curtly. I have no further clear memory of the scene in the driveway. I recall a babble of anxious voices, tense voices - "Where in the hell are the stretchers... get a doctor out here... He's on the way... Come on, easy there." And from somewhere, nervous sobbing.

## DIAL NINE ...

I raced down a short stretch of sidewalk, into a hospital corridor. The first thing I spotted was a small clerical office, more of a booth than an office. Inside, a bespectacled man stood shuffling what appeared to be hospital forms. At a wicket much like a bank teller's cage, I spotted a telephone on the shelf. "How do you get outside?" I gasped. "The President has been hurt and this is an emergency call." "Dial nine," he said, shoving the phone toward me. It took two tries before I successfully dialed the Dallas UPI number. Quickly I dictated a bulletin saying the

President had been seriously, perhaps fatally, injured by an assassin's bullets while driving through the streets of Dallas.

Litters bearing the President and the Governor rolled by me as I dictated, but my back was to the hallway and I didn't see them until they were at the entrance of the emergency room about 75 or 100 feet away. I knew they had passed, however, from the horrified expression that suddenly spread over the face of the man behind the wicket. As I stood in the drab buff hallway leading into the emergency ward trying to reconstruct the shooting for the UPI man on the other end of the telephone and still keep track of what was happening outside the door of the emergency room, I watched a swift and confused panorama sweep before me.

DALLAS LOCATIONS -- Map shows where fatal shots were fired at President Kennedy, the Trade Mart where he was headed to make a speech, and Parkland Hospital where he died 30 minutes after the assassin shot him.

## PRIESTS HURRY IN

Kilduff of the White House press staff raced up and down the hall. Police captains barked at each other, "Clear this area." Two priests hurried in behind a Secret Service agent, their narrow purple stoles rolled up tightly in their hands. A police lieutenant ran down the hall with a large carton of blood for transfusions. A doctor came in and said he was responding to a call for "all neurosurgeons." The priests came out and said the President had received the last sacrament of the Roman Catholic Church. They said he was still alive, but not conscious. Members of the Kennedy staff began arriving.

They had been behind us in the motorcade, but hopelessly bogged for a time in confused traffic. Telephones were at a premium in the hospital and I clung to mine for dear life. I was afraid to stray from the wicket lest I lose contact with the outside world. My decision was made for me, however, when Kilduff and Wayne Hawks of the White House staff ran by me, shouting that Kilduff would make a statement shortly in the so-called nurses room a floor above and at the far end of the hospital.

## DIED AT 1 O'CLOCK

I threw down the phone and sped after them. We reached the door of the conference room and there were loud cries of "Quiet!" Fighting to keep his emotions under control, Kilduff said, "President John Fitzgerald Kennedy died at approximately one o'clock." I raced into a nearby office. The telephone switchboard at the hospital was hopelessly jammed. I spotted Virginia Payette, wife of UPI's Southwestern division manager and a veteran reporter in her own right. I told her to try getting through on pay telephones on the floor above. Frustrated by the inability to get through the hospital switchboard, I appealed to a nurse.

She led me through a maze of corridors and back stairways to another floor and a lone pay booth. I got the Dallas office. Virginia had gotten through before me. Whereupon I ran back through the hospital to the conference room. There Jiggs Fauver of the White House transportation staff grabbed me and said Kilduff wanted a pool of three men immediately to fly back to Washington on Air Force 1, the presidential aircraft. "He wants you downstairs, and he wants you right now," Fauver said. Down the stairs I ran and into the driveway, only to discover Kilduff had just pulled out in our telephone car.

## DASH TO AIRPORT

Charles Roberts of Newsweek magazine, Sid Davis of Westinghouse Broadcasting and I implored a police officer to take us to the airport in his squad car. The Secret Service had requested that no sirens be used in the vicinity of the airport, but the Dallas officer did a masterful job of getting us through some of the worst traffic I've ever seen. As we piled out of the car on the edge of the runway about 200 yards from the presidential aircraft, Kilduff spotted us and motioned for us to hurry. We trotted to him and he said the plane could take two pool men to Washington; that Johnson was about to take the oath of office aboard the plane and would take off immediately thereafter.

I saw a bank of telephone booths beside the runway and asked if I had time to advise my news service. He said, "But for God's sake, hurry." Then began another telephone nightmare. The Dallas office rang busy. I tried calling Washington. All circuits were busy. Then I called the New York bureau of UPI and told them about the impending installation of a new President aboard the airplane.

## 'YOU DROPPED YOUR COMB'

Kilduff came out of the plane and motioned wildly toward my booth. I slammed down the phone and jogged across the runway. A detective stopped me and said, "You dropped your pocket comb." Aboard Air Force 1 on which I had made so many trips as a press association reporter covering President Kennedy, all of the shades of the larger main cabin were drawn and the interior was hot and dimly lighted. Kilduff propelled us to the President's suite two-thirds of the way back in the plane. The room is used normally as a combination conference and sitting room and could accomodate eight to ten people seated.

I wedged inside the door and began counting. There were 27 people in this compartment. Johnson stood in the center with his wife, Lady Bird. U.S. District Judge Sarah T. Hughes, 67, a kindly faced woman stood with a small black Bible in her hands, waiting to give the oath. The compartment became hotter and hotter. Johnson was worried that some of the Kennedy staff might not be able to get inside. He urged people to press forward, but a Signal Corps photographer, Capt. Cecil Stoughton, standing in the corner on a chair, said if Johnson moved any closer, it would be virtually impossible to make a truly historic photograph.

It developed that Johnson was waiting for Mrs. Kennedy, who was composing herself in a small bedroom in the rear of the plane. She appeared alone, dressed in the same pink wool suit she had worn in the morning when she appeared so happy shaking hands with airport crowds at the side of her husband. She was white-faced but dry-eyed. Friendly hands stretched toward her as she stumbled slightly. Johnson took both of her hands in his and motioned her to his left side. Lady Bird stood on his right, a fixed half-smile showing the tension.

## 'I DO SOLEMNLY SWEAR...'

Johnson nodded to Judge Hughes, an old friend of his family and a Kennedy appointee. "Hold up your right hand and repeat after me," the woman jurist said to Johnson. Outside a jet could be heard droning into a landing. Judge Hughes held out the Bible and Johnson covered it with his large left hand. His right arm went slowly into the air and the jurist began to intone the constitutional oath, "I do solemnly swear I will faithfully execute the office of President of the United States..."

The brief ceremony ended when Johnson in a deep, firm voice, repeated after the judge," ... So help me God." Johnson turned first to his wife, hugged her about the shoulders and kissed her on the cheek. Then he turned to Kennedy's widow, put his left arm around her and kissed her cheek. As others in the group - some Texas Democratic House members, members of the Johnson and Kennedy staffs - moved toward the new President, he seemed to back away from any expression of felicitation.

## 'LETS GET AIRBORNE'

The two-minute ceremony concluded at 2:38 p.m. CST and seconds later, the President said firmly, "Now, let's get airborne." Col. James Swindal, pilot of the plane, a big gleaming silver and blue fan-jet, cut on the starboard engines immediately. Several persons, including Sid Davis of Westinghouse, left the plane at that time. The White House had room for only two pool reporters on the return flight and these posts were filled by Roberts and me, although at the moment we could find no empty seats.

At 2:47 CST, the wheels of Air Force 1 cleared the runway. Swindal roared the big ship up to an unusually high cruising altitude of 41,000 feet where at 625 miles an hour, ground speed, the jet hurtled toward Andrews Air Force Base outside Washington. When the President's plane reached operating altitude, Mrs. Kennedy left her bedchamber and walked to the rear compartment of the plane. This was the so-called family living room, a private area where she and Kennedy, family and friends had spent many happy airborne hours chatting and dining together. Kennedy's casket had been placed in this compartment, carried aboard by a group of Secret Service agents.

Mrs. Kennedy went into the rear lounge and took a chair beside the coffin. There she remained throughout the flight. Her vigil was shared at times by four staff members close to the slain chief executive - David Powers, his buddy and personal assistant; Kenneth P. O'Donnell, appointments secretary and key political adviser; Lawrence O'Brien, chief Kennedy liaison man with Congress, and Brig. Gen. Godfrey McHugh, Kennedy's Air Force aid. Kennedy's military aide, Maj. Gen. Chester V. Clinton, was busy most of the trip in the forward areas of the plane, sending messages and making arrangements for arrival ceremonies and movement of the body to Bethesda Naval Hospital.

### 'THIS IS A SAD TIME'

As the flight progressed, Johnson walked back into the main compartment. My portable typewriter was lost somewhere around the hospital and I was writing on an oversized electric typewriter which Kennedy's personal secretary, Mrs. Evelyn Lincoln, had used to type his speech texts. Johnson came up to the table where Roberts and I were trying to record the history we had just witnessed.

"I'm going to make a short statement in a few minutes and give you copies of it," he said. "Then when I get on the ground, I'll do it over again." It was the first public utterance of the new chief executive, brief and moving: "This is a sad time for all people. We have suffered a loss that cannot be weighed. For me it is a deep personal tragedy. I know the world shares the sorrow that Mrs. Kennedy and her family bear. I will do my best. That is all I can do. I ask for your help - and God's."

When the plane was about 45 minutes from Washington, the new President got on a special radio-telephone and placed a call to Mrs. Rose Kennedy, the late president's mother. "I wish to God there was something I could do," he told her, "I just wanted you to know that." Then Mrs. Johnson wanted to talk to the elder Mrs. Kennedy. "We feel like the heart has been cut out of us," Mrs. Johnson said. She broke down for a moment and began to sob. Recovering in a few seconds, she added, "Our love and our prayers are with you."

Seconds before the shooting: President Kennedy, his wife, and Texas Governor
Connally

## 'WE ARE PRAYING FOR YOU'

Thirty minutes out of Washington, Johnson put in a call for Nellie Connally, wife of the seriously wounded Texas governor. The new President said to the governor's wife: "We are praying for you, darling, and I know that everything is going to be all right, isn't it? Give him a hug and a kiss for me." It was dark when Air Force I began to skim over the lights of the Washington area, lining up for a landing at Andrews Air Force base. The plane touched down at 5:59 p.m. EST. (4:59 CST in Dallas).

I thanked the stewards for rigging up the typewriter for me, pulled on my raincoat and started down the forward ramp. Roberts and I stood under a wing and watched the casket being lowered from the rear of the plane and borne by a complement of armed forces body bearers into a waiting hearse. We watched Mrs. Kennedy and the late President's brother, Atty. Gen. Robert F. Kennedy, climb into the hearse beside the coffin. The new President repeated his first public statement for the broadcast and newsreel microphones, shook hands with some of the government and diplomatic leaders who turned out to meet the plane, and headed for his helicopter.

Roberts and I were given seats on another 'copter bound for the White House lawn. In the compartment next to ours in one of the large chairs beside a window sat Theodore C. Sorensen, one of Kennedy's closest associates, with the title of special counsel to the President. He had not gone to Texas with his chief but had come to the air base for his return. Sorensen sat wilted in the large chair, crying softly. The dignity of his deep grief seemed to sum up all of the tragedy and sadness of the previous six hours. As our helicopter circled in the balmy darkness for a landing on the White House south lawn, it seemed incredible that only six hours before, John Fitzgerald Kennedy had been a vibrant, smiling, waving and active man.

# 6

# MEDICAL ASPECTS IN FOREIGN COUNTRIES

## 6.1 LAYMAN TREATMENT AND EMERGENCY MEDICINE

### 6.1.1 Special Introductory Remarks

In 1943, Joseph Pulitzer II recommended that a story about an operation performed on-board an American Submarine be considered for the Pulitzer Reporter's Prize. The entry, written by George Weller, a special correspondent for the *Chicago Daily News* and the *St. Louis Post-Dispatch*, was placed before a jury which had to look "for a distinguished example of a reporter's work during the year, the test being accuracy and terseness, the preference being given to news stories published in a daily newspaper prepared under the pressure of edition time relating to matters of special interest of a local or regional character." Pulitzer himself thought that the unusual story by Weller was "an example of vivid, colorful, dramatic writing. It's, to my way of thinking," he added, not 'the best', but certainly outstanding." George Weller earned the Pulitzer Reporting award "for his graphic story of how a U.S. Navy Pharmacist's Mate under enemy waters in a submarine performed an operation for appendicitis saving a sailor's life" in 1942.

Reporter Joel Brinkley and photographer Jay Mather of the Louisville *Courier-Journal* in 1979 visited refugee camps in Cambodia and Thailand and stated: "Elderly Cambodians recall an ancient prophecy: One day our people will be able to choose only between being devoured by tigers or swallowed by crocodiles. Despite the rescue efforts of a dozen nations, the prophecy is being fulfilled. Half of Cambodia's people have been killed or driven out since 1970." Brinkley's and Mather's outstanding series entitled 'Living the Cambodian Nightmare' "brought the suffering and torment, the puzzlement and confusion of displacement in the homes of *Courier-Journal* readers more effectively than the TV screen," a Pulitzer Prize jury wrote in its report and continued: "They added dimensions to reporting that mark print journalism as the most conclusive, the most detailed available to us today... A victim himself of disease that has added to the refugee complication, reporter Brinkley nevertheless produced his report in full on a deadline basis despite the pangs of his illness." The Advisory Board gave the 1980 Pulitzer Prize for International Reporting to Brinkley and Mather "for stories from Cambodia" including medical care problems in Thai refugee camps.

## 6.1.2 An Appendectomy in a Submarine near Australia

[Source: George Weller: Yank Sub Crew in Action; Stops; Snips Appendix. Saves Life of Stricken Youth as Craft Hides from Jap Ships, in: *The Chicago Daily News* (Chicago, Il.), 67th Year/No. 293, December 14, 1942, p. 1, col. 6; p. 5, cols. 1-5; reprinted by permission of the Chicago Sun-Times, Inc., Chicago, Il.]

"They are giving him ether now," was what they said back in the aft torpedo rooms. "He's gone under and they're getting ready to cut him open," the crew whispered sitting on their pipe bunks cramped between torpedoes.

One man went forward and put his arm quietly around the shoulders of another man who was handling the bow diving planes. "Keep her steady, Jake," he said. "They've just made the first cut. They're feeling around for it now." "They" were a little group of anxious-faced men with their arms thrust into reversed white pajama coats. Gauze bandages hid all their expressions except the tensity in their eyes.

### 'IT' IS ACUTE APPENDIX

"It" was an acute appendix inside Dean Rector of Chautauqua, Kas. The stabbing pains had become unendurable the day before, which was Rector's first birthday at sea. He was 19. The big depth gauge that looks like a factory clock and stands beside the "Christmas tree" of red and green gauges regulating the flooding chambers showed where they were. They were below the surface. And above them - and below them, too - were enemy waters crossed and recrossed by whirring propellers of Jap destroyers, transports and submarines.

The nearest naval surgeon competent to operate on the young seaman was thousands of miles and many days away. There was just one way to prevent the appendix from bursting and that was for the crew to operate upon their shipmate themselves. And that's what they did; they operated upon him. It was probably one of the largest operations in number of participants that ever occurred.

## READY TO TAKE CHANCE

"He says he's ready to take his chance," the gobs whispered from bulkhead to bulkhead. "That guy's regular" - the word traveled from bow planes to propeller and back again. They kept her steady. The chief surgeon was a 23-year-old pharmacist's mate wearing a blue blouse with white-taped collar and squashy white duck cap. His name was Wheeler B. Lipes. He came from Newcastle near Roanoke, Va., and had taken the Navy hospital course in San Diego, thereafter serving three years in the naval hospital in Philadelphia, where his wife lives at 853 N. 22d st.

Lipes' specialty as laboratory technician was in operating a machine that registers heartbeats. He was classified as a electrocardiographer. But he had seen Navy doctors take out one or two appendices and thought he could do it. Under the sea he was given his first chance to operate. There was difficulty about the ether. When below the surface, the pressure inside a boat is above the atmospheric pressure. More ether is absorbed under pressure. The submariners did not know how long their operation would last. They did not know how long it would take to find the appendix. They did not know whether there would be enough ether to keep the patient under throughout the operation.

They didn't want the patient waking up before they were finished. They decided to operate on the table in the officers' wardroom. In the newest and roomiest American submarines, the wardroom is approximately the size of a Pullman car drawing room. It is flanked by bench seats, attached to the wall and a table occupies the whole room - you enter with knees already crooked to sit down. The only way anyone can be upright in the wardroom is by kneeling. The operating table was just long enough so that the patient's head and feet reached the two ends without hanging over.

## READ UP ON IT

First they got out a medical book and read up on the appendix while Rector, his face pale with pain, lay in the narrow bunk. It was probably the most democratic surgical operation ever performed. Everybody from box plane man to the cook in the galley knew his role. The cook provided the ether mask. It was an inverted tea strainer. They covered it with gauze. The young surgeon had as his staff of fellow physicians men all his senior in age and rank. His anesthetist was Lt. Franz Hoskins, communications officer, of Tacoma, Wash.

Before they carried Rector to the wardroom the submarine captain, Lt.Cmdr. W. B. Ferrall of Pittsburgh, asked Lipes as the surgeon to have a talk with the patient. "Look, Dean, I never did anything like this before," he said. "You don't have much chance to pull through anyhow.

What do you say?" "I know just how it is, doc," said Rector. "Let's get going."

## 'DOC' FOR THE FIRST TIME

It was the first time in his life that anybody had called Lipes "doc." But there was in him, added to the steadiness that goes with a submariner's profession, a new calmness worthy of an Aesculapius. The operating staff adjusted gauze masks while members of the engine room crew pulled tight their reversed pajama coats over their extended arms. The tools were laid out. They were far from perfect or complete for a major operation. The scalpel had no handle.

But submariners are used to "rigging" things. The medicine chest had plenty of hemostats, which are small pincers used for closing blood vessels. The machinist "rigged" a handle for the scalpel from a hemostat. When you are going to have an operation, you must have some kind of antiseptic agent. Rummaging in the medicine chest, they found sulfanilimide tablets and ground them to powder.

## ONE THING LACKING

One thing was lacking: There was no means of holding open the wound after the incision had been made. Surgical tools used for this are called "muscular retractors." What would they use for retractors? There was nothing in the medicine chest that gave the answer, so they went as usual to the cook's galley.

In the galley they found tablespoons made of monel metal. They bent these at right angles and had their retractors. Sterilizers? They went to one of the greasy copper-colored torpedoes waiting beside the tubes. They milked alcohol from the torpedo mechanism and used it as well as boiling water. The light in the wardroom seemed insufficient; operating rooms always have big lamps. So they brought one of the big floods used for night loadings and rigged it inside the wardroom's sloping ceiling.

The moment for the operation had come. Rector, very pale and stripped, stretched himself out on the wardroom table under the glare of the lamps. Rubber gloves dipped in torpedo alcohol were drawn upon the youthful "doc's" hands. The fingers were too long. The rubber ends dribbled limply over.

## LIKE 'MICKEY MOUSE'

"You look like Mickey Mouse, doc," said one onlooker. Lipes grinned behind the gauze. Rector on the wardroom table wet his lips, glancing a sidelook at the tea-strainer ether mask. With his superior officers as his subordinates, Lipes looked into their eyes, nodded and Hoskins put the tea mask down over Rector's face. No words were spoken; Hoskins already knew from the book that he should watch Rector's eye pupils dilate.

The surgeon, following the ancient hand rule, put his little finger on Rector's subsiding umbilicus, his thumb on the point of the hip bone and, by dropping his index finger straight down, found the point where he intended to cut. At his side stood Lt. Norvell Ward, of Indianhead, Md., who was his assistant surgeon. "I chose him for his coolness and dependability," said the doc afterward of his superior officer. "He acted as my third and fourth hands."

Ward's job was to place tablespoons in Rector's side as Lipes cut through successive layers of muscles. Engineering officer Lt. Charles S. Manning of Cheraw, S.C., took the job which in a formal operating room is known as "circulating nurse." His job was to see that packets of sterile, carlisle dressings kept coming and that the torpedo alcohol and boiling water arrived regularly from the galley.

They had what is called an "instrument passer" in Chief Yeoman H. F. Wieg of Sheldon, N.D., whose job was to keep the tablespoons coming and coming clean. Submarine Skipper Ferrall too had his part. They made him "recorder." It was his job to keep count of the sponges that went into Rector. A double count of the tablespoons used as retractors was kept: one by the Skipper and one by the cook who was himself passing them out from the galley.

It took Lipes in his flapfinger rubber gloves nearly 20 minutes to find the appendix. "I have tried one side of the Caecum," he whispered after the first minutes. "Now, I'm trying the other."

### WHISPER BULLETINS

Whispered bulletins seeped back into the engine room and crews' quarters. "The doc has tried one side of something and now is trying the other side." After more search, Lipes finally whispered, "I think I've got it. It's curled way up into the blind gut."

Lipes was using the classical McBurney's incision. Now was the time when his shipmate's life was completely in his hands. "Two more spoons." They passed the word to Lt. Ward. "Two spoons at 14.45 hours," wrote Skipper Ferrall on his notepad. "More flashlights. And another battle lantern," demanded Lipes.

The patient's face, lathered with white petrolatum, began to grimace. "Give him more ether," ordered the doc. Hoskins looked doubtfully at the original five pounds of ether now sunken to hardly three-quarters of one can, but once again the tea-strainer was soaked in ether. The fumes mounted up thickening the wardroom air and making the operating staff giddy.

"Want those blowers speeded up?" the captain asked the doc. The blowers began to whirr louder. Suddenly came the moment when the doc reached out his hand, pointing toward the needle threaded with 20-day chromic catgut.

One by one the sponges came out. One by one the tablespoons bent into right angles were withdrawn and returned to the galley. At the end it was the skipper who nudged Lipes and pointed to the tally of bent tablespoons. One was missing. Lipes reached into the incision for the last time and withdrew the wishboned spoon and closed the incision.

They even had the tool ready to cut off the thread. It was a pair of fingernail scissors, well scalded in water and torpedo juice. At that moment the last can of ether went dry. They lifted up Rector and carried him into the bunk of Lt. Charles K. Miller of Williamsport, Pa. Miller alone had had control of the ship as diving officer during the operation.

## IN THERE PITCHING

It was half an hour after the last tablespoon had been withdrawn that Rector opened his eyes. His first words were, "I'm still in there pitching." By that time the sweat-drenched officers were hanging up their pajamas to dry. It had taken the amateurs about two and one half hours for an operation ordinarily requiring 45 minutes. "It was not one of those 'snappy valve' appendices," murmured Lipes apologetically as he felt the first handclaps upon his shoulder.

Within a few hours the bow and stern planesmen who, under Miller's direction, had kept the submarine from varying more than half a degree vertically in 150 minutes below the stormy sea, came around to receive Rector's winks of thanks. They were C. R. Weekley of Dover, N. H., and West Onion, W. Va.; L. L. Rose of St. Louis, E. W. Grismore of Pandora, Ohio, and W. J. Hilburn of Foley, Ala. And Rector does not forget also the three shipmates who did the messenger work for torpedo alcohol and galley spoons: S. D. Lang of Baltimore, A. A. Boheme of Geneva, Idaho, and A. E. Daniels of Sugarland, Tex.

His only remark was "Gee, I wish Earl were here to see this job." His brother Earl, a seaman on the Navy submarine tender Pigeon, is among the list of missing at Corregidor, probably captured. "I'd like to show that cut to Capt. Voge," said Lipes. "I used to tell him how I got my first experience at a morgue and never missed a patient coming or going. I had just as soon try a colostomy on one of that gang. Bet I could get away with brain surgery if I had do."

Lipes formerly served under a Chicagoan, Lt.Cmdr. Richard Voge, until the pharmacist of his present submarine was wounded in the Cavite bombing. Although Lipe's arm was steady in operating on his shipmates, he had himself suffered four shrapnel wounds when the Japs bombed Cavite. When the submarine surfaced that night, all hands who had been near the wardroom found themselves frequently grabbing the sides of the conning tower and slightly unsteady on the black, vertical ladders. It was because of the ether they had breathed, which came out again at the lessening of surface pressure.

But all their intoxication was not ether: some was joy. The submarine again began "patrolling as usual." And 13 days later Rector was manning the battle phones. And the submarine was again launching her torpedos. And in one of the bottles vibrating on the submarine's shelves, swayed the first appendix ever known to have been removed below enemy waters.

## 6.1.3  Medical Care in Thailand Refugee Camps

[Source: Joel Brinkley: For medical missionaries from Louisville, desperate patients arrive thousands at a time, in: *The Courier-Journal* (Louisville, Ky.), Vol. 249/No. 155, December 2, 1979, Special section, p. 2, cols. 1-6; p. 3, cols. 1-6; reprinted by permission of the Courier-Journal Company, Louisville, Ky.]

The ominous thud of mortar fire wakes them so often they've had to make a joke. "It's just a car door slamming," Kenneth Rasmussen assures his wife, Marjorie. They know the Vietnamese may cross the nearby border into Thailand and attack their town of Aranyaprathet at any moment. And they know that would end their work.

Rasmussen is a doctor. His wife is a nurse. Six months ago he worked in the emergency room at Louisville's Norton-Children's Hospital. But in July they sold their Klondike Lane house, packed their belongings in a warehouse and moved to Thailand. Today they call this oppressive refugee camp "home" and insist there's no place they'd rather be. But they're prepared to flee at any moment.

The Vietnamese may soon launch major attacks that would send another half-million Cambodians fleeing into Thailand. Many fear that Hanoi's troops will enter Thailand in hot pursuit of the enemy. The Rasmussens' blue Datsun pickup will be tuned and ready. Cans of spare gasoline are stored under their tiny house. And they know by heart the way to an old airbase where American planes can lift them out.

They are medical missionaries. They made their extraordinary move "only because this is where we thought we could help the most," and they don't see anything so unusual about that. They spend their days with misery and death, and by 8 o'clock most nights they're too exhausted to stay awake. They eat rice and drink Thai tea three times a day. Their meals are prepared by a local woman, and at home the Rasmussens take off their shoes in deference to her Buddhist traditions.

Their primitive living conditions are of little consequence to them. Instead, they prefer to talk of the people, the sick and dying people they treat. One who stuck in their minds was the smooth-skinned child with an unnatural part in his shiny black hair. His Cambodian mother brought him to Rasmussen at the Aranyaprathet Khmer Refugee Center one day last month. "A beautiful child," Rasmussen recalled that evening. "But sad, sad, sad."

The woman complained that her son "forgets a lot," Rasmussen said. "He puts down his toys and a moment later forgets they're beside him. He'll go out and forget to come home. She give him a pill, and he doesn't remember to put it in his mouth." The woman wasn't eager to tell her 5-year-old's story, but Rasmussen coaxed it from her through his translator, also a refugee. The Vietnamese army was approaching the woman's Western Cambodian village a few weeks earlier, and the Khmer Rouge forces of Premier Pol Pot, in power since 1975, were preparing to evacuate.

As a parting gesture - and anything but an uncharacteristic one for the Khmer Rouge - the soldiers kicked her husband and four of her five children to their knees. Then they chopped each on the back of the neck with a sharp machete. She stood watching. The 5-year-old boy clung to her leg. When her husband and four children were dead, the soldiers threw the woman a shovel and forced her to dig their graves. Her work lagged a bit, so one soldier grabbed the shovel and smacked the small boy on the head.

He fell unconscious. She dug faster. Later, after the soldiers left, a Vietnamese doctor put some salve on the boy's head wound. And now, weeks later, the woman was asking Rasmussen to fix her son's forgetfulness. "There was nothing I could do but put some cream on his scar," he said, shaking his head. "We get cases like that all the time." People of another land who challenged Rasmussen to treat bodies as well as souls started the couple on the long journey that led to Thailand.

Thirty-three years ago Kenneth Rasmussen found himself in the Sudan working as a missionary, putting to use what he had learned as a divinity student at Pittsburgh Theological Seminary. He and Marjorie had married just a few weeks before. She remained in the United States to earn a degree in nursing. Then, as now, the New York-based International Rescue Committee sponsored Rasmussen's missionary work. In Africa, he found that people "couldn't understand why we could heal their souls and not their bodies."

When he returned to the United States the next year, he began studying to be a doctor, finally graduating from the University of Maryland medical school in 1961. Later came working trips to the Sudan again and to Ethiopia, where the Rasmussens became accustomed to squatting over primitive toilets, boiling all their water and eating unfamiliar foods at every meal. Similar inconveniences dog the Rasmussens in Thailand, but they're nothing contrasted with the real horrors surrounding them. Horrors that have made Rasmussen willing to lie to save lives.

By this past summer, hundreds of thousands of Cambodians had streamed into Thailand, seeking refuge from the hated Khmer Rouge soldiers who had beaten and tortured them and their kin. Early in the year, Thai officials had said, "No more." The Cambodians wouldn't listen and sneaked over the border at night, into the refugee camps, desperately searching for food and sanctuary. Rasmussen hid them among the legal

Staff Map by Steve Durbin

**Dr. Kenneth Rasmussen works at the Aranyaprathet camp.**

immigrants and lied when Thai officials came by so he could treat their diseases, which grew in variety and severity as the months passed.

Malaria and tuberculosis were common from the start. But as autumn crept in, Rasmussen and others noticed that a surprising number of escaping Cambodians were suffering from severe malnutrition and dehydration. They were starving. "You could tell it the minute you saw them," he said. And all had tales of others - friends and family members - who had already starved to death. Still, Thai officials refused to accept more, saying they already had too many refugees for such a poor country. Rasmussen was on the scene when the policy changed. One Saturday night in early October, he said, "a U.N. representative came to our door and told us they expected a big influx (of refugees) the next day."

If the Rasmussens were to help, they were told, they would have to pretend to be working for the U.N. High Commission for Refugees. "We met early the next morning and drove about 20 kilometers north. As we headed toward the border, there they were, thousands of them, streaming down the road. They were dirty and moving very slowly, some of them dying, and everyone was wearing dusty black." (When Pol Pot took over Cambodia in 1975, he forced every man, woman and child in the nation to dress always in identical black pajamas.) They just came in one big mass, staggered over the border and plopped right there in the elephant grass," Mrs. Rasmussen said. "About 30,000 of them. And not one of them said a word or made a sound. Not even a murmur. It's something I'll never forget. It looked like a scene from 'Exodus.'"

"They weren't intentionally escaping into Thailand. The fighting had pushed them here and pushed them there. Finally it just pushed them right over the border, and they collapsed," Rasmussen said. The Rasmussens and other volunteer doctors spent the day dispensing pills and hanging bags of intravenous fluids from bushes and banyan trees. The bodies of several dozen Cambodians who died that first day were hauled off for cremation. The Rasmussens returned the next day and again the following Sunday, when the prime minister of Thailand, Kriangsak Chomanan, arrived for an inspection.

Like other visitors, Kriangsak was stunned by the scene, and after a quick look at the huddled mass of people - who had improved considerably since their arrival a week earlier - he declared: "These people can't be allowed to die here." Kriangsak ordered his military to move the refugees to a new, inland camp and declared that any future Cambodian refugees would be accepted on Thai soil - at least temporarily. Since that day, there've been no more late-night knocks on the Rasmussens' door, though hundreds of thousands of Cambodians are camped on the border only a few miles away. Almost everyone in Thailand expects many to cross over soon.

But even if they do, Mrs. Rasmussen can't help. A mosquito carrying dengue, or "bone-break fever," bit her that first Sunday morning on the border. She has been in a Bangkok hospital, or helpless at home, ever since. Her husband continues working at the camp, treating the old-timers and new refugees who straggle in. He starts the day by making hospital rounds, laughing and joking with patients who can't understand a single word he says. A small troupe of refugees follows him as he moves from bed to bed, watching.

The hospital's 20 beds are nearly always filled with miserably sick people ... a motionless, blank-faced young man with tuberculosis who has wasted away to almost nothing and lies, stinking, in his own urine. ... an old woman lying naked and still under a mosquito net, a small wad of cotton hanging from a huge, ugly cancerous growth over her right eye. ... a few people with malnutrition, including one infant girl who dies by morning. ... a second little girl, mostly just bones, wimpering softly. "This one's a miracle," Rasmussen said. "I didn't expect her to live through the night. I guess I pulled her through."

Most patients are newcomers who have just crossed the border, and Rasmussen treats them all as best he can. But a majority of the 5,000 refugees have been in the Aranyaprathet camp for years, many since the camp opened in 1976. There they lie on their backs inside narrow, aluminum-roofed huts. They eat rice and fish donated by international relief agencies, make babies and get sick. There's little else to do.

One day a few weeks ago, a British relief volunteer, in a panic, asked Rasmussen to leave his clinic to help some wounded refugees nearby. Rasmussen refused. "My philosophy," he said, "is never leave the one you're working on, because he might die."

## 6.2  HOSPITALS AT THE FRONT AND AMERICAN SOLDIERS

### 6.2.1  Special Introductory Remarks

*Associated Press* War Correspondent Harold V. (Hal) Boyle reported all phases of American participation in the European war since the African landings in 1942. He reached his peak in 1944 while preparing his 'Leaves from a War Correspondent's Notebook,' daily columns that pictured graphically the lives, the hardships, the dreams and the humor of the American soldier. Boyle's columns appeared in more than 400 afternoon newspapers. He drew his material from living at the front lines; he hobnobbed with soldiers in London, Paris, Belgium and Germany. During his front-line excursions, Boyle frequently found himself in the center of fast-breaking news stories, and on these occasions he returned to spot news reporting, a good example of which is a feature story of a field hospital somewhere in France. A Pulitzer Prize jury and the Advisory Board were impressed by the variety and quality of Boyle's dispatches, and he won the 1945 Pulitzer Correspondence Prize "for distinguished war correspondence during the year 1944."

Another press agency journalist, Jim G. Lucas of the Scripps-Howard Newspaper Alliance, was a successful war correspondent during the 1950s. In covering the Korean War, Lucas filed a daily dispatch for the general newspaper alliance wire: front-line battle accounts, straight news stories, human interest stories and interviews. The Scripps-Howard management thought that many American newspapers lacked adequate and realistic coverage of the Korean War and that therefore there was a real need for down-to-earth stories. So it became Jim Lucas' prime duty to present "an accurate, true-to-life account of the Korean War and of the men" who were fighting. During the prisoner-of-war exchanges, he wrote as many as eight to ten stories a day for different papers, including features on front hospitals. In 1954, Jim G. Lucas was awarded the Pulitzer International Reporting Prize "for his notable front-line human

interest reporting of the Korean War..., climaxing 26 months of distinguished service as a war correspondent."

## 6.2.2  A World War Army Hospital in France

[Source: Harold V. Boyle: Boyle visits a Hospital. The Nurses - The Work - The
Cures, in: *The Evening Sun (Baltimore, Md.)*, Vol. 70/No. 48, December 12,
1944, p. 17, cols. 6-8; reprinted by permission of the Associated Press, New
York, N.Y.]

Mary T. Pattie has not had a raise in pay in more than two years -
but that does not bother her so much as the fact that, in the same length
of time, she has not been able to buy or wear "a real fussy hat." Now -
with her third winter overseas coming up - she still is worrying more
about "the boys" than about herself.

"The boys" are wounded American soldiers, hundreds of whom
Mary has tended in Africa, Sicily, Italy and France. And they remember
her - this pretty, freckly girl who knows how to ease an aching wound
with a soft bandage or soothe a hurt and battle-troubled spirit with a kind
word or a wry bit of humor.

### UNSUNG HEROINE

Mary, a second lieutenant, is one of those hard-working army
nurses who receive their main recognition from the unspoken gratitude
that shines in the eyes of their war-sick soldier-patients. I first met her in
Tebessa in January, 1943, during the Tunisian campaign. She and the
other nurses in the 9th Evacuation Hospital were shivering in cold, un-
heated tents and leading anything but the life of Riley - but they loved it.

"It was all so new to us then," said Mary. "We only had three
blankets, and it was so cold in those Algerian hills that water froze in our
helmets overnight and in the morning, before we could wash our faces,
we had to break up the ice. Yes, we had fewer conveniences and more
difficulties then - but we didn't really mind them."

### "SAME OLD MUD"

Mary and the other nurses still live in stoveless tents through which
leak the chill winter winds. And they are camped in a pasture turned into
a calf-deep quagmire by churning ambulance wheels. "Yes, we are back
in the same old mud again," said Mary. "But we are numb now. We do
not have the same enthusiasm we did - but we don't need it so much. We
do things faster and better now because we learned how to work under
these conditions."

From Portsmouth, Va., Mary used to nurse ailing Rockettes in the Radio City Music Hall. Of her experiences overseas, she says: "I remember most the unfailing humor of our American boys. There is nothing like it anywhere. You just can't let them down. And you can't help keep your chins up around them - they are so darn cheerful. Even when you can't see much for them to be cheerful about."

## WISTFUL THOUGHT

Some of the nurses she came over with are back in the States now, but Mary kind of wants to stick it out. Most nurses do. Only with that third rough winter coming up, Mary can't help thinking back a little wistfully of the time when neither clothing nor her hours were so regimented. "What I really want is a fussy hat," she said. "I want to walk down Fifth avenue in a fussy hat." Laughing, she filled up a hot-water bottle. "The 9th Evacuation will lead the way to health and victory!"

That was the refrain line of a pep song sung by nurses of the 9th Evacuation Hospital when they left England for Africa two years ago this month. The girls don't sing that now - they are long past the pep-song stage - but they still are living up to it in their daily lives. In two years overseas most military outfits change personnel so much they hardly are recognizable, but not "the Fighting 9th Evac." "We still have about 75 per cent of our original personnel," said Col. William E. Stone, of Booneville, Mo., their commander, "and that applies to doctors and nurses as well as enlisted men."

## "STONE'S RANGERS"

The girls call themselves "Stone's Rangers" - a nickname which always brings a grin to the chunky, middle-aged physician who has led them through five countries since they left America. He has been a good shepherd. There have been only two deaths - both in auto accidents - among his 47 officers, 53 nurses and 294 men. "We've had a few shells land near our area, but no actual casualties," said Stone, who was warming himself before a stove while his personal clerk, Corporal Alan W. Eighler, of Allen, Mich., popped corn. Outside, the rain fell in a black night, but inside the big, flapping hospital tent it was warm and bright.

## 40,000 PATIENTS

"We've been idle only three weeks in 25 months overseas," he continued, "and in that time we treated just under 40,000 soldiers - including about 7,000 since we landed in France." That isn't a record. One or two other evacuation hospitals - those through which were funneled wounded from the bloody Anzio beachhead - have handled more casualties, and two hospitals beat the 9th Evac into action by a few days. But there isn't a better-known hospital along the battle front.

Just as certain battle units such as the 1st and 3d Infantry Divisions distinguished themselves by combat vigor and valor, the 9th Evac has made a name for itself by its tight-knit unity and one of the finest surgical records in any theater. Its personnel is as proven as a scrappy football team. They like being referred to as "the Fighting 9th Evac," but are getting a little bashful about using it themselves.

## WANT TO SEE PARIS

"Other evacs already call it 'the Ultra Swanks' and 'the Sigh Brows,'" explained Lieut. Anna H. Turse, of Hazelton, Pa. "None of us would mind another winter if they'd just give us a jeep each and let us light out for a couple of peeks at Paris," laughed Lieut. Allison Hale, a little blonde from Jersey City, N.J. "We want to get some of that perfume before it's just a memory. Nursing is all right - but in the next war I'm going to be a doughnut girl and hand out doughnuts and glamor, instead of pills. It's easier on your feet."

The Goum crept tiredly into the hospital receiving tent. He looked bad from his leather slippers all the way up to the topknot which these native French troops from Morocco leave growing on otherwise shaven skulls so the angel of death can haul them into heaven. "What's wrong?" asked the soldier clerk. The Goum doubled up with pain and said it was his stomach. It hurt him terribly. "I have walked three days and three nights across the mountains to get to you," he said proudly.

## NEWS TRAVELS

"Why did you do that?" asked the surprised clerk. "Because," replied the Goum naively, "I heard from many soldiers that here one can lie in a warm bed and eat good food." That is the best testimonial received by the 9th Evacuation Hospital which has handled 40,000 patients during more than two years service in four Mediterranean campaigns. "It isn't every hospital that the patient will walk three days to reach," dryly observed Lieut. Col. Gurney Taylor, New York city, who is in charge of the medical ward.

For several months the hospital was set up in Italy as a general hospital for French troops and the staff - most of whom come from Roosevelt Hospital in Manhattan - remember many interesting experiences at treating Colonial soldiers. Along with the usual battle casualties, the hospital now is receiving a substantial number of malaria cases. This is surprising to most soldiers, who associate malaria with hot weather, but was foreseen by the medical staff.

## MALARIA MENACE

"Many of our troops contacted malaria while fighting in the Pontine marshes in Italy, which is one of the worst infested spots in the world," said Taylor. "It had been lying dormant then and cropped out again because of lowered resistance among troops, the result of exposure and weariness from days and nights in the front lines without a rest." There have been more cases of gas gangrene noted at the hospital also since it came to France and its commander, Lieut. Col. William E. Stone, Booneville, Mo., who knows soil from his years in the farm belt, has a ready explanation.

### PENICILLIN BIG HELP

"We had relatively few cases of gas gangrene in Africa because there were fewer germs in the soil, and so wounds that came in contact with it didn't infect so easily. But, in France, the soil has been fertilized heavily with manure for centuries and was teeming with organisms which may cause gas gangrene."

Penicillin is the answer. As autumn weather has steadily worsened, soggy rains and cold nights have brought the reappearance of trench foot, bane of the soldiers of World War I. Frequent changes of heavy socks and rest in an area behind the front keep most of the sufferers from becoming hospital cases.

## 6.2.3  A Field Hospital's Situation in Korea

[Source: Jim G. Lucas: Wounded Return From Porkchop Hill by Trainload, in: *El Paso Herald-Post* (El Paso, Tx.), Vol. LXXIII/No. 164, July 10, 1953, p. A 1, cols. 2-3; reprinted by permission of the Scripps-Howard Company, Cincinnati, Oh.]

They're bringing our wounded by the trainload from Porkchop Hill these days. People like Bill Brown and Marg Coghill, a couple of first lieutenants, just forget about sleep. Bill's a doctor from Houston. Marg is a nurse from Chicago.

Their hospital train pulled into Seoul with a load of wounded South Koreans at 2:30 this morning. Bill and Marg had been on the road for 20 hours. They stayed in Seoul long enough to take on more water, to replenish the train's air conditioning, and to drink scads of hot coffee. At 4 a.m., they were on their way back to pick up more wounded. This time I went with them.

### TAKEN ABOARD

Our train reached the first pickup station on what once was the Seoul Wonsan line at dawn. Wounded GI's and ROK's were taken aboard. Still farther north, at Sintan-Ni, another group had to be picked up. Marg Coghill stayed behind with the wounded we already had. Bill Brown was to take the engine and three cars on to Sintan-Ni.

Bill shouted to the Korean engineer. "Sick men, hurt men!" he yelled. "Hubba hubba!" The Korean made helpless gestures. After a while, the train gave a tentative lurch and then we were rolling. Bill Brown fought back his impatience. When we finally reached Sintan-Ni, he jumped from the train.

## INTO TENT

"Let's see what we have here," he said to Sfc. George Naugle of San Antonio. The sergeant took him into a tent; Lieutenant Brown emerged shaking his head. "The 7th Division caught it again," he said. "These men were on a hill just behind Porkchop," explained Dr. Gerard Aiken, a first lieutenant from Boundbrook, N.J. "They all were hit by shell fragments."

The wounded began going aboard. The first had a back wound. The second a thigh wound. No. 3, head wound. A Negro was carried aboard with wounds in arm, leg and head. One man was crying. Several had ugly face wounds. "Reds shelled the rail line last night," Lieutenant Aiken said conversationally. The cars filled rapidly. "We'll take all we can," Bill Brown told Sergeant Naugle. "We can put some two to a bunk." At 10:50, we were under way, the wards filled. One GI's wound broke open as he was lifted into a top bunk. Bill Brown worked to stop the flow of blood. "How many left in Fox company?" one GI asked another. "I hear Charley Company was wiped out," a second man said. "My buddy got it in the belly," said a wounded corporal close to tears. "A burp gun got me," said another. "Around midnight. He was as close to me as you are now. Our guys got him."

## NO BUGGING

"I don't hold with bugging out (running away)," a Negro private said between clenched teeth. "No man in my company ever bugged. It ain't right." We reached the pickup station where Marg Coghill waited. Her face was white. "There's one poor ROK, Bill," she said. "You must see him. I'm afraid it's gangrene. He's going to lose his leg." In the kitchen car, the temperature was at 115 degrees. But at noon, roast chicken was served. For many of the wounded, it was the first real meal in days.

## AMBULANCES WAIT

At 5 p.m. we were back in Seoul. Thirty ambulances were waiting along the siding. Bill Brown and Marg Coghill climbed out. "You need coffee," said a lieutenant, greeting them. Bill nodded gratefully. "Pardon me, sir," interrupted Sergeant Naugle. "There's a man in Kearney's car who's in pain." Bill set down the cup of coffee untasted. From somewhere, he managed to find the strength to run.

## 6.3    DEVELOPING COUNTRIES AND FOOD SHORTAGE

### 6.3.1   Special Introductory Remarks

Changing weather, a widening pattern of global crop failures, and the inexorable rise of population threaten to starve half a billion people in the last quarter of this century. In 1974, already an estimated 460 million people were considered permanently hungry by experts who feared the world may be on the brink of the greatest disaster in human history. *Chicago Tribune* readers got a frightening, close-up look at the problem in "The Faces of Hunger," a series of articles and photographs by reporter William Mullen and photographer Ovie Carter. The series was published in October 1974, after Mullen and Carter spent three months traveling 10,000 miles through Africa and Asia. A Pulitzer Prize jury saw the story of world hunger, food supply and population as a subject of continuing importance and enormous impact. And based on writing skill, content significance, reportorial enterprise and reader impact the jury was impressed with the Mullen/Carter entry. The Board did not hesitate in giving the 1975 Pulitzer International Reporting award to both journalists "for their coverage of famine in Africa and India."

Early in 1984 - long before covering famine deaths in Africa became fashionable again and shortly after international relief reports predicted a widening disaster - *Newsday* of Long Island, N.Y., put together a team of two reporters and a photographer to travel across the continent to find out what was happening. The project was part of the newspaper's commitment to the plight of the hungry. When television brought the news of famine deaths in Ethiopia to viewers all over the world *Newsday* was already there and delivered in-depth reporting to its readers. While most media reports remained focused only on the agony of Ethiopia, the team continued its coverage from other countries not as severely impacted but just as tragic. "Obvious planning, anticipation and recognition of a major story enabled *Newsday* to  produce the most comprehensive, incisive report on the subject seen by the jury," stated the Pulitzer Prize jurors in their report. So reporters Josh Friedman and Dennis Bell and photographer Ozier Muhammad won the 1985 Pulitzer International Reporting Prize "for their series on the plight of the hungry in Africa."

## 6.3.2 Consequences of the Overspill Population in India

[Source: William Mullen: Birth control fails, too. 'Green revolution' turns to dust; India's food production in ruins, in: *Chicago Tribune* (Chicago, Il.), 128th Year/No. 290, October 17, 1974, p. 1, cols. 3-5; p. 12, cols. 1-6; reprinted by permission of the Chicago Tribune Company, Chicago, Il.]

There are no classes in the Indra Devi Girls School this year, but an important lesson is being taught there nonetheless. The school is a compound of long, low buildings behind a high wall in this small district capital in West Bengal. It is a quiet place, just as the concentration camps of Nazi Germany were quiet. Like the concentration camps, it is packed with wrecked forms of humanity, room upon room filled with gaunt-faced men, skeletal women, and hollow-eyed children with haunted, glassy stares.

So far this year, the world has ignored the people in the school. Nobody from outside India has come with food or medicine or money to relieve the misery and stave off death. Indian government officials say publicly that they will somehow find food for these and 200 million other hungry people this year. Privately they express concern that there isn't enough food available on the world market, and that as many as 500,000 to one million people could perish in the next six months. The vision of that many people dying while the world stands by is a searing one, a scarring one like the vision of the camps in Germany.

It is happening today in Cooch Behar. "The relief we are able to give them is not enough," said N. N. Kar, who is in charge of relief for the Cooch Behar district. "We can distribute about four kilograms [less than nine pounds] of wheat each week for each family, and that is about all." In the Indra Devi school, it was obvious that it was not enough. Children lay listlessly on the ground in the courtyard or in the street running in front of the school. Fathers looked on in embarrassment as their wives came to two visitors, pushing sick babies to them as tho the visitors, as Americans, might be able to help simply by touching them.

One baby had open running sores on its back, and a massive swelling lump on its spine. An official at the school said there was no doctor to attend the children, that the injury could not be treated. "We had a medical team here a few weeks ago to administer smallpox inoculations," he said, "but they didn't have time for anything else. There is nothing we can do." There were 450 people living at the school, one of five schools in the small town being used as refugee camps. Kar said 31,000 people in the district were suffering in similar circumstances, living in schools, makeshift tents, warehouses, wherever people could get a roof over their heads and wait for food.

Cooch Behar is but one district in West Bengal, a state reeling at one end from floods, at another from drouth. The government estimates 625,000 people are in dire need, and admits that estimate might be conservative. West Bengal is but one state in India. The condition of its people is no worse and is in some cases better than of the people of Assam, Bihar, Orissa, Rajasthan, Gujarat, and Kerala, other states facing severe food problems. Since 1971, India's food production has fallen apart. It has produced substantially less food in the last two years than it did in the late 1960s and early 1970s at the height of the so-called "green revolution."

The exploding population has added 60 million mouths to feed in the country since 1970. Money that the country should be using to find ways to grow more food is now being spent to buy emergency supplies to make up for crop failures. The government is having trouble finding food in a world plagued with crop failures this year, growing 2 per cent less grain that it did last year. It means 200 million Indians are living on diets one official called "slow starvation." Instead of getting better, it promises to get worse as India's food growing ability continues on a pattern of steady deterioration started three years ago with failing weather and rising energy costs.

In the Punjab and Haryana, two farming states that became the beneficiaries of the "green revolution," where farmers fed most of India when they learned how to use irrigation and fertilizer, the mood is black. The farmers there have watched their crops diminish and their profits disappear because of lack of fertilizer and failure of rain. They complain that the government has deserted them by not protecting them from the soaring cost of fuel needed to operate irrigation wells and by fixing maximum prices they can charge for their harvest. "For awhile, farming was like heaven," said Haqiqat Singh, a Punjabi farmer whose home in the late 1960s began sprouting the accoutrements of middle class luxuries once he had mastered irrigation and fertilizers. "Now I'm just passing time, making a subsistence living again." Singh, a turbaned, bearded Sikh, described the vicious circle of failures that was turning his farm into a losing proposition.

The monsoon rains failed this summer, so it drastically cut hydroelectric production in the Punjab. He was dependent on the electricity to power his well pumps to draw water for his fields that were drying from lack of rain. "Now I have to spend 20 rupees [$2,50] a day just to run my tractor engine to draw water because the electricity isn't on." The gasoline expense cuts deeply into the $350 to $500 he expects to earn annually from his farm. "I feel stranded," he said. He and other Punjabi farmers are fighting back by hoarding much of the grain they managed to harvest this year. The government won't let them sell it at a price they think is fair, so they are trying to drive the price up by making the food scarce.

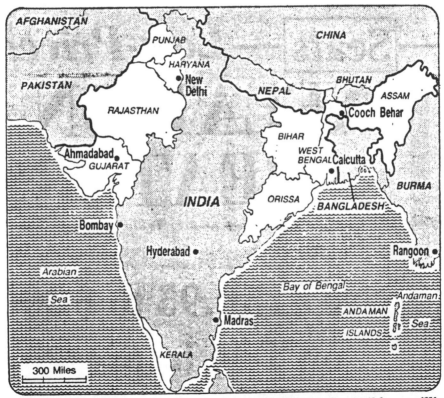

**The starving states of India: At least 500,000 and possibly a million people will die there in the next six months.**

The people in the greatest danger in India are villagers who live in rural areas where food prices are the highest and money is the most scarce. There, too, in the rural areas, is where the birthrates are the highest, the families are the largest, and the parents are the poorest. "Our children are on the brink of disaster," said Tara Gopaldas, a nutrional consultant for CARE in New Delhi. "They are the first victims of malnutrition, and we are a very young nation. Forty per cent of our people are under 20 years old, and 80 per cent of those suffer in some stage of malnutrition." About 80 per cent of India's population, which passed the 600 million mark in September, live in the rural areas.

Except for the progressive farmers of the Punjab, Haryana, and a few other scattered areas, they continue to live in a hand-to-mouth subsistence, almost feudalistic agricultural society. Part of the building tragedy in India is that the peasants themselves, deeply ingrained with tradition and resistant to change, are contributing to their own destruction. The government long ago recognized that it couldn't seriously attack the poverty of its people until it attacked the population problem. For several years India has conducted the most expensive and vigorous birth control program in the world, offering free counseling, contraceptive devices, vasectomies, and tubectomies to anyone who asked.

The campaign never succeeded because rural people, conditioned by the cycle of good years and bad years, were frightened. Their only hedge against hunger and starvation in their old age is the number of children who survive to adulthood. They continue to have six or seven children when they know they won't always be able to feed that many. A few will die, but two or three will survive as social security. "That is the way it has always been," said Santos Naskar, 50, a rice farmer in the Sundarban lowland swamps.

He was spending a summer afternoon on the stoop of his mud hut, working a little on some fish traps he was hoping to sell in the local market, but mostly just lazing the day away with his six children. He grows only one crop of rice a year, and while he waited to harvest it this autumn, he and his family were going thru their annual belt-tightening period, eating only one meal a day. He admitted being hungry every day, was uncomfortable, especially for his children, but it always happened this way in the end of the summer. "We'll get by, and I can always build a few fish traps," he said. "I'm not much for big plans."

Agricultural scientists insist that families like Naskar's wouldn't have to go hungry every year if they would only accept new cropping methods they have developed and plant more than one crop a year. But they would need to irrigate and fertilize their land, and farmers who are "not much for big plans" are frightened by the investment it would take to get them started. "The peasant farmer is a very religious person," said Dr. M. S. Swaminathan, head of the India Council for Agricultural Research. "Even if we offer credit to get him started on fertilizing and irrigation, he won't take it because he doesn't want to die an indebted man."

They prefer to pay the price of survival in other ways like the 3,000 people in the village of Pasodutoi a few miles away from Cooch Behar. They may be squatting all day in their rags waiting in front of a government rationing shop. There isn't enough food for everyone, so the government divides evenly among them, two pounds of wheat for each person every 15 days. Even when they know they will not get any food, they come anyway, seven days a week, arriving before sunrise to sit and wait until dusk. There is nothing else to do.

## 6.3.3 *The Gigantic Famine Problems in Ethiopia*

[Source: Josh Friedman: Ethiopia - a Nation dying. Death in the Camps, in: *Sunday Newsday* (Long Island, N.Y.), Vol. 45/No. 63, November 4, 1984, p. 5, cols. 1-3; p. 26, cols. 1-2; p. 28, cols. 1-2; reprinted by permission of Newsday, Inc., Long Island, N.Y.]

Abadit Gurmay, 28, stared vacantly into space, her hands bound to a post behind her with rough, hand-woven cloth. A few feet away, her 8-year-old daughter Araday held her month-old sister on her lap and stared at her mother. Moans, hacking coughs and cries filled the air in the corrugated tin shelter, packed with 400 sick and starving people. The air was sweet with the smell of rotting flesh and human feces, which collected on the raised dirt platforms that passed for beds.

"She lost her mind completely yesterday," Abadit's husband, Haddish Wolde Aregay, 33, said. "But she started going six months ago when her father died." He said his father-in-law had starved to death before the little family managed to trek to this refugee camp. "She never had any sickness before," he added, "but maybe it's sadness."

This arid area in the mountains of northern Ethiopia has known the sadness of recurrent drought and famine for centuries. But of the scores of people interviewed during a tour this past week of the Tigre and Wello provinces by a Newsday reporter and photographer, none could remember a time like this. It is the fourth year of drought in Ethiopia. No one knows precisely how many are dying, but clearly the numbers are huge. It is almost impossible to get precise figures in places like Tigre and Wello, the two most devastated of Ethiopia's 14 provinces, because much of the death takes place in the countryside, where there are no government authorities.

But statistics from Ethiopia's Relief and Rehabilitation Commission and first-hand observation by relief workers give a disturbing clue to the magnitude. In Tigre, the commission estimates that 1.3 million people will need food aid this year and next - nearly twice the number it aided last year. About 50,000 of them have taken refuge in the provincial capital, Makale, where relief workers say 20 to 30 are dying daily. In Wello, the commission says 1.8 million people will need food this year and next. In and around Korem, a huge refugee camp whose population is now between 20,000 and 30,000, the daily death rate stands at about 60. "The dying is three times as bad in the countryside. The people are weaker. There is no medical attention, no food," said Belay Ashebir, secretary of the Tigre branch of the Ethiopian Red Cross.

As in much of the rest of Africa, there has been no rain of any substance in northern Ethiopia for three to four years. Each year has been worse. This year, even the prickly pear cactus, which provides the peasants with an emergency food during droughts, failed to fruit. Grain from the south, another fallback, never materialized because the drought this year has ruined the harvest in all but two provinces. When the rains didn't come last July, the farmers ate their seeds. Then they sold the oxen used to plough the fields. Cattle, goats and sheep that weren't sold or eaten began to die. About six weeks ago, all food ran out and the people in the area started dying in great numbers. The elderly and infants went first. The able-bodied fled to the outskirts of large towns like Makale and Korem. Both are approximately a two-to-three-day drive over unpaved mountain roads from the capital of Addis Ababa, but the roads are often closed and the area is somewhat inaccessible.

The refugees sleep in drainage ditches and open lots. The lucky ones are packed into camps. Each morning, the living quietly remove the bodies of those who died in the cold mountain night. Oddly, life in the towns near these scenes goes on with a veneer of normalcy. One morning last week in Makale - a town that has grown from 70,000 to 120,000 in the past two months - children dressed in colorful modern clothing walked and skipped to school. In downtown Makale, where 2-story buildings surround a small park dominated by pictures of Marx, Engels and Lenin, merchants swept the stoops of their empty stores. There are pictures of the three throughout the town, on freshly painted billboards emblazoned with political slogans marking the recent week-long September celebration of the 10-year anniversary of Ethiopia's Marxist revolution - which came about in protest of the monarchy's inability to cope with the 1973-74 drought that swept this area and cost 200,000 lives.

Army trucks rumbled through the streets, bearing troops to the perimeter 2 kilometers outside the town to protect it from the Tigrean rebels who control much of the countryside beyond it. Amid this activity, thousands of starving peasants shuffled along the roads in search of food. About 20,000 of the fortunate ones already are enrolled in special feeding programs set up in and around the town by the government and international relief organizations. But another 20,000 are not. They wait outside the enclosed feeding centers or jam the roads leading to town. A crowd of several hundred starving refugees squatted in front of a special children's feeding station run by the International Red Cross. Some of those seated outside made feeble begging motions to passersby, waving their hands to their mouths as if yawning.

The program has room for only 600 children. But the people keep waiting. Last Sunday the crowd had swelled to nearly 3,000 when director Grete Weichlenger emerged to select 200 new children for the program. "I don't have enough food so I select the sick ones. I leave the good ones alone. It is really nonsense because then the good ones become sick," said Weichlenger, a Swiss public health nurse. "I think we never will have enough food for everyone. Each day we distribute more but the situation is getting worse." Ayene Aragay, 65, stood in front of the center with a defiant look. A month ago, he had walked with his wife, two daughters and two grandchildren from the village of Geralta, 40 miles away. His three grown sons remained in the village, too weak to walk. "I never saw anything like this in my life," he said. "I never thought I would have to beg."

Each day hundreds of new refugees pour into the area. They are dressed in the remnants of their traditional clothing. Many have sold jewelry and other valuables for food. Some still have earrings. Most women have tatooed beauty marks and even in their weakened state, they find time to braid each other's hair in intricate patterns. Many women carry wood to sell in the town for a few cents. Some carry poles. Some carry little baskets of twigs. Some men lead mules laden with the reddish roots of the few remaining trees in the areas - a process that disrupts the cycle of evaporation and reduces the possibility of normal rainfall ever returning.

From the air, it looks as though the ground will never be green again. All is brown, like a black-and-white movie with a sepia tint. Once fertile fields are distinguishable only by the stone walls that separate them or the terraces that were built to stem the erosion by rains. Camps have been set up on the outskirts of Makale to intercept the refugees so

## The Hardest Hit Countries

| | Food aid needed (thousand tons) | Cost to provide food, in millions | Millions of people affected | % of Population affected |
|---|---|---|---|---|
| **Burkina Faso** | | | | |
| | 165 | $33 | 1.3 | 20 |
| **Chad** | | | | |
| | 125 | $25 | 3 | 64 |
| **Ethiopia** | | | | |
| | 800 | $160 | 6.4 | 13 |
| **Mali** | | | | |
| | 200 | $40 | 2.4 | 34 |
| **Mauritania** | | | | |
| | 160 | $32 | 1.1 | 66 |
| **Mozambique** | | | | |
| | 520 | $104 | 3 | 24 |
| **Niger** | | | | |
| | 475 | $95 | 2.4 | 43 |
| **Sudan** | | | | |
| | 650 | $130 | 4.5 | 22 |

SOURCE: United Nations Disaster Relief Agency

## The Scope of the Famine

SOURCE: United Nations Disaster Relief Agency

that they do not linger in town. People coming from the hills to the east are concentrated in a camp in nearby Quiha. As of last week, the 5,000 people in an International Red Cross camp there had not received food for five days.

This particular camp is under the control of Farmers' Associations which have been created by the revolutionary government. The association portions out small bits of food to a squad of men who control the rest of the refugees with sticks. A few are armed with World War I-era bold-action rifles. The guards rush around, beating starving people who are fighting over turf, which is delineated by little piles and berms of stones and dirt. Young boys push old ladies back as they attempt to snatch morsels of food that have been hoarded for the sick who lie motionless under blankets in small pits. Old men attempt to slither into the pits to filch food.

Seven to eight people a day are dying there, but there were many more who died before they were able to leave the villages up in the mountains, and the elderly and young who were left behind apparently are dying rapidly now. "Fifteen or 20 days ago, the dying started in our village," said one official of the Farmers' Association, Solomon Hadera, 47, wrapped in a homespun robe and leaning on a staff. Hadera, who had led the strongest of his people down the hill to the camp, had not eaten in three days, nor had any of his eight children, he said. "For a while we were able to eat leaves but without the rains we ran out of the leaves."

Even for those who reach the towns - and who have money or can sell their possessions - food is difficult to obtain and prices are soaring because of scarcity. Irish-born Father Kevin O'Mahoney, 54, has lived and taught in a seminary in Adigrat, a city 65 miles north of Makale. He says food prices have trebled since May and, for the last five weeks, the area has been without flour. O'Mahoney recalls that old writings in the seminary describe a similar situation during the Tigre famine of 1892, when one-third of the province's population died. According to notes left by priests at the time, it cost the same to buy a chicken after the famine started in 1892 as it had cost to buy a cow the year before.

Adigrat, a town of 40,000, has more than doubled its population in the last several months and the death toll is rising, he says. "I have seen men of 65 just lie down and die. The will to live is gone - maybe his wife is dead or his children," he said. "But the women are great. They'll fight like hell. If she has a child on her back, she won't go easily." At one Makale center, relief workers reported six adults had died the night before. So had two children who lived in the same tent. Their mothers sat together wailing and clutching their friends. Children who die are quickly interred. Only adults are given brief ceremonies if relatives insist.

Two of the dead were Afra nomads, who normally travel in the hot desert. Now they huddle under blankets in free-form circles. Abraham Mohamad, 30, said 20 of the 300 in his group died last month before they reached Makale. "Before the drought, we had cattle and everything we needed. We were able to travel. But now we are left without cattle and we want to settle down," he said, adding that four of his five cows and 28 of his 30 sheep and goats had died before he sold the survivors and came to the camp. The shocking daily death rate in the Makale camps, from 20 to 30 people each day, is dwarfed by that in a massive refugee camp at Korem, 75 miles to the south. In a single day in early October, the death toll there hit a high of 101. Now it has tapered off, to an average of 60 a day.

The camp is crowded with between 20,000 and 30,000 people, barely surviving. Many have been there for several months, some for more than a year. They are beaten down - with none of the anger of the recent arrivals in Makale - and are kept in check by a force of 50 stick-wielding residents, who are paid in food. Another 440 residents are given extra food to roam the camp with shovels, burying human excrement wherever it is lying. Many of the residents are emaciated and have a stubbly growth on their heads - a product of the compulsory delousing process in which their heads are shaved and their clothes steamed. The camp is spread on a high plateau on the mountain, like the site of a medieval battle. The refugees cover acres - living in the open or in black or green tents, in shelters made of sorghum stalks or corrugated tin sheds.

The sickest are kept in two giant tin sheds, where each raised dirt bed is shared by two to four people. There are emaciated teenagers who look like small children, withered men and skeletal women, some with babies on their breasts. Each morning, five to 10 are dead. The remainder of the daily dead are found lying in the open fields, in the town, or in a children's' clinic near the camp. Dr. Serge Bechet, 29, a Belgian member of Medicins Sans Frontières, displayed the medical records of his dead patients one morning: Male, 2. Arrived yesterday. Dehydration. Female, 50. Arrived yesterday. Massive bleeding and gynecological infection. Female, 1. Arrived yesterday. Diarrhea. Male, 5. Arrived yesterday. Coma, gasping, diarrhea. Male, 40. Arrived one week ago. Bloody diarrhea.

Death by starvation comes in many guises - all brought on by the weakened condition and low resistance of the starving people. If they reach Bechet's clinic, the cause of death is usually recorded as diarrhea brought on by parasites or bacteria, anemia, something called relapsing fever, tuberculosis, typhus, measles, or other diseases. "You can call it dehydration or diarrhea but it's really starvation," says Bechet. In Makale, many cough themselves to death in the cold nights that drop to 40 degrees. Others are said to die of violent vomiting and diarrhea when they get food after a long period of starvation.

Bechet is one of 10 Medicin Sans Frontières Health workers staff in the camp by day, returning each night at 6 to Korem. They take their medicine with them to keep it from falling into the hands of Tigrean guerrillas, who have free run of the camp during the night. Somehow the guerrillas seem to be getting sufficient food, perhaps by raiding government supplies or army stores. A retired California couple, just released by the Tigreans after spending a week as their hostages, report their captors were lean but well-nourished. The couple had been seized in a tourist spot between Korem and Makale. There had been speculation that food does not get into the hinterlands because of guerrilla control of the roads, but an aerial view of the region shows there are virtually no roads to be held.

The problem is one of transport on existing roads, according to relief workers. And while the Ethiopian army is said to have loaned 50 trucks to the government's Relief and Rehabilitation Commission, the local drought-relief agency, none was seen hauling food in this week-long tour of the north. In Korem, most of the food coming into the camp is from Europe and even China. There is little American presence there. Most of the expatriate relief workers are European. Bechet complained his medical team has gotten no support from the United States except a donation of expired medicine that reportedly arrived a month ago from the U.S. embassy in Addis Ababa. However, Catholic Relief Services, the largest distributor of American food in Ethiopia, now is starting to relay American food to supplement a Save the Children program at the camp. U.S. wheat, probably channeled through the World Food program, appeared for the first time this past week in Korem.

There are more than 7,000 children under 5 in the camp. They run behind any white visitor chanting the Amharic word for "white man." Adults rush up to exhibit ulcerated arms and dripping infections, or dying children and elderly relatives. The orphans live separately from other children. During the day, they huddle like roosting birds under gray blankets, cared for by teenage girls who are long-time camp residents. There is no attempt to treat emotional wounds. The orphans are expected to comfort each other, says Save the Children nutritionist Samarab Barhay, 25. "Minds, I don't know about their minds," he said. "But physically, they are recovering. We have a weigh-in each week. They receive extra calories each day."

Another Save the Children nutritionist, Judith Appleton, is gloomy about the camp. "The condition of the people coming in is getting worse," she says. "Last year, less than 40 percent were below 80 percent of their normal weight and length. Now it's 60 percent. It means they're hanging on too long up there before coming down." Many of the camp residents seem to have given up on ever returning home, an incredible step for peasants whose families have lived in the same place for centuries - possibly millenia. "I think I don't go back again to that place," said Kasaye Tamaraz, who now lives with his wife, Weynu Adamaso, and a son, Landa, 7, in one of the four jammed tin sheds at the camp set aside for weakened or recuperating refugees. He had left Sekota, 60 miles away, last June after his 4-year-old daughter died.

Tamaraz had spent the last three years, after selling his animals and eating his seed, gathering firewood to provide food for his family. "We had nothing left. We sold everything. An empty home is like nothing. We couldn't stay there. Everybody's out. A lot of people are dying there and some of them are dying here, too." As in Makale, it is the lucky who reach the camp. Last week, Baylayes Meritay, 25, showed up in the camp with his wife, Mayitu Abebe, 21, and 4-year-old son, Negush. They left Sekota with 10 other families. Seven families made it to the camp. He thinks the other three have perished. "Those who had property sold it so they could eat. Those who didn't were in bad trouble," he said. His wife, apparently in shock, sat on the ground, unaware of scores of flies climbing into her son's mouth, nose, ears and eyes.

# 7

## *FIRST ORIENTATION*
## *BIBLIOGRAPHY*

## *PRELIMINARY REMARKS*

Since the content of this book mainly is based on three central aspects - medical communication, media morality and a journalism award-system - the following bibliography is devided into sections covering the various areas. It should be pointed out that only monographs could be accepted for the three lists of literature and that the quantity of titles in each segment was limited to thirty books.

## *7.1   MEDICAL AND HEALTH JOURNALISM*

**Bäder**, B., Medizin und Presse im Wandel der Zeit, PhD dissertation, University of Munich, 1954.

**Best**, G. et al., Health, the Mass Media and the National Health Service, London 1977.

**Boes**, U., AIDS-Berichterstattung in der Tagespresse. Inhaltsanalytische Untersuchung von 'Frankfurter Allgcmeine Zeitung' und 'Welt' im Zeitraum 1982-1989, Bochum/Germany, 1991.

**Burkett**, W., News reporting. Science, Medicine and High Technology, Ames, Ia., 1986.

**Claire**, W., The Physician as Writer, Albany, N.Y., 1984.

**Collins**, M., Communication in health care, St. Louis, Mo., 1977.

**Davidson**, H. A., Guide to Medical Writing, New York 1957.

**Day**, S. B., Health Communications, New York 1979.

**Deneke**, J. F. V., Arzt und Medizin in der Tagespublizistik des 17. und 18. Jahrhunderts, Cologne - Berlin 1969.

**Deneke**, J. F. V., Aspekte und Probleme der Medizinpublizistik. Bestandsaufnahmen und Analysen zur historischen und aktuellen Präsentation von Medizin in Massenmedien, Bochum/Germany 1985.

**Fischer**, H.-D., Berlin, Medizin und Medien, Cologne 1986.

**Fischer**, H.-D., Handbuch der Medizinkommunikation. Informationstransfer und Publizistik im Gesundheitswesen, Cologne 1988.

**Fischer**, H.-D., Medizinpublizistik. Prämissen, Praktiken, Probleme, Frankfurt - Bern - New York - Paris 1990.

**Fischer**, H.-D., Publizistikwissenschaftler und Medizinkommunikation im deutschsprachigen Raum, Bochum/Germany 1990.

**Fletcher**, C. M., Communication in medicine, London 1973.

**Girstenbrey**, W., Mit Journalisten leben. Ein Ratgeber für Ärzte, Cologne 1976.

**Gunn**, W. et al., Attitudes toward the Swine Flu Immunization Program and Media Coverage of Events, Atlanta, Ga., 1981.

**Karpf**, A., Doctoring the Media. The Reporting of Health and Medicine, London 1988.

**Kreps**, G. L. and B. C. **Thornton**, Health Communication - Theory and Practice, New York - London 1984.

**Krieghbaum**, H., When Doctors Meet Reporters, New York 1957.

**Leather**, D. et al., Health Education and the Media, 2 vols., Oxford 1981-86.

**Merscheim**, H., Medizin in Illustrierten. Berichterstattungs-Analyse von *Bunte*, *Neue Revue*, *Quick*, und *stern*, Bochum/Germany 1978.

**Roloff**, E. K., Die Berichterstattung über Herztransplantationen in der westdeutschen Presse. Eine aussagenanalytische Fallstudie zu Phänomenen des Medizinjournalismus, PhD dissertation, University of Salzburg/Austria, 1972.

**Rowlandson**, T. and M. H. **Saffron**, Medical caricatures, New York (1971).

**Schmidt**, F. and H. N. **Weiner**, Public Relations in Health and Welfare, New York 1966.

**Schwager**, E., On Medical Communication, St. Paul, Minn., 1982.

**Swanberg**, H., History of the American Medical Writers' Association and its Previous Associated Organizations, Quincy, Ill., 1965.

**Wagner**, H. and H. **Starkulla**, Medizin und Medien. Krankt die Gesundheit am Journalismus?, 2nd ed., Munich 1984.

**Wende**, D., Über die medizinische Berichterstattung von Krebs in Tageszeitungen und deren kritische Bewertung, Bochum/Germany 1990.

**Wittenborn**, J. R. et al., Communication and drug abuse, Springfield, Ill., 1970.

## 7.2   MEDIA ETHICS AND RESPONSIBLITIES

**Boventer**, H., Ethik des Journalismus. Zur Philosophie der Medien-kultur, Konstanz/Germany 1984.

**Boventer**, H., Medien und Moral. Ungeschriebene Regeln des Journalismus, Konstanz/Germany 1988.

**Christians**, C. G. et al., Media Ethics. Cases and Moral Reasoning, New York - London 1983.

**Christians**, C. G. and C. L. **Covert**, Teaching Ethics in Journalism Education. The Teaching of Ethics III, New York 1980.

**Crawford**, N., The Ethics of Journalism, New York 1924.

**Erbring**, L. et al., Medien ohne Moral. Variationen über Journalismus und Ethik, Berlin 1988.

**Fischer**, H.-D. et al., Die Presseräte der Welt. Struktur, Finanzbasis und Spruchpraxis von Medien-Selbstkontrolleinrichtungen im internationalen Vergleich, Bonn 1976.

**Fischer**, H.-D. and J. C. **Merrill**, International and Intercultural Communication, New York 1976.

**Flint**, L. N., The Conscience of the Newspaper. A Case Book in the Principles and Problems of Journalism, New York 1925.

**Gerald**, J. E., The Social Responsibility of the Press, Minneapolis, Minn., 1963.

**Goodwin**, H. E., Groping for Ethics in Journalism, Ames, Ia., 1983.

**Hocking**, W. E., Freedom of the Press. A Framework of Principle, Chicago 1947.

**Hodges**, L., Social Responsibility - Journalism, Law, Medicine, Lexington, Va., 1978.

**Hulteng**, J. H., The Messenger's Motives. Ethical Problems in the News Media, Englewood Cliffs, N.J., 1976.

**Hutchins**, R. M., A Free and Responsible Press, Chicago 1947.

**Huter**, A., Grundlinien einer Ethik der Massenkommunikation, Vienna/Austria 1980.

**International Press Institute**, Press Councils and Press Codes, 2nd ed., Zurich 1962.

**Lambeth**, E. B., Committed Journalism. An Ethic for the Profession, Bloomington, Ind., 1986.

**Löffler**, M. and J. L. **Hébarre**, Form und Funktion der Presse-Selbstkontrolle, Munich 1968.

**Lowenstein**, R. L., Press Councils - Idea and Reality, Columbia, Mo., 1973.

**Merrill**, J. C. and R. D. **Barney**, Ethics and the Press. Readings in Mass Media Morality, New York 1975.

**Meyer**, P., Editors, Publishers and Newspaper Ethics, Washington, D.C., 1983.

**Phelan**, J. M., Disenchantment. Meaning and Morality in the Media, New York 1980.

**Rivers**, W. L. and W. **Schramm**, Responsibility in Mass Communication, New York 1969.

**Rubin**, B., Questioning Media Ethics, New York 1978.

**Sarkar**, C., Press Councils and Their Role, New Delhi 1965.

**Swain**, B. M., Reporters' Ethics, Ames, Ia., 1978.

**Thayer**, L., Ethics, Morality and the Media. Reflections on American Culture, New York 1980.

**UNESCO**, Collective Consultations on Codes of Ethics for the Mass Media, Paris 1974.

**Vogel**, J. B., Ethical Codes and Courts of Honour in the Press of the Free World, PhD dissertation, University of Iowa, 1961.

## 7.3   PULITZER AND PULITZER PRIZES

**Barrett**, J. W., Joseph Pulitzer and his *World*, New York 1941.

**Bates**, J. D., The Pulitzer Prizes. The Inside Story of America's Most Prestigeous Award, New York 1991.

**Beasley**, M. H. and R. R. **Harlow**, Voices of Change - Southern Pulitzer Winners, Washington, D.C., 1979.

**Fischer**, E. J. and H.-D. **Fischer**, American Reporter at the International Political Stage. Herbert Bayard Swope and his Pulitzer Prize-winning Articles from Germany in 1916, Bochum/Germany 1982.

**Fischer**, H.-D., *The New York Times* Facing World War II. Articles, Maps and Statistics from a 1941 Pulitzer Prize winning Entry, Frankfurt - Bern - New York - Paris 1990.

**Fischer**, H.-D., Outstanding International Press Reporting. Pulitzer Prize Winning Articles in Foreign Correspondence, I: 1928-1945. From the Consequences of World War I to the End of World War II, Berlin - New York 1984.

**Fischer**, H.-D., Outstanding International Press Reporting. Pulitzer Prize Winning Articles in Foreign Correspondence, II: 1946-1962. From the End of World War II to the Various Stations of the Cold War, Berlin - New York 1985.

**Fischer**, H.-D., Outstanding International Press Reporting. Pulitzer Prize Winning Articles in Foreign Correspondence, III: 1963-1977. From the Escalation of the Vietnam War to the East Asian Refugee Problems, Berlin - New York 1986.

**Fischer**, H.-D., Outstanding International Press Reporting. Pulitzer Prize Winning Articles in Foreign Correspondence, IV: 1978-1989. From Roarings in the Middle East to the Destroying of the Democratic Movement in China, Berlin - New York 1991.

**Fischer**, H.-D. and E. J. **Fischer**, The Pulitzer Prize Archive - International Reporting 1928-1985. From the Activities of the League of Nations to present-day Global Problems, Munich - London - New York - Oxford - Paris 1987.

**Fischer**, H.-D. and E. J. **Fischer**, The Pulitzer Prize Archive - National Reporting 1941-1986. From Labor Conflicts to the Challenger Disaster, Munich - London - New York - Paris 1988.

**Fischer**, H.-D. and E. J. **Fischer**, The Pulitzer Prize Archive - Local Reporting 1947-1987. From a County Vote Fraude to a Corrupt City Council, Munich - London - New York - Paris 1989.

**Fischer**, H.-D. and E. J. **Fischer**, The Pulitzer Prize Archive - Political Editorials 1916-1988. From War-related Conflicts to Metropolitan Disputes, Munich - London - New York - Paris 1990.

**Fischer**, H.-D. and E. J. **Fischer**, The Pulitzer Prize Archive - Social Commentary 1969-1989. From University Troubles to a California Earthquake, Munich - London - New York - Paris 1991.

**Fischer**, H.-D. and C. G. **Trump**, Education in Journalism. The 75th Anniversary of Joseph Pulitzer's Ideas at Columbia University (1904-1979), Bochum/Germany 1980.

**Hohenberg**, J., The Pulitzer Prizes. A History of the Awards in Books, Drama, Music, and Journalism, Based on the Private Files over Six Decades, New York - London 1974.

**Hohenberg**, J., The Pulitzer Prize Story. News Stories, Editorials, Cartoons, and Pictures from the Pulitzer Prize Collection at Columbia University, New York - London 1959.

**Hohenberg**, J., The Pulitzer Prize Story II. Award-Winning News Stories, Columns, Editorials, Cartoons, and News Pictures, 1959-1980, New York 1980.

**Juergens**, G., Joseph Pulitzer and the New York *World*, Princeton, N.J., 1966.

**Laub**, G. J., Joseph Pulitzer - Schöpfer der modernen amerikanischen Tagespresse, PhD dissertation, University of Vienna/Austria, 1959.

**Lewis**, A. A., Man of the *World*. Herbert Bayard Swope: A Charmed Life of Pulitzer Prizes, Poker and Politics, Indianapolis - New York 1978.

**Lisby**, G. C., Julian Harris and the *Columbus Enquirer-Sun* - The Consequences of Winning the Pulitzer Prize, Columbia, S.C., 1988.

**Reynolds**, W. R., Joseph Pulitzer, PhD dissertation, Columbia University, New York 1950.

**Rothmyer**, K., Winning Pulitzers. The Stories Behind Some of the Best News Coverage of Our Time, New York 1991.

**Siebert**, H., Pulitzer als Journalist und Verleger, PhD dissertation, University of Munich/Germany, 1956.

**Sloan**, W. D., Pulitzer Prize Editorials. America's Best Editorial Writing, 1917-1979, Ames, Ia., 1980.

**Sloan**, W. D. et al., The Best of Pulitzer Prize News Writing, Columbus, Oh., 1986.

**Sovern**, M. I., The Pulitzer Prizes 1917-1991, New York 1991.

**Swanberg**, W. A., Pulitzer, New York 1967.

**Wills**, K. J., The Pulitzer Prizes. A legacy of distinguished reporting, powerful and unforgettable images from America's best journalists, New York 1987 ff. (annually).

# INDEX